PORTABLE
ELECTRONICS
DATA
BOOK

PORTABLE
ELECTRONICS
DATA
BOOK

John Douglas-Young

Prentice Hall, Englewood Cliffs, New Jersey 07632

Library of Congress Cataloging-in-Publication Data

Douglas-Young, John.
    Portable electronics data book / John Douglas-Young.
       p. cm.
    ISBN 0-13-685827-9
    1. Electronics—Handbooks, manuals, etc.   2. Electronics—Tables.
I. Title.
TK7825.D68   1989
621.381'0212—dc19   89-30593
                                                              CIP

Editorial/production supervision: Elaine Lynch
Cover design: Wanda Lubelska Design
Manufacturing buyer: Robert Anderson

© 1989 by Prentice-Hall, Inc.
A Division of Simon & Schuster
Englewood Cliffs, New Jersey 07632

The publisher offers discounts on this book when ordered
in bulk quantities. For more information, write:
    Special Sales/College Marketing
    Prentice-Hall, Inc.
    College Technical and Reference Division
    Englewood Cliffs, NJ 07632

Printed in the United States of America
10 9 8 7 6 5 4 3 2

ISBN 0-13-685827-9

Prentice-Hall International (UK) Limited, *London*
Prentice-Hall of Australia Pty. Limited, *Sydney*
Prentice-Hall Canada Inc., *Toronto*
Prentice-Hall Hispanoamericana, S.A., *Mexico*
Prentice-Hall of India Private Limited, *New Delhi*
Prentice-Hall of Japan, Inc., *Tokyo*
Simon & Schuster Asia Pte. Ltd., *Singapore*
Editora Prentice-Hall do Brasil, Ltda., *Rio de Janeiro*
Prentice-Hall, Inc., *Englewood Cliffs, New Jersey*

THE UNIQUE, PRACTICAL VALUE
THIS BOOK OFFERS

In our work in electronics, we always like being asked questions for which we know the answers—especially the right answers, sharp and clear, not fuzzy! The trouble is that we are all specialists nowadays, so a great deal of what we once knew about things outside our immediate area of expertise gets mothballed and does not come readily to mind. To make matters worse, the "state of the art" keeps advancing so that what we do recollect may turn out to be rather old-fashioned. These problems account for the popularity of reference books of all kinds, expensive though many of them are.

Such books should be both comprehensive and easy to use, but these desirable features do not always go together. Most books with masses of information provide a table of contents and an index. A table of contents does not list everything, however, and it is tedious, not to say frustrating, to wade through it and still not be able to find what you want. A good index is much better, but tends to overkill, since for some items it gives several page numbers, and you may have to examine all of them before you find what you want.

One type of reference book that does not share these problems is the dictionary. Each entry is in alphabetical order, so you turn to it directly. There is no guesswork about where it is located. Even better is the encyclopedia since it contains both minor and major entries. If a minor entry is better understood if it is tabulated or included in a larger article that covers the whole subject, it is cross-referred to the major reference.

This is the method used in this book, for the content consists of a great many major references, with minor references between. Many of the latter do no more than direct you to a major reference because the item is dealt with better that way. There is no table of contents and no index. They are, as it were, built in.

Many major references also contain computer programs that may be used to do calculations. They are, of course, no better in this respect than your pocket calculator, but they have the advantage of helping you use the right data and algorithms, so that you get dependable results. These programs are written in mainstream BASIC and have been run on IBM, TRS80, Commodore, and other well-known microcomputers.

The listings given are reproductions of computer printouts, so there will not be any errors unless you introduce them yourself in copying them into your own machine. Instructions to output to a printer have not been included because you probably will not need them. However, you can alter the program to do this if you want to.

Interpretive BASIC is used as the language for these programs because it has become the most popular computing language in the world. Despite its increased power, it remains simple and easy to learn. We can admire those who program in loftier, cryptic, and more obscure languages, but we do not have to emulate them. Like the English language, BASIC has many dialects and accents, but it has a central core that is common to all versions, and we have restricted our programs to using that core and have avoided less-used, more obscure, or special-purpose words.

We—not the royal "We," but the publisher and author—have made every effort to ensure that these programs are accurate and complete. However, as this book is written for general readership, we have no knowledge about or ability to control anyone's use of the programs. Therefore, we cannot guarantee that they will enable you or anyone else to achieve any particular result.

While we have included a huge mass of useful facts and figures, we have excluded much that is outdated, yet still clutters many other reference books. There is no sense in paying for stuff that no one will ever use again. Also, we assumed we would be insulting you if we told you how to do simple mathematics. However, there is a section on the Calculus—not how to do it, but the standard formulas in use, including a computer program to do integration—and a section containing mathematical tables. We thought a bit about the latter since everyone has a calculator. But if these tables were left out, someone would be sure to complain!

Although the emphasis in this book is on facts and formulas, a certain amount of explanatory text is included in some major references where the subject is not widely known as, for instance, text on transducers and vacuum tubes. Although the latter are not in general use any more, some are used in high-power applications, in industrial, broadcasting, and microwave equipment, as well as in the familiar picture tube and cathode-ray tube.

This book contains so much vital, essential, and helpful material that we expect you will make it your constant companion and that it will be the first place you look for the answers to those questions mentioned in the first paragraph.

John Douglas-Young

A *See* Ampere.

AC *See* Alternating Current.

Admittance See Alternating Current.

Air-Core Inductor *See* Inductors.

Alpha *See* Transistors.

ALTERNATING CURRENT

Admittance Formulas

Admittance is the measure of the ease with which alternating current flows in a circuit. The following formulas apply:

The general formula is:

$$Y = 1/Z$$

where:

Y = admittance in siemens.

Z = impedance in ohms.

For series circuit:

$$Y = 1/\sqrt{R^2 + X^2}$$

where:

Y = admittance in siemens.

R = resistance in ohms.

X = reactance in ohms.

For parallel circuit:

$$Y = \sqrt{G^2 + B^2}$$

where:

Y = admittance in siemens.

G = conductance in siemens.

B = susceptance in siemens.

(*See also* Conductance, Reactance.)

Angular Velocity Formula

The rate at which an angle changes, expressed in radians per second, given by:

$$\omega = 2\pi f$$

where:

ω = angular velocity (ω is Greek lower-case omega).

π = 3.1415927 . . . .

f = frequency in hertz.

Average Value Formulas

See Root-Mean-Square Values.

Effective Value Formulas

See Root-Mean-Square Values.

Instantaneous Value Formulas

For current:

$$i = I_m \sin \theta$$

where:

i = instantaneous current value.

θ = phase angle

Less than 90°, = θ

90°–180°, = $180 - \theta$

180°–270°, = $\theta - 180$

270°–360°, = $360 - \theta$

I_m = peak current value.

For voltage:

$$v = V_m \sin \theta$$

where:

v = instantaneous voltage value.

θ = phase angle

Less than 90°, = θ

90°–180°, = $180 - \theta$

180°–270°, = $\theta - 180$

270°–360°, = $360 - \theta$

V_m = peak voltage value.

Ohm's Law for AC Formulas

For voltage:

$$v = iZ$$

For current:

$$i = v/Z$$

For impedance:

$$Z = v/i$$

where:

v = instantaneous voltage across impedance Z.

i = instantaneous current through impedance Z.

Z = impedance (q.v. under particular device).

Peak-to-Peak Value Formulas

See Root-Mean-Square Values.

Peak Value Formulas

See Root-Mean-Square Values.

Phase Angle Formulas

$$\theta = \arctan (X_L/R)$$

$$\theta = \arctan (X_C/R)$$

where:

θ = angle of lead or lag in degrees.

X_L = *inductive reactance* in ohms (*see* Inductors).

X_C = *capacitive reactance* in ohms (*see* Capacitors).

Power Factor Formulas

Power factor, the ratio of the true power to apparent power in an AC circuit, is given by:

$$pf = P_T/P_A$$
$$= \cos \theta$$

where:

pf = power factor (percentage).

P_T = true power, in watts.

P_A = apparent power, in volt-amperes.

θ = phase angle between current and voltage.

For a purely resistive circuit:

$$\theta = 0°$$
$$pf = 1$$

For a resonant circuit:

$$\theta = 0°$$
$$pf = 1$$

For a purely reactive circuit:

$$\theta = 90°$$
$$pf = 0$$

Root-Mean-Square (RMS) Values

The following table can be used to convert sinusoidal voltage or current values from one measurement unit to another. First find the given unit in the left-hand column. Then find the heading for the desired unit over one of the right-hand columns. To convert the value in the given unit to the value in the desired unit, multiply the given value by the factor listed in the column under the desired unit.

Average, RMS, Peak, and Peak-to-Peak Conversion Table

Given unit	Multiplying factor to get			
	Average	RMS	Peak	Peak-to-peak
Average		1.11	1.57	3.14
RMS	0.9		1.414	2.828
Peak	0.637	0.707		2.0
Peak-to-Peak	0.32	0.3535	0.5	

Figure A-1 One cycle of alternating voltage as supplied by the power company. There are 360 degrees in a cycle, and two voltage peaks, one positive and one negative. Although the peak voltage is 165 V, the RMS value of 117 V is generally used. The RMS value has the same power as the DC value, so a lamp or heater that works on 117 V RMS will work equally well on 117 V DC. The voltage at each point on the wave is the value of the peak voltage multiplied by the sine of the angle at that point, so the wave is called a *sine wave*. (For instance, sin 45 deg = 0.707, and 0.707 × 165 = 117 V RMS, and so on.) Each cycle lasts for 1/60th of a second, so there are 60 cycles per second. The modern metric unit for a cycle per second is a *hertz*, so this is expressed as 60 hertz (or 60 Hz). [3]

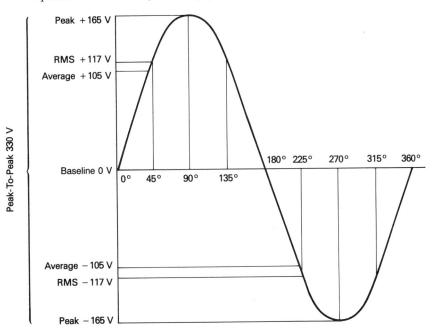

TABLE A-1 Table of Standard Annealed Bare Copper Wire Using American Wire Gauge (B & S).—[6]

Gauge (AWG) or (B&S)	Diameter inches			Area	Weight	Length	Resistance at 68°F			Current* capacity (Amps) Rubber Insulated
	Min.	Nom.	Max.	Circular Mils	Pounds per M'	Feet per Lb.	Ohms per M'	Feet per Ohm'	Ohms per lb.	
0000	.4554	.4600	.4646	211600.	640.5	1.561	0.4901	20400.	.00007652	225
000	.4055	.4096	.4137	167800.	507.9	1.968	.06180	16180.	.0001217	175
00	.3612	.3648	.3684	133100.	402.8	2.482	.07793	12830.	.0001935	150
0	.3217	.3249	.3281	105500.	319.5	3.130	.09827	10180.	.0003076	125
1	.2864	.2893	.2922	83690.	253.3	3.947	.1239	8070.	.0004891	100
2	.2550	.2576	.2602	66370.	200.9	4.977	.1563	6400.	.0007778	90
3	.2271	.2294	.2317	52640.	159.3	6.276	.1970	5075.	.001237	80
4	.2023	.2043	.2063	41740.	126.4	7.914	.2485	4025.	.001966	70
5	.1801	.1819	.1837	33100.	100.2	9.980	.3133	3192.	.003127	55
6	.1604	.1620	.1636	26250.	79.46	12.58	.3951	2531.	.004972	50
7	.1429	.1443	.1457	20820.	63.02	15.87	.4982	2007.	.007905	
8	.1272	.1285	.1298	16510.	49.98	20.01	.6282	1592.	.01257	35
9	.1133	.1144	.1155	13090.	39.63	25.23	.7921	1262.	.01999	
10	.1009	.1019	.1029	10380.	31.43	31.82	.9989	1001.	.03178	25
11	.08983	.09074	.09165	8234.	24.92	40.12	1.260	794.	.05053	
12	.08000	.08081	.08162	6530.	19.77	50.59	1.588	629.6	.08035	20
13	.07124	.07196	.07268	5178.	15.68	63.80	2.003	499.3	.1278	
14	.06344	.06408	.06472	4107.	12.43	80.44	2.525	396.0	.2032	15
15	.05650	.05707	.05764	3257.	9.858	101.4	3.184	314.0	.3230	
16	.05031	.05082	.05133	2583.	7.818	127.9	4.016	249.0	.5136	6
17	.04481	.04526	.04571	2048.	6.200	161.3	5.064	197.5	.8167	
18	.03990	.04030	.04070	1624.	4.917	203.4	6.385	156.5	1.299	3
19	.03553	.03589	.03625	1288.	3.899	256.5	8.051	124.2	2.065	
20	.03164	.03196	.03228	1022.	3.092	323.4	10.15	98.5	3.283	
21	.02818	.02846	.02874	810.1	2.452	407.8	12.80	78.11	5.221	
22	.02510	.02535	.02560	642.4	1.945	514.2	16.14	61.95	8.301	
23	.02234	.02257	.02280	509.5	1.542	648.4	20.36	49.13	13.20	
24	.01990	.02010	.02030	404.0	1.223	817.7	25.67	38.96	20.99	
25	.01770	.01790	.01810	320.4	.9699	1031.	32.37	30.90	33.37	
26	.01578	.01594	.01610	254.1	.7692	1300.	40.81	24.50	53.06	
27	.01406	.01420	.01434	201.5	.6100	1639.	51.47	19.43	84.37	
28	.01251	.01264	.01277	159.8	.4837	2067.	64.90	15.41	134.2	
29	.01115	.01126	.01137	126.7	.3836	2607.	81.83	12.22	213.3	
30	.00993	.01003	.01013	100.5	.3042	3287.	103.2	9.691	329.2	
31	.008828	.008928	.009028	79.7	.2413	4145.	130.1	7.685	539.3	
32	.007850	.007950	.008050	63.21	.1913	5227.	164.1	6.095	857.6	
33	.006980	.007080	.007180	50.13	.1517	6591.	206.9	4.833	1364.	
34	.006205	.006305	.006405	39.75	.1203	8310.	260.9	3.833	2168.	
35	.005515	.005615	.005715	31.52	.09542	10480.	329.0	3.040	3448.	
36	.004900	.005000	.005100	25.00	.07568	13210.	414.8	2.411	5482.	
37	.004353	.004453	.004553	19.83	.06001	16660.	523.1	1.912	8717.	
38	.003865	.003965	.004065	15.72	.04759	21010.	659.6	1.516	13860.	
39	.003431	.003531	.003631	12.47	.03774	26500.	831.8	1.202	22040.	
40	.003045	.003145	.003245	9.888	.02993	33410.	1049.	0.9534	35040.	
41	.00270	.00280	.00290	7.8400	.02373	42140.	1323.	.7559	55750.	
42	.00239	.00249	.00259	6.2001	.01877	53270.	1673.	.5977	89120.	
43	.00212	.00222	.00232	4.9284	.01492	67020.	2104.	.4753	141000.	
44	.00187	.00197	.00207	3.8809	.01175	85100.	2672.	.3743	227380.	
45	.00166	.00176	.00186	3.0976	.00938	106600.	3348.	.2987	356890.	
46	.00147	.00157	.00167	2.4649	.00746	134040.	4207.	.2377	563900.	

*Note: Values from National Electrical Code.

AM *See* Amplitude Modulation.

American Wire Gauge Table *See* Table A-1.

Ammeter *See* Meters.

Ammeter Shunt Low-value resistance connected between the terminals of an ammeter to increase its range. Its value is given by:

$$R = R_m/(N - 1) = I_m R_m/I_s$$

where:

R = resistance of shunt, in ohms.

R_m = meter resistance, in ohms.

N = scale multiplication factor.

I_m = meter current, in amperes.

I_s = shunt current, in amperes.

For more than one range (see Figure A-2):

$$R_2 = [(R_1 + R_2) + R_m]/N$$

where:

R_2 = intermediate value, in ohms.

$R_1 + R_2$ = total shunt resistance for lowest full-scale reading, in ohms.

R_m = meter resistance, in ohms.

N = scale multiplication factor.

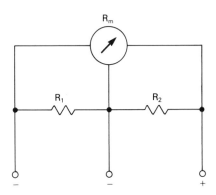

Figure A-2 Multirange Ammeter Shunt.

Ampere Metric (*Système Internationale d'Unités* or *S.I.*) base unit of electric current. The ampere is that constant current which—if maintained in two straight parallel conductors of infinite length and negligible cross-section and placed one meter apart in a vacuum—would produce, between these conductors, a force equal to 2×10^{-7} newtons per meter of length. An ampere is also the current that is produced by an electromotive force of 1 volt applied across a resistance of 1 ohm ($I = V/R$).

Ampere-Hour A current of 1 ampere flowing for 1 hour, given by:

$$AH = AT = 3600 \text{ coulombs}$$

where:

$$AH = \text{ampere-hours.}$$

$$A = \text{current, in amperes.}$$

$$T = \text{time, in hours.}$$

Ampere-hour is used to denote the amount of energy a battery can deliver before it must be recharged or replaced.

Amplification Factor *See* Amplifiers.

Amplifier Classification *See* Amplifiers.

Amplifier Gain *See* Amplifiers.

AMPLIFIERS*

Amplifier Formulas

(*Note*: Definitions of variables appear on pages 9–11).

Transistors. Alpha (current gain of common-base transistor):

$$\alpha = \Delta I_c / \Delta I_e \text{ (with } V_c \text{ constant)}$$

Bandwidth:

$$f_{hfe} = f_{hfb} / h_{fe}$$

or

$$f_{hfb} = h_{fe} f_{hfe}$$

Base current:

$$I_b = I_e - I_c = I_c / h_{fe}$$

Beta (current gain of common-emitter transistor):

$$\beta = \Delta I_c / \Delta I_b \text{ (with } V_c \text{ constant)}$$

Collector current:

$$I_c = I_e - I_b = \alpha I_e = h_{fe} I_b$$

Collector power:

$$P_c = V_{cc} I_c$$

Current gain (general):

$$A_i = \Delta I_c / \Delta I_b \text{ (with } V_c \text{ constant)}$$

*See end of Amplifier section for computer programs.

Emitter current:

$$I_e = I_b + I_c \text{ (total current)}$$

Emitter resistance (small signal):

$$r_e = 26/I_e$$

where:

I_e = emitter current, in milliamperes.

Input capacitance:

$$C_{in} = g_m/6.28f_{hfb}$$

Input resistance:

$$R_i = \Delta V_i/\Delta I_i$$

Output resistance:

$$R_o = \Delta V_o/\Delta I_o$$

Power gain:

$$A_p = \Delta P_o/\Delta P_i$$

Transconductance:

$$g_m = I_e/26$$

where:

I_e = emitter current, in milliamperes.

Upper frequency limit:

$$f_u = g_m/6.28f_{hfb}$$

Voltage gain:

$$A_v = \Delta V_c/\Delta V_b \text{ (with } I_c \text{ constant)}$$

where:

α = current gain of common-base amplifier ($\alpha = \beta/(1 + \beta)$

A_v = voltage gain.

A_i = current gain.

A_p = power gain.

β = current gain in common-emitter amplifier.

C_t = total capacitance, in picofarads.

C_{in} = input capacitance, in farads.

Δ = variation or change in value.

f_u = upper frequency limit, in megahertz.

f_{hfe} = beta cutoff frequency, in megahertz.

f_{hfb} = alpha cutoff frequency, in megahertz.

g_m = transconductance, in microsiemens.

h_{fe} = β = $\alpha/(1 - \alpha)$

I_b = base current, in amperes.

I_c = collector current, in amperes.

I_e = emitter current, in amperes.

I_i = input current, in amperes.

I_o = output current, in amperes.

P_c = collector power, in watts.

P_i = input power, in watts.

P_o = output power, in watts.

R_i = input resistance, in ohms.

R_o = output resistance, in ohms.

r_e = small-signal emitter resistance, in ohms.

V_b = base voltage, in volts.

V_c = collector voltage, in volts.

V_{ce} = collector-emitter voltage, in volts.

V_i = input voltage, in volts.

V_o = output voltage, in volts.

See also Biasing, Characteristic Curves, Feedback.

Vacuum tubes. Amplification factor:

$$\mu = \Delta E_b/\Delta E_c \text{ (with } I_b \text{ constant)}$$

AC (Dynamic) plate resistance:

$$r_p = \Delta E_b/\Delta I_b \text{ (with } E_c \text{ constant)}$$

Mutal conductance (Transconductance):

$$g_m = \Delta I_b/\Delta E_c \text{ (with } E_b \text{ constant)}$$

Gain of amplifier stage:

$$\text{Gain} = \mu R_L/(R_L + r_p)$$

where:

μ = amplification factor.

Δ = variation or change in value.

E_b = plate voltage, in volts.

E_c = grid voltage, in volts.

I_b = plate current, in amperes.

R_L = plate load resistance, in ohms.

r_p = AC plate load resistance, in ohms.

g_m = mutual conductance, in siemens.

Classifications

Class	Conduction angle (degrees)
A	360
AB	180–360
B	180
C	<180

Darlington Pair

A Darlington pair consists of two matched transistors, with both collectors connected directly to the power source, and the emitter of the first connected directly to the base of the second, so that emitter of the first is returned to ground through the base-emitter junction of the second. (See Figure A-3.) The overall current gain of the pair is given by:

$$A_{ic} = I_{out}/I_{b2}$$
$$= (h_{fe})^2$$

where:

A_{ic} = overall current gain.

h_{fe} = forward current transfer ratio of each transistor.

I_{b2} = base current of input transistor.

I_{out} = total collector current.

Figure A-3 Darlington Pair. [2]

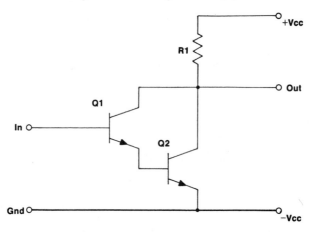

Differential Amplifier (*See* Figure A-4.)

Common-mode signal:

$$v_c = (v_1 + v_2)/2$$

Common-mode rejection ratio:

$$CMRR = 20 \log (A_d/A_c)$$

Figure A-4 Differential Amplifier. [2]

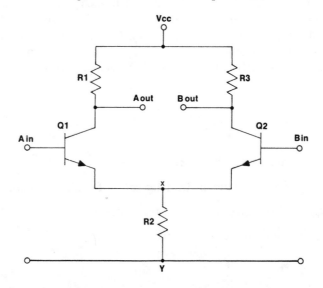

Differential-mode signal:

$$v_d = v_2 - v_1$$

Emitter current:

$$I_E = I_{E1} + I_{E2}$$

Emitter resistor value:

$$R_E = (V_{EE} - V_{BE})/I_E$$

where:

A_c = common-mode gain, which equals $\beta(i_{b1} + i_{b2})/2$.

A_d = differential-mode gain, which equals $\beta(i_{b2} - i_{b1})$.

β = forward current transfer ratio (beta).

$CMRR$ = common-mode rejection ratio, in decibels.

I_E = total DC emitter current, in amperes.

I_{E1} = DC emitter current, in amperes ($Q1$).

I_{E2} = DC emitter current, in amperes ($Q2$).

R_E = total DC emitter resistance, in ohms.

V_{BE} = base-to-emitter DC voltage.

v_c = common-mode signal voltage.

v_d = differential-mode signal voltage.

V_{EE} = emitter DC supply voltage.

v_1 = first-transistor input signal voltage.

v_2 = second-transistor input signal voltage.

Operational Amplifiers (Inverting)

(For definitions of variables, see page 15.)

For all practical purposes, op amps are ICs, the 741 being a typical specimen. (See Figure A-5.)

Closed-loop gain:

$$A_c = -V_{out}/V_{in} = -R_{FB}/R_{IN} = -Z_{FB}/Z_{IN}$$

Feedback current:

$$I_{FB} = V_{out}/R_{FB} = V_{out}/Z_{FB} = I_{in}$$

Input current:

$$I_{in} = V_{in}/R_{in} = V_{out}/Z_{in}$$

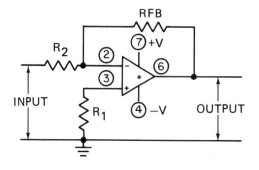

Figure A-5 Inverting Operational Amplifier. (* is a 741 IC with pin numbers shown) [7]

Input impedance:

$$Z_{in} = R_{in}$$

Input voltage:

$$V_{in} = V_{out}/A_c$$

Inverting input resistor:

$$R_1 = (R_2 \times R_{FB})/(R_2 + R_{FB})$$

Output voltage:

$$V_o = -A_c V_{in} = -(Z_{FB}/Z_{in})V_{in} = -(R_{FB}/R_{IN})V_{IN}$$

Operational Amplifiers (Noninverting) (*See* Figure A-6.)

(For definitions of variables, see page 15.)

Closed-loop gain:

$$A_c = V_{out}/V_{in} = (R_1 + R_{FB})/R_1 = 1 + (R_{FB}/R_1)$$

Common-mode signal:

$$v_c = (v_1 + v_2)/2$$

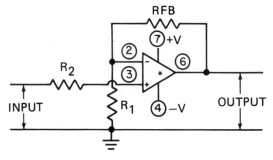

Figure A-6 Noninverting Operational Amplifier. (* is a 741 IC with pin numbers shown) [7]

Feedback current:

$$I_{FB} = I_{in}$$

Input current:

$$I_{in} = V_{in}/R_{in}$$

Input voltage:

$$V_{in} = I_{in}R_{in} = V_{out}/A_c$$

Input resistor:

$$R_2 = (R_1 \times R_{FB})/(R_1 + R_{FB})$$

Output voltage:

$$V_o = A_c V_{in} = I_{FB}(R_{in} + R_{FB})$$
$$= I_{in}(R_{in} + R_{FB}) = V_{R1} + V_{RFB}$$
$$= [(R_1 + R_{FB})/R_1]V_{IN}$$

where:

A_c = closed-loop gain.

I_{FB} = feedback current, in amperes.

I_{IN} = input current, in amperes.

R_{FB} = feedback resistance, in ohms.

R_{IN} = input resistance, in ohms.

R_1 = (see figure), in ohms.

R_2 = (see figure), in ohms.

v_c = common-mode signal voltage.

V_{in} = input signal voltage.

V_{IN} = input voltage.

V_{out} = output signal voltage.

V_{RFB} = voltage developed across R_{FB}.

V_{R1} = voltage developed across R_1.

v_1 = common-mode signal voltage at input 1.

v_2 = common-mode signal voltage at input 2.

Z_{FB} = feedback impedance, in ohms.

Z_{IN} = input impedance, in ohms.

Summing Amplifier (*See* Figure A-7.)

(For definitions of variables, see page 17.)

This amplifier delivers an output voltage which is proportional to the sum of two or more input voltages or currents. Other names for summing amplifier are averaging or mixer amplifier.

Figure A-7 Summing Amplifier. (* is a 741 IC with pin numbers shown) [7]

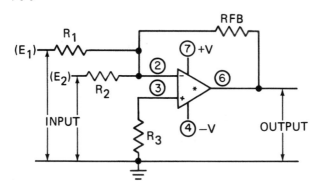

Feedback current:

$$I_{FB} = V_o/R_{FB}$$

Gain per channel:

$$A_1 = -R_{FB}/R_1$$
$$A_2 = -R_{FB}/R_2$$

Input current:

$$I_{R1} = E_1/R_1$$
$$I_{R2} = E_2/R_2$$
$$I_T = I_{R1} + I_{R2}$$

Input impedance:

$$Z_{E1} = R_1$$
$$Z_{E2} = R_2$$

Output/voltage:

$$V_o = -R_{FB}(E_1/R_1 + E_2/R_2), \text{ or}$$
$$V_o = -A_1E_1 + A_2/E_2, \text{ or}$$
$$V_o = -[(R_{FB}/R_1)E_1 + (R_{FB}/R_2)E_2]$$

Noninverting input resistor:

$$R_3 = 1(1/R_1 + 1/R_2 + 1/R_{FB})$$

where:

A_1 = channel 1 gain.

A_2 = channel 2 gain.

E_1 = channel 1 input voltage, in volts.

E_2 = channel 2 input voltage, in volts.

I_{FB} = feedback current, in amperes.

I_{R1} = current in R_1, in amperes.

I_{R2} = current in R_2, in amperes.

I_T = total input current, in amperes.

R_{FB} = feedback resistance, in ohms.

R_1 = channel 1 input resistance, in ohms.

R_2 = channel 2 input resistance, in ohms.

R_3 = noninverting input resistance, in ohms.

V_o = output voltage, in volts.

Z_{E1} = channel 1 input impedance, in ohms.

Z_{E2} = channel 2 input impedance, in ohms.

Common-Emitter and Common-Source Voltage Amplifier Programs

Figure A-8(a) shows a standard type of common-emitter voltage amplifier with voltage feedback (*see* Feedback), using a PNP bipolar junction tran-

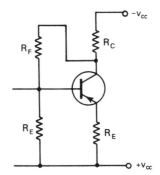

Figure A-8(a) Common-Emitter Voltage Amplifier with Voltage Feedback.

R_F is the feedback resistor; if there were no feedback, R_F would be connected directly to $-V_{cc}$. [4]

sistor. Figure A-8(b) gives a BASIC program that requires that you enter the transistor parameters h_{fe}, h_{oe}, h_{ie}, and h_{re}. (*See* Transistors.) With this information, it then does the following:

Figure A-8(b) First Part of BASIC Program to Analyze the Amplifier Shown in Figure A-8(a)

This portion prints load resistance values from 5000 ohms to 35000 ohms, together with values of power gain and input resistance, for the transistor defined by the h parameters you enter. From these you choose the combination you deem best. Usually this would be the combination that gives the highest G_P. If you are interested in a value for R_L outside this range you should change line 300; if you want different increments, you should change line 190.

However, if you answer by entering N to the prompt in line 30, the program jumps to line 1000.

```
10 PRINT"COMMON-EMITTER VOLTAGE AMPLIFIER DESIGN"
20 PRINT"DO YOU WANT TO FIND RL AND RI FOR"
30 INPUT "MAXIMUM POWER GAIN (Y/N)";A$
40 IF A$<>"Y" THEN 1000
50 PRINT"I AM ASSUMING THAT IC REMAINS THE SAME"
60 PRINT"SO VCC INCREASES FOR EACH RL INCREMENT"
70 PRINT"ENTER H PARAMETERS FOR BJT TRANSISTOR"
80 INPUT"HFE=";A
90 INPUT"HOE=";B
100 INPUT"HIE=";C
110 INPUT"HRE=";D
120 PRINT"I WILL PRINT 2 SCREENS OF DATA"
130 PRINT"PRESS <HOLD> TO KEEP FIRST SCREEN"
140 PRINT"PRESS <HOLD> AGAIN FOR SECOND SCREEN"
150 INPUT"PRESS Y TO CONTINUE";B$
160 IF B$="Y"THEN 170
170 N=0:M=0
180 M=M+1
190 N=N+5000
200 I=A*A*N/((B*N+1)*((C*B-A*D)*N+C))
210 J=(C+(B*C-A*D)*N)/(1+B*N)
220 K=10*LOG(I)/LOG(10)
230 IF M>1 THEN 250
240 PRINT"HFE=";A:PRINT"HOE=";B:PRINT"HIE=";C:PRINT"HRE=";D:PRINT""
250 A$="######"
260 PRINT"RL=";USING A$;N
270 PRINT"GP=";USING A$;I
280 PRINT"RI=";USING A$;J
290 PRINT"GP (DB) =";USING A$;K:PRINT""
300 IF N>30000 THEN 320
310 GOTO 180
320 PRINT"NOTE: OTHER INCREMENTS AND LIMITS FOR RL"
330 PRINT"MAY BE PROGRAMMED"
340 INPUT"DO YOU WANT TO REPEAT THIS (Y/N)";C$
350 IF C$="Y"THEN 120 ELSE 2000
```

1. If desired, prints out power gain G_p and value in ohms for R_I for a range of R_L values, from which you can select the best R_L and R_I values for your transistor; or computes the best R_L and R_I values for your transistor for minimum limits of G_p and R_I supplied by you.

2. From this information, calculates and prints voltage gain A_v, current gain A_i, final values of G_p and R_O, for an amplifier without feedback.

3. Asks if feedback is intended, and if so, what is the value of the feedback resistor; then prints perturbed values of the h parameters you entered originally, followed by new values for A_v, A_i, G_p, R_I, and R_O.

4. Finally, asks if you want a check of current stability S_I and voltage stability S_V. If the answer is affirmative, asks for R_E, R_I, R_F, R_L, and h_{fb}. (If you do not have h_{fb}, it equals $-h_{fe}/(1 + h_{fe})$. If the amplifier does not have feedback, R_F has the value of the resistor connected between V_{cc} and the transistor base.

Figure A-8(b) Continued
This portion of the program will only be done if you enter N in response to the prompt in line 30. It asks for the minimum power gain you will accept and input resistance required. The result will be more precise than that given in the previous section, but if the computed value is 100,000 or more the program will ask you to enter other limits.

```
1000 PRINT"I ASSUME YOU HAVE DECIDED ON MINIMUM"
1010 PRINT"POWER GAIN (GP) & INPUT RESISTANCE (RI)"
1020 PRINT"ENTER H PARAMETERS OF BJT TRANSISTOR"
1030 INPUT"HFE=";A
1040 INPUT"HOE=";B
1050 INPUT"HIE=";C
1060 INPUT"HRE=";D
1070 INPUT"GP MINIMUM LIMIT=";E
1080 INPUT"RI MINIMUM LIMIT=";F
1090 N=0:M=0:PRINT""
1100 M=M+1:N=N+1000
1110 I=A*A*N/((B*N+1)*((C*B-A*D)*N+C))
1120 J=(C+(B*C-A*D)*N)/(1+B*N)
1130 K=10*LOG(I)/LOG(10)
1140 IF (I>E)*(J*F) THEN 1190
1150 IF I>99999 THEN 1220
1160 IF J>99999 THEN 1220
1170 IF N>99999 THEN 1220
1180 GOTO 1100
1190 A$="######"
1200 PRINT"RI=";USING A$;J
1210 PRINT"RL=";USING A$;N:GOTO 2000
1220 PRINT"COMPUTED VALUE IS GREATER THAN 99999"
1230 PRINT"ENTER OTHER LIMITS": GOTO 1070
```

Figure A-8(b) Continued

This portion of the program is done after either of the two previous sections. It asks you to enter the R_L and R_I you have decided on, and then proceeds to compute the values for A_V, A_I, G_P, R_I, and R_O to be expected from this circuit.

These values are for a circuit without voltage feedback. However, the program then asks if the circuit is to have voltage feedback, and if your response is Y it jumps to line 3000. Alternatively, it asks if you want it to check for current and voltage stability without feedback, and if your response is Y it jumps to line 4000.

```
2000 PRINT"IF YOU HAVE MADE YOUR FINAL CHOICE FOR"
2010 PRINT"RL AND RI, YOU SHOULD NOW ENTER THEM"
2020 INPUT"RL=";E
2030 INPUT"RI=";F
2040 PRINT""
2050 G=A*E/((C*B-A*D)*E+C)
2060 A$="#####.##"
2070 PRINT"AV=";USING A$;G
2080 H=A/(B*E+1)
2090 PRINT"AI=";USING A$;H
2100 I=A*A*E/((B*E+1)*((C*B-A*D)*E+C))
2110 PRINT"GP=";USING A$;I
2120 J=(C+(B*C-A*D)*E)/(1+B*E)
2130 PRINT"RI=";USING A$;J
2140 K=(C+F)/(B*C-D*A+B*F)
2150 PRINT"RO=";USING A$;K
2160 IF D$="Y"THEN 2200
2170 PRINT"IS THIS AMPLIFIER TO HAVE VOLTAGE"
2180 INPUT"FEEDBACK? ENTER Y/N";D$
2190 IF D$="Y"THEN 3000
2200 PRINT"DO YOU WANT TO CHECK VOLTAGE & CURRENT"
2210 INPUT"STABILITY. ENTER Y/N";E$
2220 IF E$="Y"THEN 4000 ELSE 2230
2230 END
```

This portion of the program computes the perturbed h parameters resulting from voltage feedback, and then goes back to line 2040 to recalculate and print the voltage, current, and power gain, and input and output resistances resulting therefrom.

```
3000 INPUT"ENTER VALUE OF FEEDBACK RESISTOR RF";Z
3010 C=C*Z/(Z+C)
3020 A=(A*Z-C)/(Z+C)
3030 D=(C*(1-D))/(Z+C)
3040 B=B+((1+A)*(1-D))/(Z+C)
3050 A$="######":PRINT""
3060 PRINT"HIE(P)=";USING A$;C
3070 PRINT"HFE(P)=";USING A$;A
3080 B$="##.####"
3090 PRINT"HRE(P)=";USING B$;D
3100 C$="##.######"
3110 PRINT"HOE(P)=";USING C$;B
3120 GOTO 2040
```

Figure A-8(b) Continued

This portion will be done if your response to the program's prompt about checking current and voltage stability was affirmative. After you enter the component values called for the program will print out values for current stability S_I and voltage stability S_V. If there is no feedback resistor, enter the value of the resistor connected between $-V_{cc}$ and the transistor's base.

Ideally, S_I values should be zero. Practical values that do not exceed 1 are very good. Any double-digit value is not.

```
4000 INPUT"RE=";RE
4010 INPUT"RI=";RB
4020 INPUT"RF=";RF
4030 INPUT"RL=";RC
4040 INPUT"HFB=";FB
4050 SI=(1/RE)/(1/RB+1/RF+(1-FB)/RE)
4060 SV=-(SI*RE+RC*(1+FB*SI))
4070 A$="###.###":PRINT""
4080 PRINT"SI=";USING A$;SI
4090 A$="#######"
4100 PRINT"SV=";USING A$;SV
4110 END
```

Figure A-8(c) is a screen print of a run of this program. The program does not provide for a printout to printer, but you can include this in the program, if desired. Also, lines 250, 1190, 2060, 3050, 3080, 3100, 4070, and 4090 mean nothing to a Commodore machine. If you are using one of these, and you want to pretty up the output to the screen, you could use this subroutine:

```
5000 A$=STR$(N):FOR X=1 TO LEN(A$)
5010 IF MID$(A$,X,1)="."THEN GOTO 5040
5020 NEXT:AA$=A$
5030 RETURN
5040 A=A$+"000000000000":AA$=LEFT$(A$,X+Z)
5050 RETURN
```

Sample Program

```
10 INPUT"ENTER NUMBER OF DECIMAL PLACES";Z
20 INPUT"ENTER NUMBER TO BE FORMATTED";N
30 GOSUB 5000
```

40 PRINT AA$
50 END

The program must have a predetermined value for the number of decimal places, Z, before the subroutine is entered.

Figure A-8(c) What You Should See When You Run the Program.

```
Ready
>RUN
COMMON-EMITTER VOLTAGE AMPLIFIER DESIGN
DO YOU WANT TO FIND RL AND RI FOR
MAXIMUM POWER GAIN (Y/N)? Y
I AM ASSUMING THAT IC REMAINS THE SAME
SO VCC INCREASES FOR EACH RL INCREMENT
ENTER H PARAMETERS FOR BJT TRANSISTOR
HFE=? 60
HOE=? .00005
HIE=? 1250
HRE=? .0003
I WILL PRINT 2 SCREENS OF DATA
PRESS <HOLD> TO KEEP FIRST SCREEN
PRESS <HOLD> AGAIN FOR SECOND SCREEN

PRESS Y TO CONTINUE? Y
HFE= 60
HOE= 5E-05
HIE= 1250
HRE= 3E-04

RL=  5000
GP=  9779
RI=  1178
GP (DB) =      40

RL= 10000
GP= 14159
RI=  1130
GP (DB) =      42


RL= 15000
GP= 16092
RI=  1096
GP (DB) =      42

RL= 20000
GP= 16822
RI=  1070
GP (DB) =      42


RL= 25000
GP= 16931
RI=  1050
GP (DB) =      42

RL= 30000
GP= 16712
RI=  1034
GP (DB) =      42
```

Figure A-8(c) Continued

```
RL= 35000
GP= 16320
RI=  1021
GP (DB) =     42

NOTE: OTHER INCREMENTS AND LIMITS FOR RL
MAY BE PROGRAMMED
DO YOU WANT TO REPEAT THIS (Y/N)? N
IF YOU HAVE MADE YOUR FINAL CHOICE FOR
RL AND RI, YOU SHOULD NOW ENTER THEM
RL=? 25000
RI=? 1050

AV=   634.92
AI=    26.67
GP=16931.20
RI= 1050.00
RO=23711.30
IS THIS AMPLIFIER TO HAVE VOLTAGE
FEEDBACK? ENTER Y/N? Y
ENTER VALUE OF FEEDBACK RESISTOR RF? 120000

HIE(P)=   1237
HFE(P)=     59
HRE(P)= 0.0102
HOE(P)= 0.000543

AV=   514.35
AI=     4.07
GP= 2095.69
RI=   198.04
RO= 3595.89
DO YOU WANT TO CHECK VOLTAGE & CURRENT
STABILITY. ENTER Y/N? Y
RE=? 1400
RI=? 1050
RF=? 120000
RL=? 25000
HFB=? .99

SI=   0.738
SV= -44299
```

This is what you get if your response to line 30 is N.

```
COMMON-EMITTER VOLTAGE AMPLIFIER DESIGN
DO YOU WANT TO FIND RL AND RI FOR
MAXIMUM POWER GAIN (Y/N)? N
I ASSUME YOU HAVE DECIDED ON MINIMUM
POWER GAIN (GP) & INPUT RESISTANCE (RI)
ENTER H PARAMETERS OF BJT TRANSISTOR
HFE=? 60
HOE=? .00005
HIE=? 1250
HRE=? .0003
GP MINIMUM LIMIT=? 16931
RI MINIMUM LIMIT=? 1050

RI=   1057
RL= 23000
```

Figure A-8(d) is another program for computing A_V for a MOSFET amplifier, first with the source resistor bypassed, and second with it not bypassed. Underneath the program listing, you can see how the screen looks when this program is run. The circuit is shown in Figure A-8(e).

Figure A-8(d) Program to Compute Voltage Gain for the MOSFET Amplifier Shown in Figure A-8 (e), and Sample Run.

```
10 PRINT"VOLTAGE GAIN OF COMMON-SOURCE AMPLIFIER"
20 PRINT""
30 PRINT"WITH BYPASSED SOURCE RESISTOR"
40 INPUT"GFS (SIEMENS)=";A
50 INPUT"ROS (OHMS)=";B
60 INPUT"RL (OHMS)=";C
70 D=A*B*C/(B+C)
80 A$="#####.##"
90 PRINT"AV =";USING A$;D
100 PRINT""
110 PRINT"WITH UNBYPASSED SOURCE RESISTOR"
120 INPUT"GFS (SIEMENS)=";E
130 INPUT"ROS (OHMS)=";F
140 INPUT"RL (OHMS)=";G
150 INPUT"RS (OHMS)=";H
160 AA=E*F*G/(F+(E*F-1)*H+G)
170 PRINT"AV =";USING A$;AA
180 PRINT""
190 PRINT"OUTPUT RESISTANCE WITH UNBYPASSED"
200 PRINT"SOURCE RESISTOR"
210 INPUT"GFS (SIEMENS)=";I
220 INPUT"ROS (OHMS)=";J
230 INPUT"RS (OHMS)=";K
240 N=J*I+1
250 RR=J+N*K
260 PRINT"RO (OHMS) =";RR
270 END


Ready
>RUN
VOLTAGE GAIN OF COMMON-SOURCE AMPLIFIER

WITH BYPASSED SOURCE RESISTOR
GFS (SIEMENS)=? .006
ROS (OHMS)=? 15000
RL (OHMS)=? 8000
AV =    31.30

WITH UNBYPASSED SOURCE RESISTOR
GFS (SIEMENS)=? .006
ROS (OHMS)=? 15000
RL (OHMS)=? 8000
RS (OHMS)=? 750
AV =     8.02

OUTPUT RESISTANCE WITH UNBYPASSED
SOURCE RESISTOR
GFS (SIEMENS)=? .006
ROS (OHMS)=? 15000
RS (OHMS)=? 1000
RO (OHMS) = 106000
```

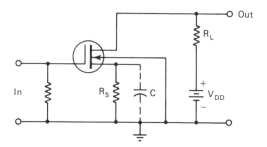

Figure A-8(e) Common Source Voltage Amplifier for Program in Figure A-8(d). [4]

AMPLITUDE MODULATION

Amplitude Modulation (AM) is modulation in which the amplitude of the carrier is varied in accordance with the intelligence to be transmitted. The amount of modulation, referred to as the percentage of modulation, is given by:

$$M = [(V_C - V_T)/2V_{av}] \times 100$$

where:

V_{av} = average amplitude of modulated carrier.

V_C = amplitude of crest of modulated carrier.

V_T = amplitude of trough of modulated carrier.

M = percentage of modulation.

Measurement of Modulation Percentage

Apply the modulated carrier to the Y input of an oscilloscope, and the modulating wave to the X input. A "trapezoidal" waveform will appear of the screen, as shown in Figure A-9. The modulation percentage M is given by:

$$M = [(H_1 - H_2)/(H_1 + H_2)] \times 100$$

Figure A-9 Measurement of Amplitude Modulation Percentage.
Using an oscilloscope as described in the text gives one of these figures on the screen. [5]

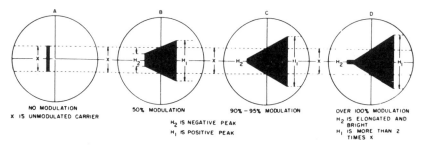

where:

H_1 and H_2 are the dimensions shown in the figure.

Power

Sideband power:

$$P_{SB} = (M^2/2) \times P_C$$

Total radiated power:

$$P_T = P_{SB} + P_C$$

where:

M = modulation percentage.

P_C = carrier power, in watts.

P_{SB} = total sideband power, in watts.

P_T = total radiated power, in watts.

ANTENNAS

Radio waves are transmitted through space without wires, but they are produced and detected by electrical circuits in which electrons flow in wires. An antenna is the means of converting radiation energy into electrical energy, and vice versa. Any piece of wire or metal rod can act as an antenna but, like every other conductor, it has the properties of resistance, inductance, and capacitance. Therefore, there will be some frequency at which the antenna will be resonant. At this frequency, the antenna will transmit or receive better than at others. The main determining factor in an antenna's resonance is its length; therefore, there is a proper length for best reception or transmission at each frequency. The length is generally a multiple or submultiple of the wavelength.

Half-Wavelength Antenna in Space

$$L = 492/f$$

Half-Wavelength Antenna in the Atmosphere
$$L = 468/f$$

One Wavelength in Feet

$$L = 984V/f$$

Electrical Length

$$\lambda_{FT} = 984/f$$

Long-Wire Antenna Length

$$L = [492(N - 0.05)]/f$$

Quarter-Wave Antenna Length

$$L = 246V/f$$

Radiation Resistance

$$R = P/I^2$$

Efficiency

$$E_{ff} = 100R/(R + R_w + R_L)$$

Total Number of Lobes in Radiation Pattern

$$L_T = 2N$$

where:

E_{ff} = antenna efficiency, in percent.

F = frequency, in megahertz.

I = effective current (at maximum current point), in amperes.

L = length, in feet.

λ_{FT} = wavelength, in feet.

L_T = total number of lobes.

N = number of halfwaves on antenna.

P = radiated power, in watts.

R = radiation resistance, in ohms.

R_L = equivalent resistance of other losses, in ohms.

R_w = effective wire resistance, in ohms.

V = velocity factor of transmission line (see transmission lines).

(*Note:* Wavelength, denoted by λ (lambda), is normally given in meters. To convert meters to feet, multiply by 3.2808.)

Antilogarithm *See* Mathematical Tables.

Apparent Power *See* Alternating Current.

Argon Lamp *See* Lamps.

Arrester, Lightning There are two types. The heavy-duty type used to safeguard house wiring from surges of 2000 V or more contains a spark gap that is wide enough to block ordinary voltages but across which the high voltage produced by lightning can easily jump and escape to ground.

A plug-in surge or spike arrester for surges less than 2000 V may also be used at receptacles serving delicate electronic equipment. It consists of a voltage-sensitive resistor made of silicon carbide (a "varistor"). A similar device is available for use with the antenna transmission line of a receiver. The current normally passing through it is negligibly small, but if a high voltage surge occurs it is shunted to ground. Current through the resistor is given by:

$$I = KV^n$$

where:

V = voltage across the resistor, in volts.

I = current through the resistor, in amperes.

K = a constant, equal to the current, in amperes, at V = 1 volt.

n = a constant dependent on voltage, usually between 4 and 5.

Astable Multivibrator *See* Oscillators.

ATTENUATORS

An attenuator is a resistive network that provides a known reduction in the amplitude of a signal without introducing appreciable distortion. If its input and output impedances are equal, the attenuator is said to be *symmetrical*. If they are unequal, it is called a *pad*. Pads are often used to match dissimilar impedances, and then are designed to introduce as low an insertion loss as possible. These pads are called *minimum-loss pads*.

Symmetrical attenuators, both balanced and unbalanced, are shown in Figure A-10. Underneath each is a formula for determining the resistance of each resistor. To perform the calculation, substitute for Z the required impedance, and for A, B, or C the value from the appropriate column in Table A-2 corresponding to the attenuation desired.

Figure A-10 Symmetrical Attenuators. [5]

UNBALANCED   **BALANCED**

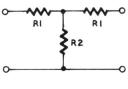

T Pad
R1 = ZA; R2 = ZB

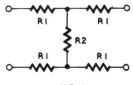

H Pad
$R1 = \dfrac{ZA}{2}$; R2 = ZB

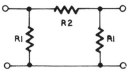

π Pad
$R1 = \dfrac{Z}{A}$; $R2 = \dfrac{Z}{B}$

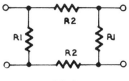

O Pad
$R1 = \dfrac{Z}{A}$; $R2 = \dfrac{Z}{2B}$

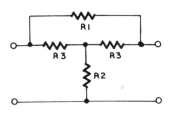

Bridged T Pad
$R1 = \dfrac{Z}{C}$; R2 = ZC; R3 = Z

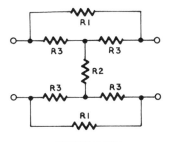

BRIDGED H PAD
$R1 = \dfrac{Z}{2C}$; R2 = ZC; $R3 = \dfrac{Z}{2}$

TABLE A-2   Values for Formulas in Figure A-10

ATTENUATION dB	A	B	C
−0.1	0.00576	86.9	86.4
−0.2	0.0115	43.4	42.9
−0.4	0.0230	21.7	21.2
−0.6	0.0345	14.4	14.0
−0.8	0.0460	10.8	10.4
−1.0	0.0575	8.67	8.20
−2.0	0.115	4.30	3.86
−3.0	0.171	2.84	2.42
−4.0	0.226	2.10	1.71
−5.0	0.280	1.64	1.28
−6.0	0.332	1.34	1.00
−7.0	0.382	1.12	0.807
−8.00	0.431	0.946	0.661
−9.00	0.476	0.812	0.550
−10.0	0.519	0.703	0.462
−12.0	0.598	0.536	0.335
−14.0	0.667	0.416	0.249
−16.0	0.726	0.325	0.188
−18.0	0.776	0.256	0.144
−20.0	0.818	0.202	0.111
−22.0	0.853	0.160	0.0863
−24.0	0.881	0.127	0.0673
−26.0	0.905	0.100	0.0528
−28.0	0.923	0.0797	0.0415
−30.0	0.939	0.0633	0.0327
−35.0	0.965	0.0356	0.0181
−40.0	0.980	0.0200	0.0101
−50.0	0.994	0.00632	0.00317
−60.0	0.998	0.00200	0.00100
−80.0	0.999	0.000200	0.000100
−100.0	0.999	0.0000200	0.0000100

Minimum-loss pads are shown in Figure A-11, together with formulas for calculating their resistor values. $Z1$ is always the larger impedance, connected to the higher of the impedances to be matched.

Figures A-12 through A-15 are computer programs in BASIC that may be used instead of manual calculation.

Audible Signaling Device *See* Transducers.

Audio Amplifiers *See* Amplifiers.

Audio Output Transformer *See* Transformers.

Avalanche Diode See Zener Diodes.

Figure A-11 Minimum-Loss Pads. [5]

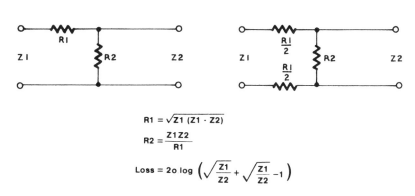

Figure A-11 Minimum-Loss Pads. [5]

$$R1 = \sqrt{Z1\,(Z1 - Z2)}$$

$$R2 = \frac{Z1\,Z2}{R1}$$

$$\text{Loss} = 20 \log \left(\sqrt{\frac{Z1}{Z2}} + \sqrt{\frac{Z1}{Z2} - 1} \right)$$

Figure A-12 BASIC Program for T or H Attenuator

Larger impedance must be entered first. Minimum loss cannot be 0 dB. R3 is the output series resistance (the right-hand R1 in Figure A-10). In the H type each series resistor is half the value of the corresponding series resistor in the T type.

```
10 PRINT"PROGRAM FOR DESIGN OR ANALYSIS OF T-TYPE"
20 PRINT"(UNBALANCED) OR H-TYPE (BALANCED) RESIS-"
30 PRINT"TIVE ATTENUATOR SECTION. VALUE IN OHMS."
40 PRINT
50 PRINT"ENTER INPUT IMPEDANCE Z1 AND OUTPUT IM-"
60 PRINT"PEDANCE Z2 (AS Z1,Z2)"
70 INPUT Z1,Z2
80 LET Z=Z1/Z2
90 LET Q=(SQR(Z)+SQR(Z-1))^2
100 LET M=10*(LOG(Q)/LOG(10))
110 PRINT
120 PRINT"MINIMUM LOSS IN DECIBELS = ";M
130 PRINT
140 PRINT"ENTER DESIRED LOSS IN DECIBELS"
150 INPUT L
160 LET N=EXP(2.3026*(L/10))
170 LET W=N-1
180 LET U=N+1
190 LET R3=2*(SQR(Z1*Z2*N))/W
200 LET R1=(Z1*(U/W))-R3
210 LET R2=(Z2*(U/W))-R3
220 PRINT
230 PRINT"INPUT IMPEDANCE  = ";Z1
240 PRINT"OUTPUT IMPEDANCE = ";Z2
250 PRINT"              R1 = ";R1
260 PRINT"              R2 = ";R2
270 PRINT"              R3 = ";R3
280 END
```

Figure A-13 BASIC Program for π or 0 Attenuator

Larger impedance must be entered first. Minimum loss cannot be 0 dB. R3 is the output shunt resistor (the right-hand R1 in Figure A-10). In the 0 type each series resistor is half the value of the corresponding series resistor in the π type.

```
10 PRINT"PROGRAM FOR DESIGN OR ANALYSIS OF PI-"
20 PRINT"TYPE (UNBALANCED) OR 0-TYPE (BALANCED)"
30 PRINT"RESISTIVE ATTENUATOR SECTION. VALUES IN"
40 PRINT"OHMS"
50 PRINT
60 PRINT"ENTER INPUT IMPEDANCE Z1 AND OUTPUT IM-"
70 PRINT"PEDANCE Z2 (AS Z1,Z2)
80 INPUT Z1,Z2
90 LET Z=Z1/Z2
100 LET Q=(SQR(Z)+SQR(Z-1))^2
110 LET M=10*(LOG(Q)/LOG(10))
120 PRINT
130 PRINT"MINIMUM LOSS IN DECIBELS = ";M
140 PRINT
150 PRINT"ENTER DESIRED LOSS IN DECIBELS"
160 INPUT L
170 LETN=EXP(2.3026*(L/10))
180 LET W=N-1
190 LET U=N+1
200 LET R3=(W*SQR((Z1*Z2)/N))/2
210 LET R1=1/((1/Z1)*(U/W)-(1/R3))
220 LET R2=1/((1/Z2)*(U/W)-(1/R3))
230 PRINT
240 PRINT"INPUT IMPEDANCE  = ";Z1
250 PRINT"OUTPUT IMPEDANCE = ";Z2
260 PRINT"              R1 = ";R1
270 PRINT"              R2 = ";R2
280 PRINT"              R3 = ";R3
290 END
```

Figure A-14 BASIC Program for Bridged-T
or Bridged-H Attenuator

This attenuator is symmetrical. Minimum loss cannot be 0 dB. In the Bridged-H
type each series resistor (R1 and R3 in Figure A-10) is half the value of the corresponding series resistor in the Bridged-T
type.

```
10 PRINT"PROGRAM FOR DESIGN OR ANALYSIS OF"
20 PRINT"BRIDGED-T OR BRIDGED-H RESISTIVE"
30 PRINT"ATTENUATOR SECTION. VALUES IN OHMS"
40 PRINT
50 PRINT"THIS ATTENUATOR IS SYMMETRICAL"
60 PRINT"ENTER IMPEDANCE"
70 INPUT Z
80 PRINT
90 PRINT"ENTER DESIRED LOSS IN DECIBELS"
100 INPUT L
110 LET N=EXP(2.3026*(L/10))
120 LET R2=Z/(SQR(N)-1)
130 LET R1=Z*(SQR(N)-1)
140 PRINT
150 PRINT"R1 = ";R1
160 PRINT"R2 = ";R2
170 PRINT"R3 = ";Z
180 END
```

Figure A-15 BASIC Program for Minimum-
Loss L Pad

```
10 PRINT"PROGRAM TO ANALYZE OR DESIGN MINIMUM-"
20 PRINT"LOSS L-PAD MATCHING INPUT IMPEDANCE Z1"
30 PRINT"AND OUTPUT IMPEDANCE Z2 (Z1>Z2)"
40 PRINT"(VALUES OF R AND Z IN OHMS)"
50 PRINT
60 PRINT"ENTER Z1 AND Z2 (AS Z1,Z2)"
70 INPUT Z1,Z2
80 IF Z1>Z2 THEN 100
90 PRINT"Z1 MUST BE GREATER THAN Z2":GOTO 60
100 LET R1=Z1*SQR(1-(Z2/Z1))
110 LET R2=Z2/SQR(1-(Z2/Z1))
120 LET M= SQR(Z1/Z2)+SQR((Z1/Z2)-1)
130 LET L=20*(LOG(M)/LOG(10))
140 LET D$=" DECIBELS"
150 PRINT
160 PRINT"R1   =    ";R1
170 PRINT"R2   =    ";R2
180 PRINT"LOSS =    ";L;D$
190 END
```

Bandwidth *See* Amplifiers.

Base *See* Transistors.

Battery *See* Power Sources.

Beta *See* Transistors.

BIASING METHODS

Voltage-Divider Bias Circuit

Figure B-1 shows the most widely used transistor bias circuit. The values for $R1$ and $R2$ are given by:

$$R1 = RB(V_{CC}/V_B)$$

$$R2 = R1[V_B/(V_{CC} - V_B)]$$

Figure B-1 Voltage-Divider Bias Circuit [3]

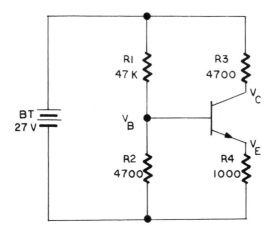

Voltage-Divider Bias Circuit with Feedback

If $R1$ in the previous circuit is connected to the transistor collector instead of to the power supply, voltage feedback (shunt feedback) is obtained. The values of $R1$ and $R2$ are given by:

$$R1 = RB(V_C/V_B)$$
$$R2 = R1[V_B/(V_C - V_B)]$$

where:

$$RB = (R1 \times R2)/(R1 + R2)$$
$$V_B = \text{desired bias voltage.}$$
$$V_C = \text{collector voltage.}$$
$$V_{CC} = \text{supply voltage from battery.}$$

When Using a Field-Effect Transistor

When using an FET, a voltage-divider bias circuit is not always required. In this case, $R1$ in Figure B-1 is eliminated, and $R2$ is usually 1 megohm. Bias is then set by the value of $R3$, as in a vacuum-tube circuit, given by:

$$R_S = V_S/I_D$$

where:

$$R_S = \text{source resistance, in ohms.}$$
$$V_S = \text{source voltage} (= V_G - V_{GS}), \text{ in volts.}$$
$$I_D = \text{drain current, in amperes.}$$

Bleeder Resistor *See* Power Sources.

Breakdown Diode *See* Diodes.

BROADCASTING

Broadcasting is concerned with the dissemination of sound and television signals. Sound broadcasting requires a relatively narrow bandwidth and therefore has fewer technical problems than television. Amplitude modulation (AM) gives satisfactory reproduction of speech and music within a modulation frequency range of about 100 Hz to 8 kHz.

High fidelity requires a modulation frequency range of 30 Hz to 15 kHz, which is extended out to 75 kHz by stereo and SCA, so it uses frequency-modulated (FM) carrier frequencies between 88 MHz and 108 MHz, where the wider bandwidth can be provided. A television station, on the other hand, needs an AM frequency channel width of 6 MHz, and its carrier frequency will be in the ranges shown for Bands I, III, IV and V in Table B-1 below. U.S. television channel frequencies are listed in Table B-2.

TABLE B-1   International Carrier-Frequency Band Allocation

Frequency	Wavelength	Frequency range	Purpose
Low	Long	150–285 kHz	AM sound
Medium	Medium	525–1605 kHz	AM sound
High	Short	Bands approximately 259 kHz wide located near 4, 6, 7, 9, 11, 15, 17, 21, 26 MHz	AM sound
Very high	Band I	47–68 MHz	Television*
	Band II	87.5–108 MHz	FM sound
	Band III	174–216 MHz	Television*
Ultra-high	Bands IV and V	470–960 MHz	Television*

*See Table B-3 for authorized power and antenna height.

Table B-2   US Television Channel Frequencies [7]

Channel Number (Low VHF)	Lower Frequency (MHz)	Picture Carrier (AM) (MHz)	Color Carrier (MHz)	Sound Carrier (FM) (MHz)	Upper Frequency (MHz)
2	54	55.25	58.85	59.75	60
3	60	61.25	64.83	65.75	66
4	66	67.25	70.83	71.75	72
5	76	77.25	80.83	81.75	82
6	82	83.25	86.83	87.75	88
7	174	175.25	178.83	179.75	180
8	180	181.25	184.83	185.75	186
9	186	187.25	190.83	191.75	192
10	192	193.25	196.83	197.75	198
11	198	199.25	202.83	203.75	204
12	204	205.25	208.83	209.75	210
13	210	211.25	214.83	215.75	216
14	470	471.25	474.83	475.75	476
15	476	477.25	480.83	481.75	482
16	482	483.25	486.83	487.75	488
17	488	489.75	492.83	493.75	494
18	494	495.25	498.83	499.75	500
19	500	501.25	504.83	505.75	506
20	506	507.25	510.83	511.75	512
21	512	513.25	516.83	517.75	518
22	518	519.25	522.83	523.75	524
23	524	525.25	528.83	529.75	530
24	530	531.25	534.83	535.75	536
25	536	537.25	540.83	541.75	542
26	542	543.25	546.83	547.75	548
27	548	549.25	552.83	553.75	554
28	554	555.25	558.83	559.75	560
29	560	561.25	564.83	565.75	566
30	566	567.25	570.83	571.75	572
31	572	573.25	576.83	577.75	578
32	578	579.25	582.83	583.75	584

Table B-2   (continued)

Channel Number	Lower Frequency (MHz)	Picture Carrier (AM) (MHz)	Color Carrier (MHz)	Sound Carrier (FM) (MHz)	Upper Frequency (MHz)
33	584	585.25	587.83	589.75	590
34	590	591.25	594.83	595.75	596
35	596	597.25	600.83	601.75	602
36	602	603.25	606.83	607.75	608
37	608	609.25	612.83	613.75	614
38	614	615.25	618.83	619.75	620
39	620	621.25	624.83	625.75	626
40	626	627.25	630.83	631.75	632
41	632	633.25	636.83	637.75	638
42	638	639.25	642.83	643.75	644
43	644	645.25	648.83	649.75	650
44	650	651.25	654.83	655.75	656
45	656	657.25	660.83	661.75	662
46	662	663.25	666.83	667.75	668
47	668	669.25	672.83	673.75	674
48	674	675.25	678.83	679.75	680
49	680	681.25	684.83	685.75	686
50	686	687.25	690.83	691.75	692
51	692	693.25	696.83	697.75	698
52	698	699.25	702.75	703.75	704
53	704	705.25	707.83	709.75	710
54	710	711.25	714.83	715.75	716
55	716	717.25	720.83	721.75	722
56	722	723.25	726.83	727.75	728
57	728	729.25	732.83	733.75	734
58	734	735.25	738.83	739.75	740
59	740	741.25	744.83	745.75	746
60	746	747.25	780.83	751.75	752
61	752	753.25	756.83	757.75	758
62	758	759.25	762.83	763.75	764
63	764	765.25	768.83	769.75	770
64	770	771.25	774.83	775.75	776
65	776	777.25	780.83	781.75	782
66	782	783.25	786.83	787.75	788
67	788	789.25	792.83	793.75	794
68	794	795.25	798.83	799.75	800
69	800	801.25	804.83	805.75	806
70	806	807.25	810.83	811.75	812
71	812	813.25	816.83	817.75	818
72	818	819.25	822.83	823.75	824
73	824	825.25	828.83	829.75	830
74	830	831.25	834.83	835.75	836
75	836	837.25	840.83	841.75	842
76	842	843.25	846.83	847.75	848
77	848	849.25	852.83	853.75	854
78	854	855.25	858.83	859.75	860
79	860	861.25	864.83	865.75	866
80	866	867.25	870.83	871.75	872
81	872	873.25	876.83	877.75	878
82	878	879.25	882.83	883.75	884
83	884	885.25	888.83	889.75	890

TABLE B-3

Channel	Maximum power (kW)[1]	Maximum antenna height[2]
2–6	100	2000 ft[3]
7–13	316	2000 ft[3]
14–69	5000[4]	2000 ft

[1]Minimum power is 100 watts in all cases.
[2]Increased height may be authorized, but output power must be reduced accordingly.
[3]In Northeast USA, maximum height is 1000 ft.
[4]Limited to 1000 kW within 250 miles of Canadian border.

Other requirements for U.S. TV stations are:

Channel width	6 MHz
Picture carrier location	1.25 MHz ± 1000 Hz above lower boundary of channel
Aural center frequency	4.5 MHz ± 1000 Hz above visual carrier
Aural transmitter power	20 percent of peak visual power
Modulation	AM composite picture and sync signal on visual carrier and FM audio signal on sound carrier. (See Figure B-2.)

Figure B-2 US Television Channel Frequency Spectrum (For actual frequencies, see Table B-2) [6]

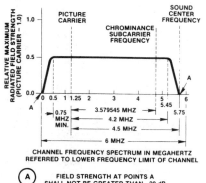

CHANNEL FREQUENCY SPECTRUM IN MEGAHERTZ
REFERRED TO LOWER FREQUENCY LIMIT OF CHANNEL

(A) FIELD STRENGTH AT POINTS A SHALL NOT BE GREATER THAN -20 dB

Scanning lines	525 lines per frame, interlaced two to one
Scanning sequence	Horizontally from left to right, vertically from top to bottom
Horizontal scanning frequency	2/455 times chrominance subcarrier frequency (15,734.264 ± 0.044 Hz)
Vertical scanning frequency	2/525 times the horizontal scanning frequency (59.94 Hz)
Chrominance subcarrier frequency	3.579545 MHz ± 10 Hz
Blanking level*	75.0 ± 2.5 percent of peak carrier level
Reference black level*	92.5 ± 2.5 percent of amplitude of blanking level above reference white level
Reference white level*	Luminance signal of reference white is 12.5 ± 2.5 percent of peak carrier level
Horizontal pulse timing tolerance	±0.5 percent of average interval
Horizontal pulse repetition stability	±0.15 percent per second
Audio modulation (FM)	Same as FM radio
Audio distortion	Same as FM radio
Color signal	Luminance component transmitted as AM of the picture carrier, and chrominance components as AM sidebands of two suppressed subcarriers in quadrature. (See Figure B-4.)
I-channel bandwidth	Flat within 2 dB to 1.3 MHz
Q-channel bandwidth	Flat within 2 dB to 400 kHz

Subsidiary signals (test, cue, and control signals) are transmitted in lines 17 through 20 of the vertical blanking interval. Coded patterns for identification of the program may be transmitted in the intervals within

*See Figure B-3.

Figure B-3 Television Composite Signal.

U.S. and European signals are similar, except that they are of opposite phase. The sync pulses are "upside down" in the European signal. [6]

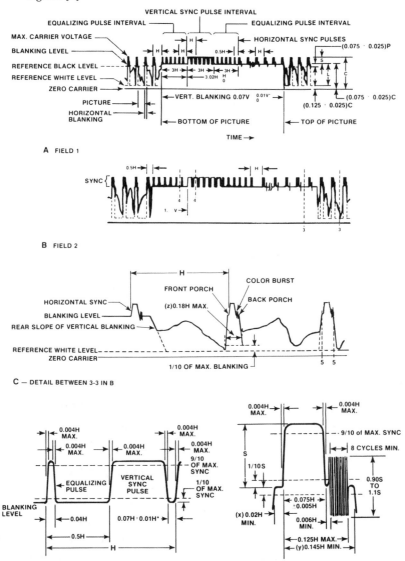

the first and last 10 microseconds of lines 22 through 24 and 260 through 262. The aural FM signal may also be multiplexed for communication between station control and transmitter sites, as it is in FM radio.

U.S. Instructional Television

Assigned transmission frequencies are in the band from 2.5 to 2.68 GHz,

Figure B-4 In color modulation any hue can be represented by a phasor having a specific phase angle and an amplitude corresponding to the degree of saturation. Two subcarriers are used. The colors to be transmitted are separated into their orange (+) and cyan (−) components, which amplitude-modulate the I carrier; and their magenta (+) and yellow-green components (−), which amplitude-modulate the Q carrier. Both carrier frequencies are 3.579545 MHz, but they differ in phase by 90 degrees. Intermediate colors consist of the vector addition of their component amplitudes on both carriers, as shown above for red, green, and blue. [2]

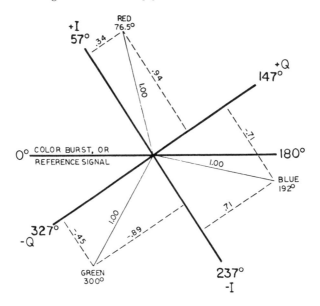

and power is limited to a maximum of 10 watts. Other requirements are the same as for commercial television. Directive transmitting and receiving antenna arrays are preferred.

U.S. Television Satellites

TV relay satellites occupy circular equatorial orbits at a height of about 36,000 km, with a period of 23 h 56 m. Allocated bands are 2.5 to 2.69 GHz (community reception only), 3.7 to 4.2 GHz down, and about 6 GHz up (current U.S. satellites), 11.7 to 12.5, 12.1 to 12.7, and 11.7 to 12.2 GHz.

European Television

The United Kingdom started TV broadcasting with a 405-line system, and France with an 819-line system, but the standard for Europe now is a

625-line system, with 25 pictures (50 fields) per second. The distribution of frequencies within the IF band used in this system is shown in Figure B-5.

Figure B-5 European TV Channel Frequency Spectrum.
Luminance and chrominance sidebands occupy spectrum between roll-offs at −1.25 and +5.5 MHz. V = picture carrier frequency; C = color subcarrier frequency (4.43361875 MHz above picture carrier frequency); A = audio carrier frequency (FM); X = lower limit of color sidebands.

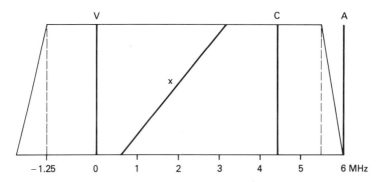

PAL Color Transmission

The *Phase Alternation Line* (PAL) system is used in the U.K., many European countries, South Africa, Australia, New Zealand, and some others. (The U.S. system is called NTSC, standing for National Television System Committee.) PAL is similar to the NTSC color system, except that the phase of one of the chrominance signals is reversed during alternate line periods. The chrominance signals are designated U and V (compared with the I and Q signals in NTSC), and the phase of the V axis component is electronically reversed after every line. By using this method, phase errors introduced in one line are reversed in the next line, so maintaining the correct hue.

SECAM Color Transmission

The *Sequential and Memory* (SECAM) system is used in France, the USSR, East Europe, and some African and Middle East countries. In this system, the three primary colors are transmitted in succession. It is therefore not compatible with either the NTSC or PAL systems. However, modern methods of digitization make it possible to translate each system into either of the others.

Sound Broadcasting

Amplitude-modulated (AM) broadcasting has the following station performance requirements:

Modulation	85–95 percent.
Audio frequency distortion	Harmonics less than 5 percent of arithmetical sum or RMS amplitude up to 84 percent modulation; less than 7.5 percent for 85–95 percent modulation.
Audio-frequency response	Transmission characteristic flat between 100 and 5000 Hz to within 2 dB, referred to 1000 Hz.
Noise	At least 45 dB, unweighted, below 100 percent modulation for the frequency band from 30 to 20,000 Hz.
Carrier-frequency stability	Within 20 Hz of assigned frequency.

Table B-4 explains the classification of U.S. broadcast stations.

Frequency-modulated (FM) broadcasting has the following station performance requirements:

Modulation	Frequency modulation with a modulating capability of 100 percent corresponding to a frequency swing of ±75 kHz.
Audio-frequency distortion	Maximum combined audiofrequency harmonic RMS voltage in system output less than:

50–100 Hz <3.5%
100–7500 Hz <2.5%
7500–15,000 Hz <3.0%

TABLE B-4 Classification of Standard U.S. Broadcast Stations
(a) Domestic

Class of channel	Class of station	Permissible power (kWh)	Signal-intensity contour of area protected from objectionable interference (microvolts/meter)		Permissible interfering signal on same channel (microvolts/meter)	
			Day[1]	Night	Day[1]	Night[3]
Clear	I-A	50	100*	500*[2]	5	25
			500†	500†[1]	5	
	I-B	10–50	100*	500*[2]	5	25
	II-A	0.25–50 day 10–50 night	500	500[1]	25	25
	II-B } II-D }	0.25–50	500	2500[1]	25	125
Regional	III-A	1–5	500	2500[1]	25	125
	III-B	0.5–5 day 0.5–1 night	500	4000[1]	25	200
Local	IV	0.25–1 day 0.25 night	500	—	25	—

Notes:
*Same channel.
†Adjacent channel.
[1] Ground wave.
[2] 50% sky wave.
[3] 10% sky wave.

(b) International

Band	Frequency (kHz)
A	5950–6200
B	9500–9775
C	11,700–11,975
D	15,100–15,450
E	17,700–17,900
F	21,450–21,750
G	25,600–26,100

Source: Federal Communications Commission Rules and Regulations, Volume III, Part 73, Sept. 1972.

Figure B-6 Standard Pre-Emphasis Curves for FM Broadcasting.
Time constant is 75 microseconds (solid line). Frequency response must be between the two lines.

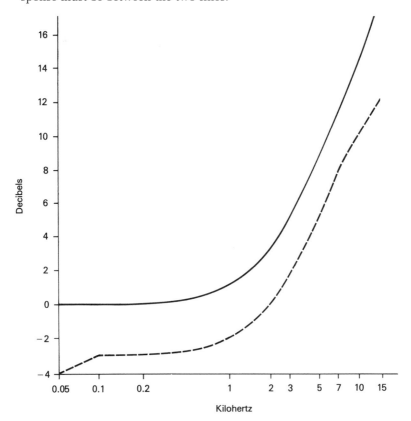

Audio-frequency response	Transmitting system capable of transmitting the band of frequencies from 50–15,000 Hz. Pre-emphasis employed and response maintained within limits given in Figure B-6.
Noise	(FM) In the band 50–15,000 Hz, at least 60 dB below 100 percent modulation at 400-Hz modulating frequency. (AM) In the band 50 to 15,000 Hz, at least 50 dB below level representing 100-percent amplitude modulation.

Center-frequency stability	Within ± 2000 Hz of assigned frequency.
Antenna polarization	Horizontal required, but circular or elliptical may be employed if desired.
Out-of-band radiation	Between 120 and 240 kHz removed from carrier, any emission must be at least 25 dB below the level of the unmodulated carrier. Any emission removed by more than 600 kHz must be at least 80 dB below the level of the unmodulated carrier, or at least $43 + 10 \log_{10} P$ watts, whichever is the lesser attenuation.

Authorized Frequencies: FM broadcasting stations are authorized for operation on 100 allocated channels, each 200 kHz wide, extending consecutively from channel 201 on 88.1 MHz to channel 300 on 107.9 MHz. Commercial broadcasting is authorized on channels 221 (92.1 MHz) through 300. Noncommercial educational broadcasting is licensed on channels 201 through 220 (91.9 MHz).

U.S. Station Service Classification:

Class *A*	Serve primarily a relatively small community, city, or town, and the rural surroundings. The coverage will not exceed the equivalent of 3 kW effective radiated power (antenna gain multiplied by antenna input power) at an antenna height of 300 feet above average terrain (average elevation between 2 and 10 miles from the antenna along eight radials evenly spaced by 45°). Minimum effective radiated power is 100 W. Class A channels are 221, 224, 228, 232, 237, 240, 252, 257, 261, 265, 269, 272, 276, 280, 285, 288, 292, and 296.
Class *B*	Serve a large community in Zone I (northeastern part of U.S.), or Zone IA (Puerto Rico, Virgin Islands, and California south of 40° N.). The coverage will not exceed the equivalent of an effective power of 50 kW at an antenna height of 500 feet above average terrain. Minimum effective radiated power is 5 kW.

Class *C*   Serve a large community in Zone II (Alaska, Hawaii, and other parts of the U.S. not in Zone I or IA). The coverage will not exceed the equivalent of an effective radiated power of 100 kW at an antenna height of 2000 feet above average terrain. Minimum effective radiated power is 25 kW.

Class *D*   Operate on a noncommercial educational channel with maximum transmitter output power of 10 W.

According to their class, FM stations must also be situated with respect to each other by not less than the minimum mileages shown in Table B-5.

TABLE B-5   Minimum Mileage Separation Between FM Stations

	Class *A*				Class *B*				Class *C*		
	Separation in kHz				Separation in kHz				Separation in kHz		
	Co-ch*	200	400	600	Co-ch*	200	400	600	Co-ch*	200	400	600
Class	Minimum mileage separations										
A	65	40	15	15	—	65	40	40	—	105	65	65
B	—	65	40	40	150	105	40	40	170	135	65	65
C	—	105	65	65	170	135	65	65	180	150	65	65

*Co-channel

Frequency Spectrum

Stereophonic transmission by FM stations uses the main channel and a stereophonic subchannel. It is important to recognize that a requirement is that monophonic receivers must receive monophonic or stereophonic programs without degradation; that is, the systems must be compatible. The main channel refers to the band of frequencies from 50 to 15,000 hertz that modulate the main carrier. The stereophonic subchannel is the band of frequencies from 23 to 53 kilohertz containing the stereophonic subcarrier and its associated sidebands. The pilot subcarrier is a control signal, and the stereophonic subcarrier is the second harmonic of the pilot subcarrier. (See Figure B-7.)

Figure B-7 FM Broadcasting Station Frequency Spectrum

Only the main channel (0-15 kHz) is used for monaural broadcasting. SCA (Subsidiary Communications Authorization) signals are used by duly authorized stations for interstation communication and for background music only, supplied to commercial customers. [6]

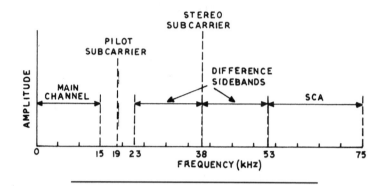

C

CALCULUS

General

The *differential calculus* applies itself to the problem of finding the slope of a curve, and the *integral calculus* deals with the area under the curve.

Differentiation

The curve in Figure C-1 is a graph of $y = f(x)$, or y equals a function of x (such as $x^2 - 1$). The slope of the curve at the point P is given by the tangent PT, which touches the curve but does not intersect it. PT is also the limiting position of the chord PQ (straight line) when Q moves up to coincidence with P.

The position of P is given by coordinates x and y. The position of Q is given by coordinates $(x + \Delta x)$ and $(y + \Delta y)$. As Q approaches P, the increments Δx and Δy get smaller until, at P, they are indistinguishable from zero.

Figure C-1 The derivative of y with respect to x at the point P is given by the slope of the tangent PT. (See text.)

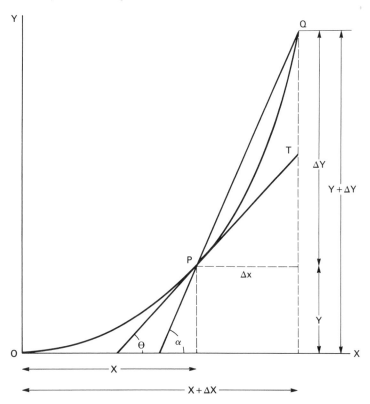

The principal steps in the differential process are:

1. Write down the function:

$$y = f(x)$$

2. Give increments to x and y:

$$y + \Delta y = f(x + \Delta x)$$

3. Subtract (1) from (2):

$$\Delta y = f(x + \Delta x) - f(x)$$

4. Divide by Δx:

$$\frac{\Delta y}{\Delta x} = \frac{f(x + \Delta x) - f(x)}{\Delta x}$$

5. Since Δy and Δx both get smaller and smaller as they approach 0 as a limit, write $\Delta y/\Delta x$ in the form:

$$\lim_{\Delta x \to 0} = \frac{\Delta y}{\Delta x}$$

6. The expression in (4) now becomes:

$$\frac{dy}{dx} = \lim_{\Delta x \to 0} \frac{f(x + \Delta x) - f(x)}{\Delta x}$$

This is the *derivative* of y with respect to x at any point x. The expression dy/dx may also be written $f'(x)$ or $D_x y$.

Geometrically, $(\Delta y/\Delta x) = \tan \alpha$, and $\Delta x \to 0$ as $Q \to P$, until PQ coincides with PT, and α becomes θ. Therefore the derivative of a function at any point represents the trigonometrical tangent of the angle between the geometric tangent to the curve at that point and the x-axis.

The derivative of a function $y = x^n$ is also given by:

$$\frac{dy}{dx} = nx^{n-1}$$

For example, the derivative of $y = x^4$ is:

$$\frac{dy}{dx} = 4x^{4-1} = 4x^3$$

and the derivative of $y = x^4 + x^2$ is:

$$\frac{dy}{dx} = 4x^3 + 2x^{2-1} = 4x^3 + 2x$$

and the derivative of $y = x^4 + x^2 + 7$ is:

$$\frac{dy}{dx} = 4x^3 + 2x + (1 \times 7^{1-1}) = 4x^3 + 2x$$

The 7 is a constant, and the derivative of a constant is always 0.
A condensed list of derivatives is given in Table C-1.

TABLE C-1   Condensed List of Derivatives and Integrals

y	$\dfrac{dy}{dx}$	$\int y dx$
x^n	nx^{n-1}	$x^{n+1}/(n + 1)$
$1/x$	$-1/x^2$	$\ln(x)$
e^{ax}	ae^{ax}	e^{ax}/a
$\ln(x)$	$1/x$	$x[\ln(x) - 1]$

TABLE C-1   Condensed List of Derivatives and Integrals (*Cont.*)

y	$\dfrac{dy}{dx}$	$\displaystyle\int y\,dx$
$\log_a x$	$\dfrac{1}{x}\log_a e$	$x\log_a\left(\dfrac{x}{e}\right)$
$\sin ax$	$a\cos ax$	$-\dfrac{1}{a}\cos ax$
$\cos ax$	$-a\sin ax$	$\dfrac{1}{a}\sin ax$
$\tan ax$	$a\sec^2 ax$	$-\dfrac{1}{a}\ln(\cos ax)$
$\cot ax$	$-a\,\mathrm{cosec}^2\,ax$	$\dfrac{1}{a}\ln(\sin ax)$
$\sec ax$	$a\tan ax\sec ax$	$\dfrac{1}{a}\ln(\sec ax+\tan ax)$
$\mathrm{cosec}\,ax$	$-a\cot ax\,\mathrm{cosec}\,ax$	$\dfrac{1}{a}\ln(\mathrm{cosec}\,ax-\cot ax)$
$\sin^{-1}(x/a)$	$1/(a^2-x^2)^{1/2}$	$x\sin^{-1}(x/a)+(a^2-x^2)^{1/2}$
$\cos^{-1}(x/a)$	$1/(a^2-x^2)^{1/2}$	$x\cos^{-1}(x/a)-(a^2-x^2)^{1/2}$
$\tan^{-1}(x/a)$	$a/(a^2+x^2)$	$x\tan^{-1}(x/a)-\dfrac{1}{2}a\ln(a^2+x^2)$
$\cot^{-1}(x/a)$	$-a/(a^2+x^2)$	$x\cot^{-1}(x/a)+\tfrac{1}{2}a\ln(a^2+x^2)$
$\sec^{-1}(x/a)$	$a(x^2-a^2)^{-1/2}/x$	$x\sec^{-1}(x/a)-a\ln[x+(x^2-a^2)^{1/2}]$
$\mathrm{cosec}^{-1}(x/a)$	$-a(x^2-a^2)^{-1/2}/x$	$x\,\mathrm{cosec}^{-1}(x/a)+a\ln[x+(x^2-a^2)^{1/2}]$
$\sinh ax$	$a\cosh ax$	$\dfrac{1}{a}\cosh ax$
$\coth ax$	$a\sinh ax$	$\dfrac{1}{a}\sinh ax$
$\tanh ax$	$a\,\mathrm{sech}^2\,ax$	$\dfrac{1}{a}\ln(\cosh ax)$
$\coth ax$	$-a\,\mathrm{cosech}^2\,ax$	$\dfrac{1}{a}\ln(\sinh ax)$
$\mathrm{sech}\,ax$	$-a\tanh ax\,\mathrm{sech}\,ax$	$\dfrac{2}{a}\tan^{-1}(e^{ax})$
$\mathrm{cosech}\,ax$	$-a\coth ax\,\mathrm{cosech}\,ax$	$\dfrac{1}{a}\ln\left(\tanh\dfrac{ax}{2}\right)$
$\sinh^{-1}(x/a)$	$(x^2+a^2)^{-1/2}$	$x\sinh^{-1}(x/a)-(x^2+a^2)^{1/2}$
$\cosh^{-1}(x/a)$	$(x^2-a^2)^{-1/2}$	$x\cosh^{-1}(x/a)-(x^2-a^2)^{1/2}$
$\tanh^{-1}(x/a)$	$a(a^2-x^2)^{-1}$	$x\tanh^{-1}(x/a)+\tfrac{1}{2}a\ln(a^2-x^2)$
$\coth^{-1}(x/a)$	$-a(x^2-a^2)^{-1}$	$x\coth^{-1}(x/a)+\tfrac{1}{2}a\ln(x^2-a^2)$
$\mathrm{sech}^{-1}(x/a)$	$-a(a^2-x^2)^{-1/2}/x$	$x\,\mathrm{sech}^{-1}(x/a)+a\sin^{-1}(x/a)$
$\mathrm{cosech}^{-1}(x/a)$	$-a(x^2+a^2)^{-1/2}/x$	$x\,\mathrm{cosech}^{-1}(x/a+a\sinh^{-1}(x/a)$
$(s^2\pm a^2)^{1/2}$ $(a^2-x^2)^{1/2}$		$\begin{cases}\tfrac{1}{2}x(x^2\pm a^2)^{1/2}\pm\tfrac{1}{2}a^2\sinh^{-1}(x/a)\\ \tfrac{1}{2}x(a^2-x^2)^{1/2}+\tfrac{1}{2}a^2\sin^{-1}(x/a)\end{cases}$
$(x^2\pm a^2)^p x$		$\begin{cases}\tfrac{1}{2}(x^2\pm a^2)^{p+1}/(p+1) & (p\neq-1)\\ \tfrac{1}{2}\ln(x^2\pm a^2) & (p=-1)\end{cases}$
$(a^2-x^2)^p x$		$\begin{cases}-\tfrac{1}{2}(a^2-x^2)^{p+1}/(p+1) & (p\neq-1)\\ -\tfrac{1}{2}\ln(a^2-x^2) & (p=-1)\end{cases}$

TABLE C-1 Condensed List of Derivatives and Integrals (*Cont.*)

y	$\dfrac{dy}{dx}$	$\int y\,dx$
$x(ax^2 + b)^p$		$\begin{cases}(ax^2 + b)^{p+1}/2a(p + 1) & (p \neq -1) \\ [\ln(ax^2 + b)]/2a & (p = -1)\end{cases}$
$(2ax - x^2)^{-1/2}$		$\cos^{-1}\left(\dfrac{a - x}{a}\right)$
$(a^2 \sin^2 x + b^2 \cos^2 x)^{-1}$		$\dfrac{1}{ab}\tan^{-1}\left(\dfrac{a}{b}\tan x\right)$
$(a^2 \sin^2 x - b^2 \cos^2 x)^{-1}$		$-\dfrac{1}{ab}\tanh^{-1}\left(\dfrac{a}{b}\tan x\right)$
$e^{ax} \sin bx$		$e^{ax}\dfrac{a \sin bx - b \cos bx}{a^2 + b^2}$
$e^{ax} \cos bx$		$e^{ax}\dfrac{(a \cos bx + b \sin bx)}{a^2 + b^2}$
$\sin mx \sin nx$		$\begin{cases}\dfrac{1}{2}\dfrac{\sin(m - n)x}{m - n} - \dfrac{1}{2}\dfrac{\sin(m + n)x}{m + n} & (m \neq n) \\ \dfrac{1}{2}\left(x - \dfrac{\sin 2mx}{2m}\right) & (m = n)\end{cases}$
$\sin mx \cos nx$		$\begin{cases}-\dfrac{1}{2}\dfrac{\cos(m + n)x}{m + n} - \dfrac{1}{2}\dfrac{\cos(m - n)x}{m - n} & (m \neq n) \\ -\dfrac{1}{2}\dfrac{\cos 2mx}{2m} & (m = n)\end{cases}$
$\cos mx \cos nx$		$\begin{cases}\dfrac{1}{2}\dfrac{\sin(m + n)x}{m + n} + \dfrac{1}{2}\dfrac{\sin(m - n)x}{m - n} & (m \neq n) \\ \dfrac{1}{2}\left(x + \dfrac{\sin 2mx}{2m}\right) & (m = n)\end{cases}$

Maxima and Minima

Wherever the tangent to a curve is horizontal, $f'(x) = 0$, this point is *critical*. In Figure C-2, the tangent to the curve at point A is horizontal,

Figure C-2 Maxima and minima are critical points on a curve where their tangents are horizontal. A is an example of a maximum, while B is a minimum. O is neither a maximum nor a minimum. (See text.)

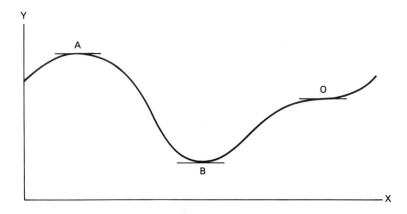

and the values of y near A are less than the value of y at A; therefore A is called a maximum point, or *maximum*. Point B is a critical point where values of y near B are greater than the value of y at B, so B is called a minimum point, or *minimum*. Point 0 is also a critical point, but it is neither a maximum nor a minimum since some values of y adjacent to 0 are greater and some are less than the value of y at 0 itself.

Integration

The curve in Figure C-3 is a graph of $y = f(x)$, and A is the area under the curve, between it and the x-axis, and between the ordinates $x = a$ and $x = b$. The area A is given by:

$$A = \int_a^b f(x)\, dx$$

Figure C-3 The definite integral is the area under the curve, between it and the x-axis, and between the ordinates $x = a$ and $x = b$.

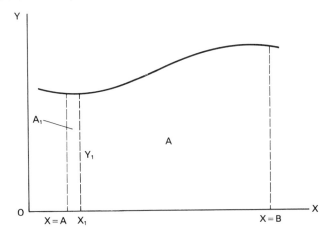

This is read, "A is equal to the integral from a to b of $f(x)$." It may also be written:

$$A = \int_a^b y\, dx$$

The more general expression for an integral is:

$$\int y\, dx$$

but this is indefinite and does not represent any particular area. The inclusion of the ordinates $x = a$ and $x = b$ makes it a definite integral.

At the starting point $x = a$, the area $A = 0$. At x_1 the area A_1 between y_1 and $x = a$ will be approximately the same as the area of this rectangle.

But it will not be the exact area because its upper boundary is a curve. However, the narrower the rectangle, the closer it will approach the correct area. In theory, an infinite number of rectangles of zero width would give the correct area. In practice, the procedure is much simpler because integration is the inverse of differentiation, as the following example will show. In the case of the curve that is the graph of:

$$y = x^2 - x - 12$$

bounded by the ordinates $x = 0$ and $x = 4$, write down:

$$A = \int_0^4 (x^2 - x - 12)\, dx$$

$$= \left[\frac{x^3}{3} - \frac{x^2}{2} - 12x \right]_0^4$$

$$= \frac{64}{3} - \frac{16}{2} - 48$$

$$= -\frac{104}{3} \text{ square units}$$

The minus sign occurs because this curve lies below the x-axis. In most cases, the sign is of no interest, but if the curve lies on both sides of the x-axis, the positive and negative parts should be integrated separately and then combined for the total area.

A condensed list of integrals is given in Table C-1.

Approximate Integration by Simpson's Rule

It often happens in practice that only an approximation of the definite integral is needed. This may be obtained by using Simpson's Rule:

$$\int_a^b f(x)\, dx \simeq \frac{\Delta x}{3} [y_0 + y_n + 4(y_1 + y_3 + \cdots) + 2(y_2 + \cdots)],$$

the terms in this function being as shown in Figure C-4(a).

In using Simpson's Rule, you must make the number of intervals (n) even. Then you can use the BASIC program given in Figure C-4(b) to evaluate the integral. It allows for up to 11 ordinates. The first is always y_0, and the last, y_n. If you use fewer than 11 ordinates, enter zeros for the unused ones. (Otherwise, the computer will ask for them by displaying ??, and it will refuse to continue until they are entered; also don't forget

Figure C-4(a) Simpson's Rule

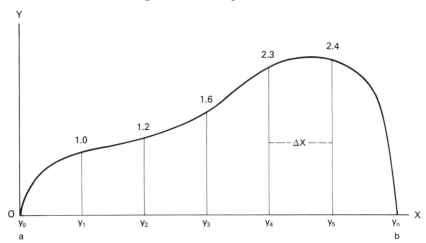

Figure C-4(b) BASIC Program for Simpson's Rule

```
5 CLS:CLEAR
10 PRINT:PRINT"DEFINITE INTEGRAL BY SIMPSON'S RULE"
20 PRINT:PRINT"ENTER ORDINATES Yo,Yn"
30 INPUT Y0,YN
40 PRINT:PRINT"ENTER ORDINATES Y1,Y3,Y5,Y7,Y9"
50 INPUT Y1,Y3,Y5,Y7,Y9
60 PRINT:PRINT"ENTER ORDINATES Y2,Y4,Y6,Y8"
70 INPUT Y2,Y4,Y6,Y8
80 PRINT:PRINT"ENTER INCREMENT (DELTA X)"
90 INPUT X
100 I=(X/3)*(Y0+YN+4*(Y1+Y3+Y5+Y7+Y9)+2*(Y2+Y4+Y6+Y8))
110 PRINT:PRINT"APPROXIMATE DEFINITE INTEGRAL = ";I
120 PRINT:PRINT"TYPE Y TO CONTINUE, Q TO QUIT"
130 INPUT Y$
140 IF Y$="Y"THEN 5
150 END
```

to enter a comma between each ordinate.) The response from your computer should look like Figure C-4(c).

Note that Δx is $(b - a)/n$, of course.

CAPACITANCE*

Capacitance of a Capacitor

$$C = 2.24 \times 10^{-13}kA[(N - 1)/d]$$

where:

C = capacitance, in farads.

*See Capacitors also.

Figure C-4(c) Sample Run of Program in Figure C-4(b), using values given in Figure C-4(a).

```
DEFINITE INTEGRAL BY SIMPSON'S RULE

ENTER ORDINATES Yo,Yn
?  0,0

ENTER ORDINATES Y1,Y3,Y5,Y7,Y9
?  1,1.6,2.4,0,0

ENTER ORDINATES Y2,Y4,Y6,Y8
?  1.2,2.3,0,0

ENTER INCREMENT (DELTA X)
?  1

APPROXIMATE DEFINITE INTEGRAL =  9

TYPE Y TO CONTINUE, Q TO QUIT
?  Q
Ready
```

k = dielectric constant.

A = area of one side of one plate, in square inches.

d = separation between plates, in inches.

N = number of plates.

Charge Stored in a Capacitor

$$q = CV$$

where:

q = quantity of charge, in coulombs.

C = capacitance, in farads.

V = potential difference between plates, in volts.

Combined Capacitance of Several Capacitors

For capacitors in parallel:

$$C_T = C_1 + C_2 + C_3 + \cdots + C_n$$

For capacitors in series (two capacitors):

$$C_T = C_1 C_2 / (C_1 + C_2)$$

For capacitors in series (more than two capacitors):

$$C_T = 1/(1/C_1 + 1/C_2 + 1/C_3 + \cdots + 1/C_n)$$

where:

$$C_T = \text{total capacitance, in farads.}$$

C_1 through C_n = capacitances of individual capacitors, in farads.

See Figures C-5 and C-6 also.

Energy Stored in a Capacitor

$$w = CV^2/2$$

where:

w = energy, in joules.

C = capacitance, in farads.

V = potential difference between plates, in volts.

Figure C-5(a) BASIC Program to Calculate
the Capacitance of up to Five Capacitors in
Series

```
10 CLS:CLEAR
20 PRINT"PROGRAM TO FIND THE TOTAL CAPACITANCE"
30 PRINT"OF UP TO 5 CAPACITORS IN SERIES"
40 PRINT"ENTER ALL VALUES IN MICROFARADS"
50 PRINT:PRINT"ENTER C1"
60 INPUT C1
70 PRINT"ENTER C2"
80 INPUT C2
90 PRINT"ENTER C3. IF NO C3, ENTER 0"
100 INPUT C3
110 IF C3=0 THEN 170
120 PRINT"ENTER C4. IF NO C4, ENTER 0"
130 INPUT C4
140 IF C4=0 THEN 170
150 PRINT"ENTER C5. IF NO C5, ENTER 0"
160 INPUT C5
170 C=(C1*C2)/(C1+C2)
180 IF C3=0 THEN 240
190 C=(C*C3)/(C+C3)
200 IF C4=0 THEN 240
210 C=(C*C4)/(C+C4)
220 IF C5=0 THEN 240
230 C=(C*C5)/(C+C5)
240 IF C<.001 THEN C=C*1E7 ELSE 260
250 GOTO 280
260 PRINT:PRINT"TOTAL CAPACITANCE = ";USING"####.#####";C;
270 PRINT" uF":GOTO 310
280 C=CINT(C)
290 PRINT:PRINT"TOTAL CAPACITANCE = ";C/10;
300 PRINT" pF"
310 PRINT:PRINT"TYPE Y TO CONTINUE, Q TO QUIT"
320 INPUT A$
330 IF A$="Y"THEN 10
340 END
```

Figure C-5(b) Sample Run of Program in (a)

```
PROGRAM TO FIND THE TOTAL CAPACITANCE
OF UP TO 5 CAPACITORS IN SERIES
ENTER ALL VALUES IN MICROFARADS

ENTER C1
? .001
ENTER C2
? .002
ENTER C3. IF NO C3, ENTER 0
? .003
ENTER C4. IF NO C4, ENTER 0
? 0

TOTAL CAPACITANCE =   545.4  pF

TYPE Y TO CONTINUE, Q TO QUIT
? Q
Ready
```

Figure C-6(a) BASIC Program to Calculate Value of Capacitor to Connect in Series with Another Capacitor (C1) to Obtain a Required Total Value

```
10 CLS:CLEAR
20 PRINT"PROGRAM TO FIND WHAT VALUE OF CAPACITANCE"
30 PRINT"IS REQUIRED IN SERIES WITH C1 TO GIVE A"
40 PRINT"DESIRED TOTAL CAPACITANCE"
50 PRINT"ENTER ALL VALUES IN MICROFARADS"
60 PRINT:PRINT"ENTER C1"
70 INPUT C1
80 PRINT:PRINT"ENTER DESIRED TOTAL CAPACITANCE"
90 INPUT C
100 IF C>=C1 THEN 110ELSE 170
110 PRINT:PRINT"TOTAL CAPACITANCE MUST BE LESS"
120 PRINT"THAN C1. TRY AGAIN"
130 N=1
140 N=N+1
150 IF N<>500 GOTO 140
160 GOTO 80
170 C2=C1/((C1/C)-1)
180 IF C2<0 THEN 190ELSE 200
190 C2=C2*(-1)
200 IF C2<.001 THEN C2=C2*1E7 ELSE 220
210 GOTO 240
220 PRINT:PRINT"REQUIRED VALUE IS ";USING"####.#####";C2;
230 PRINT" uF":GOTO 270
240 C2=CINT(C2)
250 PRINT:PRINT"REQUIRED VALUE IS ";C2/10;
260 PRINT" pF"
270 PRINT:PRINT"TYPE Y TO CONTINUE, Q TO QUIT"
280 INPUT A$
290 IF A$="Y"THEN 10
300 END
```

Figure C-6(b) Sample Run of Program in (a)

```
PROGRAM TO FIND WHAT VALUE OF CAPACITANCE
IS REQUIRED IN SERIES WITH C1 TO GIVE A
DESIRED TOTAL CAPACITANCE
ENTER ALL VALUES IN MICROFARADS

ENTER C1
? .01

ENTER DESIRED TOTAL CAPACITANCE
? .002

REQUIRED VALUE IS     0.00250 uF

TYPE Y TO CONTINUE, Q TO QUIT
? Q
Ready
```

Figure of Merit

For capacitor alone:

$$Q = X_c/R$$

where:

Q = figure of merit, or quality factor.

X_c = capacitive reactance, in ohms.

R = series resistance in circuit, in ohms.

For capacitor in series with resistor:

$$Q = 1/2\pi f RC$$

For capacitor in parallel with resistor:

$$Q = 2\pi f RC$$

where:

Q = figure of merit.

f = frequency, in hertz.

R = total resistance, in ohms.

C = capacitance, in farads.

π = 3.1415927...

Force of Attraction between Plates

$$F = AV^2/k(1504S)^2$$

where:

F = attractive force, in dynes.

A = area of one plate, in cm^2.

V = potential difference between plates, in volts.

k = dielectric constant.

S = separation between plates, in cm.

Impedance of Capacitor

$$Z = \sqrt{R^2 + X_c^2}$$

where:

Z = impedance, in ohms.

R = series resistance, in ohms.

X_c = reactance of capacitor, in ohms.

Reactance of Capacitor

$$X_c = 1/2\pi f C$$

where:

X_c = reactance of capacitor, in ohms.

f = frequency, in hertz.

C = capacitance, in farads.

π = 3.1415927. . .

CAPACITORS

Button Capacitors

Small disk-shaped capacitor consisting of a stack of silvered mica sheets encased in a silverplated brass housing. One set of plates is connected to the housing, and the other (higher voltage) to a terminal running through the center of the stack. This construction gives minimum internal series inductance, important in RF applications. Marking consists of three or six colored dots, read clockwise around the rim. (See Figure C-7.) The significance of the dots is:

1. First significant figure, in picofarads.
2. Second significant figure, in picofarads.

Figure C-7 Button Capacitor and Color Coding [5], [7]

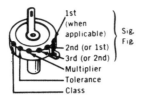

Color	1st and 2nd Digit	Multiplier	Tolerance	Voltage	Characteristics	
Black	0	1	±20%	—	A	NP0**
Brown	1	10	±1%	100V	B	N033*
Red	2	100	±2%	200V	C	N075
Orange	3	1000	±3%	300V	D	N150
Yellow	4	10,000		400V	E	N220
Green	5	—	±5%	500V*	F	N330
Blue	6	—	—	600V		N470
Violet	7	—	—	700V		N750
Gray	8	0.01	—	800V	—	—
White	9	—	—	900V	—	—
Gold	—	0.1	± 5%	1000V	—	—
Silver	—	0.01	± 10%	—	—	P100

* Assume 500 volt rating if color is missing or voltage value is not imprinted on the capacitor.
** Three temperature characteristics exist: N = negative, P = positive, NPO = negative-positive-zero. N150 means minus or negative 150, which indicates that for every degree centigrade the temperature increases, the capacitance will decrease 150 parts per million, N750 rating produces a decrease of 750 parts per million per degree increase, etc.
(See also Temperature Coefficient, later in this section.)

3. Multiplier on three-dot types; third significant figure in pico-farads on six-dot types.

4. Multiplier on six-dot types.

5. Tolerance on six-dot types.

6. Characteristic on six-dot types.

Ceramic Capacitors

Ceramic disk, tube, or slab, of steatite or barium titanate, silvered on opposite sides, and encapsulated in protective insulating coating. Markings are usually typographical, but small disk-types may have three- or five-colored dots, read clockwise around the rim, as in Figure C-7 (except for voltage). The significance of the dots is:

Three-dot types:

1. First significant figure, in picofarads.
2. Second significant figure, in picofarads.
3. Multiplier.

Five-dot types:

1. Temperature coefficient.
2. First significant figure, in picofarads.
3. Second significant figure, in picofarads.
4. Multiplier.
5. Tolerance.

Older tubular or slab types may also be color-coded.

Dielectric Constants

The ratio of the capacitance of a capacitor with a certain dielectric to the capacitance of an identical capacitor, with air as its dielectric, is termed the dielectric constant, also called permittivity, specific inductive capacity, or capacitivity. Approximate values for various dielectrics used in low-loss and medium-loss capacitors are given in Table C-2 (below).

**TABLE C-2   Dielectric Constants
of Capacitor Materials**

Material	Constant
Air (low-loss, approx. same as vacuum)	1.0
Barium titanate (medium-loss)	100–1250
Mica (low-loss)	4.0–9.0
Mylar (low-loss)	4.7
Impregnated paper (medium-loss)	1.5–3.0
Polycarbonate (low-loss)	2.9–3.2
Polyethylene (low-loss)	2.5
Polyimide (low-loss)	3.4–3.5
Polystyrene (low-loss)	2.4–3.0
Quartz, fused (low-loss)	3.78
Steatite (low-loss)	5.2–6.3
Titanium dioxide (medium-loss)	100

Disk Capacitors

Most ceramic and some mica capacitors are manufactured in disk form. *See* button, ceramic, and mica capacitors.

Electrolytic Capacitors

In these capacitors, the dielectric has been formed by electrolysis on the surface of one of the plates. This results in an extremely thin layer, so allowing higher values of capacitance in a smaller package than other types. However, most of these capacitors are polarized, which means that voltage must be applied to them in accordance with the terminal or lead markings (+ or −); otherwise, the dielectric will break down. Electrolytic capacitors are also leaky, so are classed as high-loss capacitors.

Aluminum Oxide Dielectric: These electrolytic capacitors have been used for a long time for filter capacitors in low-voltage power supplies, and the larger sizes can be obtained with two or more capacitors in the same container. Since these may have different values and working voltages, it is important to pay heed to the markings on the outside of the container identifying the terminals or leads. Capacitances are available from 0.047 to 600,000 microfarads. Maximum working voltage may go as high as 7500 V.

Tantalum Oxide Dielectric: These electrolytic capacitors are generally smaller than the aluminum oxide type for the same capacitance and are more variable in appearance. There are two principal types: solid and liquid.

Solid: This capacitor consists of two tantalum foil electrodes separated by layers of absorbent paper saturated with electrolyte. On the surface of one electrode (the anode) is a thin film of oxide formed by electrolysis. This electrode is one of the plates, but the other plate is the electrolyte itself, the second foil being its means of connection to the negative lead. Capacitances range from 0.001 through 1000 microfarads, with maximum DC working voltages from 2 V through 200 V.

Solid tantalum electrolytic capacitors are mostly tubular or disks. Some of the smaller sizes are color coded as shown in Figure C-8.

Liquid: A liquid tantalum electrolytic capacitor consists of a silver, or silverplated, "can" to which the negative lead is attached. Inside this is the anode, which may be made of tantalum foil or sintered tantalum, immersed in the electrolyte. The oxide dielectric is formed on this anode in the same way as in the solid type.

Liquid tantalum capacitors are available with capacitances from 0.25 through 4700 microfarads. Maximum DC working voltages range from 16 V through 50 V.

Nonpolarized Electrolytics: Some tantalum electrolytic capacitors are nonpolarized—that is to say, it does not matter which way they are connected with respect to the voltage in the circuit. This is an advantage where a high capacitance is needed for an AC signal, such as in speaker crossovers and audio filters.

Figure C-8 Coding of Small Tantalum Capacitors [7]

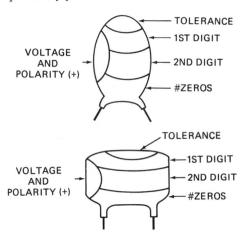

Color Code	Voltage @ 85°C	1st digit	2nd digit	Multiplier
Black	4VDC	0	0	——
Brown	6VDC	1	1	——
Red	10VDC	2	2	——
Orange	15VDC	3	3	——
Yellow	20VDC	4	4	$\times 10^4$
Green	25VDC	5	5	$\times 10^5$
Blue	35VDC	6	6	$\times 10^6$
Violet	50VDC	7	7	$\times 10^7$
Gray	——	8	8	——
White	——	9	9	——

Note: If no tolerance dot exists, the tolerance is ± 20%; silver dot is ± 10%; gold dot is ± 5%

Feedthrough Capacitors

A feedthrough capacitor is really an insulator mounted in a metal chassis or shield, through which a conductor passes, but it is designed to provide a desired value of capacitance between the conductor and the grounded metal chassis. Such capacitors are used for bypass purposes in UHF tuners and similar applications. Their capacitances are very small, from 4.7 to 470 picofarads, but maximum working voltage may be as high as 500 V DC.

Glass or Quartz Dielectric Capacitors

These capacitors are mainly trimmer capacitors, consisting of a small rectangular or cylindrical plastic case with a screwdriver adjustment. With capacitances adjustable from 6 to 50 pF (typical), they are suitable for peaking RF or IF circuits.

Leads

In most capacitors, leads connected to the two plates are brought out through the casing either axially or radially. Axial leads emerge from opposite ends of tubular or button capacitors. Radial leads come out at the sides of all types. Leads are usually tinned copper, about two inches long, except in capacitors specially designed for mounting on printed circuit boards, where they will be short, spaced so that they fit the holes in the board, and kinked close to the capacitor case so that the machine that mounts them will insert the leads to the proper depth. Some large capacitors have solder lugs or terminals instead of leads.

In many capacitors, the foil plates are rolled in such a way that one of them is the outside one, and so it can shield the inner foil from picking up undesirable signals. On these capacitors, the leads are identified so that the outer foil, when connected to the low side of the circuit, grounds whatever signals it picks up.

Mica Capacitors

Mica-dielectric capacitors have capacitances ranging from 1 picofarad to 0.01 microfarad, and a high breakdown dielectric strength of 1000 volts per mil. Epoxy-dipped types usually have their data printed on them typographically, but molded plastic types may be color coded in accordance with Figure C-9. Capacitance values are given in picofarads. (*See* Temperature Coefficient below for explanation of characteristic.)

Figure C-9 Six-Dot Mica Capacitors
Hold capacitor so that arrow points to your right. Colors of dots have same meanings as shown in Figure C-7.

Dot 1 Normally white or silver. A black dot indicates a military specification (MIL-C-5A).

Dot 2 First significant figure of capacitance value.

Dot 3 Second significant figure of capacitance value.

Dot 4 Decimal multiplier of capacitance value.

Dot 5 Tolerance.

Dot 6 Characteristic.

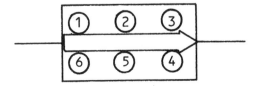

Paper Capacitors

Impregnated-paper dielectric capacitors may be tubular, with two strips of aluminum foil separated by the dielectric, and rolled up before being encapsulated in an insulating case; or alternating pieces of aluminum and paper may be stacked before encapsulation. In some types, metallizing the paper may replace foil.

Paper types are cheaper than other types, but are larger for the same amount of capacitance. Their data may be printed typographically on the body, or indicated by colored bands (some tubular types), using the same code as in Figure C-7. Capacitances range from 0.001 to 200 microfarads, and maximum DC working voltages from 50 V to 15,000 V.

Plastic Capacitors

Polystyrene and polystyrene-polyester dielectric capacitors have capacitances ranging from 5 picofarads to 10 microfarads, and maximum DC working voltages from 50 V to 2000 V. Their characteristics are independent of frequency. Disk or tubular forms are used, with data printed typographically.

Plastic-Film Capacitors

Plastic films used include polyester, polycarbonate, and polystyrene, with deposited metal. The data is printed typographically on the body, but one end may be marked with a color band or black line to identify the outer foil lead. The case may be disk or tubular, dipped in epoxy or molded. Capacitances run from 100 picofarads to 20 microfarads, and maximum DC working voltages from 25 V to 2000 V. The latter are often denoted by the color of the band on one end: red = 500 WVDC; yellow = 125 WVDC; blue = 25 WVDC.

Polarized Capacitor

An electrolytic capacitor has the dielectric film formed adjacent to only one metal electrode. Opposition to the passage of current is then greater in one direction than the other. Leads or terminals are marked + or − to indicate which should have the more positive or negative voltage to minimize direct current leakage. Reversing the connections results in currents high enough to destroy the capacitor or damage parts to which it is connected.

Quartz Dielectric Capacitors

See Glass or Quartz Dielectric Capacitors.

Temperature Coefficient

Variations in temperature affect physical dimensions of a capacitor and therefore result in variations in capacitance. The degree of variation depends upon the type and size of the component. Each has its own *temperature coefficient.* The change of capacitance with temperature of a capacitor is given by:

$$\Delta C = C \times TC \times \Delta T$$

where:

ΔC = change of capacitance, in same units as C.

C = capacitance of capacitor at 25°C.

TC = temperature coefficient in ppm/°C.

ΔT = change of temperature from 25°C, in °C.

Where the temperature coefficient is indicated on a capacitor, it may be given by a letter or a color, as shown in Table C-3.

TABLE C-3   Color Coding for Temperature Coefficient

Color	Letter	ppm/°C	Significant figure	Multiplier
Black	A	0	0.0	−1
Brown	B	−33	—	−10
Red	C	−75	1.0	−100
Orange	D	−150	1.5	−1000
Yellow	E	−220	2.0	−10,000
Green	F	−330	3.3	+1
Blue	G	−470	4.7	+10
Violet	H	−750	7.5	+100
Gray	J	+150 to −1500		+1000
White	K	+100 to −750		+10,000

Variable Capacitors

Variable capacitors can be divided into two basic types. In one type, the variable capacitor is made so that it can be adjusted continuously, as is required for tuning a communications receiver over a wide band of frequencies. This is done with variable capacitors which may be ganged on the same shaft to resonate several circuits simultaneously.

A typical capacitor for such a function is the variable air-dielectric capacitor. This consists of two sets of aluminum plates which mesh with each other without touching. One set of plates, the stator, is fixed. The other set, the rotor, is on a ball-bearing mounted shaft. It rotates so as to vary the area of the rotor plates that is within the stator plates and, consequently, the capacitance of the capacitor.

The second type is a partially variable capacitor called a trimmer. Its function is to adjust to a desired capacitance value and then remain at this value. A common use for a trimmer is as a *padder*, or small capacitor connected parallel with the RF section of the tuning capacitor, to adjust the overall tuning of the latter to enable it to track accurately with the oscillator section. Another may be provided to adjust the overall value of the tuning capacitor to agree with the markings on the receiver dial. Trimmer capacitors have screwdriver adjustments, with limited range. Trimmers are made with mica, air, teflon, ceramic, quartz, and glass dielectrics. For UHF applications, trimmers with air, glass, and quartz have very high values of *Q*. When used as padders, they are often mounted on the tuning capacitor itself.

Cathode-Ray Tube *See* Vacuum Tubes.

Central Processing Unit (CPU) *See* Microprocessor.

CHARACTERISTIC CURVES

Characteristic curves can be drawn for any transistor. Figure C-10 shows a family of curves for a transistor used as a voltage amplifier connected in the common-emitter configuration. The horizontal axis gives collector voltage (V_C). The vertical axis indicates collector current (I_C). The curves show the transistor's performance for different values of base current (I_B).

Figure C-10 A Family of Characteristic Curves for a Transistor Being Used as a Voltage Amplifier (no emitter resistor) [3]

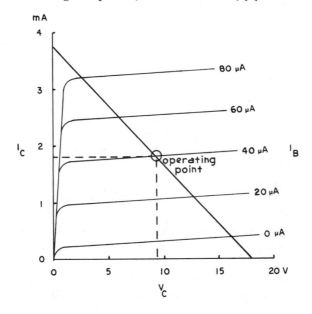

To analyze the transistor's performance, a load line is drawn from $V_{C,max} - I_{C,min}$ to $V_{C,min} - I_{C,max}$. The ends of this line define the two extremes of the transistor's range of operation. Since you would not normally want the transistor to distort the signal it is amplifying, you would choose an operating point midway along the load line so that swings of voltage on the base stay in the linear portion of the line.

See Biasing Methods.

Choke *See* Inductors.

Choke-Input Filter *See* Power Sources.

Circuit Breaker *See* Fuses and Circuit Breakers.

Coaxial Cable *See* Transmission Lines.

Coefficient of Coupling *See* Transformers.

Collector *See* Transistors.

Color Coding *See* Capacitors, Resistors.

Common-Base Amplifier *See* Transistors.

Common-Collector Amplifier *See* Transistors.

Common-Drain Amplifier *See* Transistors.

Common-Emitter Amplifier *See* Transistors.

Common-Gate Amplifier *See* Transistors.

Common-Source Amplifier *See* Transistors.

Common Logarithms *See* Mathematical Tables.

Common-Mode Ratio *See* Amplifiers.

Common-Source Amplifier *See* Transistors.

COMMUNICATIONS

Unlike broadcasting, where individual stations transmit one way to many receivers but do not themselves receive transmissions from those receivers, communication means two-way transmission between stations. Each station is capable of transmitting to and receiving from the other. Table C4 lists the permissible types of emission, and Table C-5 gives the internationally-agreed call sign prefixes for each country.

TABLE C-4   Types of Emission

Modulation type	Transmission characteristics	Symbol
Amplitude	No modulation	A0
	Telegraphy (interrupted carrier; i.e., keying of unmodulated carrier)	A1
	Telegraphy (continuous carrier with keying of modulating audio signal; or interrupted modulated carrier)	A2
	Telephony (full carrier and both sidebands)	A3
	Telephony (reduced carrier and single sideband)	A3A
	Telephony (reduced carrier, two independent sidebands)	A3B
	Telephony (suppressed carrier, single sideband)	A3J
	Facsimile	A4
	Television (vestigial sideband)	A5C
	Telegraphy (multichannel, voice frequency; reduced carrier, single sideband)	A7A
	Cases not covered by the above	A9
Frequency or Phase	No modulation	F0
	Telegraphy (frequency-shift keying of unmodulated carrier)	F1
	Telegraphy (with modulation, same as A2)	F2
	Telephony	F3
	Facsimile	F4
	Television	F5
	Four-frequency diplex telegraphy	F6
	Cases not covered by the above	F9
Pulse	No modulation	P0
	Telegraphy (same as F1)	P1
	Telegraphy (same as A2) pulse-amplitude modulation pulse-width modulation pulse-position modulation	P2D P2E P2F

TABLE C-4 Types of Emission (*Cont.*)

Modulation type	Transmission characteristics	Symbol
	Telephony	
	pulse-amplitude modulation	P3D
	pulse-width modulation	P3E
	pulse-position modulation	P3F
	pulse-code modulation	P3G
	Cases not covered by the above	P9

TABLE C-5 Call Sign Prefixes

Prefix	Country	Prefix	Country
AAA-ALZ	United States	EUA-EWZ	Belorussia
AMA-AOZ	Spain	EXA-EZZ	USSR
APA-ASZ	Pakistan	FAA-FZZ	France & Terr.
ATA-AWZ	India	GAA-GZZ	United Kingdom
AXA-AXZ	Australia	HAA-HAZ	Hungary
AYA-AZZ	Argentina	HBA-HBZ	Switzerland
A2A-A2Z	Botswana	HCA-HDZ	Ecuador
A3A-A3Z	Tonga	HEA-HEZ	Switzerland
A5A-A5Z	Bhutan	HFA-HFZ	Poland
BAA-BZZ	China	HGA-HGZ	Hungary
CAA-CEZ	Chile	HHA-HHZ	Haiti
CFA-CKZ	Canada	HIA-HIZ	Dominican Republic
CLA-CMZ	Cuba	HJA-HKZ	Colombia
CNA-CNZ	Morocco	HLA-HMZ	Korea
COA-COZ	Cuba	HNA-HNZ	Iraq
CPA-CPZ	Bolivia	HOA-HPZ	Panama
CQA-CRZ	Portuguese Terr.	HQA-HRZ	Honduras
CSA-CUZ	Portugal	HSA-HSZ	Thailand
CVA-CXZ	Uruguay	HTA-HTZ	Nicaragua
CYA-CZZ	Canada	HUA-HUZ	El Salvador
C2A-C2Z	Nauru	HVA-HVZ	Vatican State
C3A-C3Z	Andorra	HWA-HYZ	France & Terr.
DAA-DTZ	Germany	HZA-HZZ	Saudi Arabia
DUA-DZZ	Philippines	IAA-IZZ	Italy & Terr.
EAA-EHZ	Spain	JAA-JSZ	Japan
EIA-EJZ	Ireland	JTA-JVZ	Mongolia
EKA-EKZ	USSR	JWA-JXZ	Norway
ELA-ELZ	Liberia	JYA-KYZ	Jordan
EMA-EOZ	USSR	JZA-JZZ	West Irian
EPA-EQZ	Iran	KAA-KZZ	United States
ERA-ERZ	USSR	LAA-LNZ	Norway
ESA-ESZ	Esthonia	LOA-LWZ	Argentina
ETA-ETZ	Ethiopia	LXA-LXZ	Luxembourg

TABLE C-5   Call Sign Prefixes (*Cont.*)

Prefix	Country	Prefix	Country
LYA-LYZ	Lithuania	URA-UTZ	Ukraine
LZA-LZZ	Bulgaria	UUA-UQZ	USSR
L2A-L9Z	Argentina	VAA-VGZ	Canada
MAA-MZZ	United Kingdom	VHA-VNZ	Australia
NAA-NZZ	United States	VOA-VOZ	Canada
OAA-OCZ	Peru	VPA-VSZ	British Terr.
ODA-ODZ	Lebanon	VTA-VWZ	India
OEA-OEZ	Austria	VXA-VYZ	Canada
OFA-OJZ	Finland	VZA-VZZ	Australia
OKA-OMZ	Czechoslovakia	WAA-WZZ	United States
ONA-OTZ	Belgium	XAA-XIZ	Mexico
OUA-OZZ	Denmark	XJA-XOZ	Canada
PAA-PIZ	Netherlands	XPA-XPZ	Denmark
PJA-PJZ	Netherlands W. Ind.	XQA-XRZ	Chile
PKA-POZ	Indonesia	XSA-XSZ	China
PPA-PYZ	Brazil	XTA-XTZ	Upper Volta
PZA-PZZ	Surinam	XUA-XUZ	Khmer Republic
RAA-RZZ	USSR	XVA-XVZ	Vietnam
SAA-SMZ	Sweden	XWA-XWZ	Laos
SNA-SRZ	Poland	XXA-XXZ	Portuguese Terr.
SSA-SSM	Egypt	XYA-XZZ	Burma
SSN-STZ	Sudan	YAA-YAZ	Afghanistan
SUA-SUZ	Egypt	YBA-YHZ	Indonesia
SVA-SZZ	Greece	YIA-YIZ	Iraq
TAA-TCZ	Turkey	YJA-YJZ	New Hebrides
TDA-TDZ	Guatemala	YKA-YKZ	Syria
TEA-TEZ	Costa Rica	YLA-YLZ	Latvia
TFA-TFZ	Iceland	YMA-YMZ	Turkey
TGA-TGZ	Guatemala	YNA-YNZ	Nicaragua
THA-THZ	France & Terr.	YOA-YRZ	Romania
TIA-TIZ	Costa Rica	YSA-YSZ	El Salvador
TJA-TJZ	Cameroon	YTA-YUZ	Yugoslavia
TKA-TKZ	France & Terr.	YVA-YYZ	Venezuela
TLA-TLZ	Central African Rep.	YZA-YZZ	Yugoslavia
TMA-TMZ	France & Terr.	ZAA-ZAZ	Albania
TNA-TNZ	Congo	ZBA-ZJZ	British Terr.
TOA-TQZ	France & Terr.	ZKA-ZMZ	New Zealand
TRA-TRZ	Gabon	ZNA-ZOZ	British Terr.
TSA-TSZ	Tunisia	ZPA-ZPZ	Paraguay
TTA-TTZ	Chad	ZQA-ZQZ	British Terr.
TUA-TUZ	Ivory Coast	ZRA-ZUZ	South Africa
TVA-TXZ	France & Terr.	ZVA-ZZZ	Brazil
TYA-TYZ	Dahomey	2AA-2ZZ	United Kingdom
TZA-TZZ	Mali	3AA-3AZ	Monaco
UAA-UQZ	USSR	3BA-3BZ	Mauritius

TABLE C-5 Call Sign Prefixes (*Cont.*)

Prefix	Country	Prefix	Country
3CA-3CZ	Equatorial Guinea	6KA-6NZ	Korea
3DA-3DM	Swaziland	6OA-6OZ	Somali Republic
3DN-3DZ	Fiji	6PA-6SZ	Pakistan
3EA-3FZ	Panama	6TA-6UZ	Sudan
3GA-3GZ	Chile	6VA-6WZ	Senegal
3HA-3UZ	China	6XA-6XZ	Malagasy Republic
3VA-3VZ	Tunisia	6YA-6YZ	Jamaica
3WA-3WZ	Vietnam	6ZA-6ZZ	Liberia
3XA-3XZ	Guinea	7AA-7IZ	Indonesia
3YA-3YZ	Norway	7JA-7NZ	Japan
3ZA-3ZZ	Poland	7OA-7OZ	Yemen
4AA-4CZ	Mexico	7PA-7PZ	Lesotho
4DA-4IZ	Philippines	7QA-7QZ	Malawi
4JA-4LZ	USSR	5RA-5RZ	Algeria
4MA-4MZ	Venezuela	7SA-7SZ	Sweden
4NA-4OZ	Yugoslavia	7TA-7YZ	Algeria
4PA-4SZ	Sri Lanka	7ZA-7ZZ	Saudi Arabia
4TA-4TZ	Peru	8AA-8IZ	Indonesia
4UA-4UZ	United Nations	8JA-8NZ	Japan
4VA-4VZ	Haiti	8OA-8OZ	Botswana
4WA-4WZ	Yemen	8PA-8PZ	Barbados
4XA-4XZ	Israel	8QA-8QZ	Maldive Is.
4YA-4YZ	Int. Civ. Av. Org.	8RA-8RZ	Guyana
4ZA-4ZZ	Israel	8SA-8SZ	Sweden
5AA-5AZ	Libya	8TA-8YZ	India
5BA-5BZ	Cyprus	8ZA-8ZZ	Saudi Arabia
5CA-5GZ	Morocco	9AA-9AZ	San Marino
5HA-5IZ	Tanzania	9MA-9MZ	Malaysia
5JA-5KZ	Colombia	9EA-9FZ	Ethiopia
5LA-5MZ	Liberia	9GA-9GZ	Ghana
5NA-5QZ	Nigeria	9HA-9HZ	Malta
5PA-5QZ	Denmark	9IA-9JZ	Zambia
5RA-5SZ	Malagasy Republic	9KA-9KZ	Kuwait
5TA-5TZ	Mauretania	9LA-9LZ	Sierra Leone
5UA-5UZ	Niger	9MA-9MZ	Malaysia
5VA-5VZ	Togo	9NA-9NZ	Nepal
5WA-5WZ	Western Samoa	9OA-9TZ	Zaire
5XA-5XZ	Uganda	9UA-9UZ	Burundi
5YA-5ZZ	Kenya	9VA-9VZ	Singapore
6AA-6BZ	Egypt	9WA-9WZ	Malaysia
6CA-6CZ	Syria	9XA-9XZ	Rwanda
6DA-6JZ	Mexico	9YA-9YZ	Trinidad & Tobago

See Frequency for further information.

Complementary Metal-Oxide-Semiconductor (CMOS) Circuits The type of circuit shown in Figure C-11(A) is called CMOS because *p*-channel and *n*-channel insulated-gate field-effect transistors (IGFETs) are used together. CMOS finds its greatest use in integrated circuits (ICs). Since no other components (such as resistors) are required, fabrication is greatly simplified.

Figure C-11 The circuit of a MOS NAND gate is shown in A, and the familiar NAND truth table in B. [3]

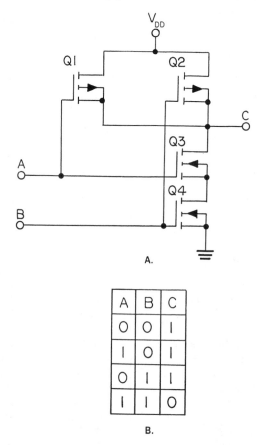

A	B	C
O	O	I
I	O	I
O	I	I
I	I	O

B.

In this circuit, $Q1$ and $Q2$ are *p*-channel IGFETs, which turn on with low voltage on their gates. $Q3$ and $Q4$ are *n*-channel IGFETs that turn on with high voltage on their gates.

When inputs A and B are both low, $Q1$ and $Q2$ are conducting, but $Q3$ and $Q4$ are not. V_{DD} (any value from 5 to 15 V) is connected to output

C by *Q*1 and *Q*2 in parallel, but current cannot flow to V_{SS} because *Q*3 and *Q*4 are not conducting. Therefore, output *C* is high (at the same value as V_{DD}).

If the voltage applied to input *A* is high, it causes *Q*1 to turn off and *Q*3 to turn on. But *Q*2 is still conducting, and *Q*4 is still not conducting, because the voltage at *B* has not changed. Therefore, output *C* remains high. If input *B* goes high while input *A* is low, *Q*2 turns off and *Q*4 turns on.

However, *Q*1 is still conducting, and *Q*3 is still off, so output *C* is still high. If both input *A* and input *B* go high, *Q*1 and *Q*2 turn off, but *Q*3 and *Q*4 turn on. The V_{DD} voltage is therefore disconnected from output *C*, but output *C* is now connected to V_{SS}, so it goes low.

This action is summarized in the truth table in Figure C-11(B), which is, of course, the NAND function.

See Logic Circuits.

Complex Numbers If $z = x + jy$, where *x* and *y* are real variables, *z* is a complex variable and is a function of *x* and *y*. This is represented graphically in Figure C-12, where it is clear that *y* cannot be added arithmetically to *x*, but must be added vectorially (hence the use of the *j* term, $j = \sqrt{-1}$).

Figure C-12 The Complex Variable *z* is a Function of *x* and *y*.

These are represented by two vectors at 90 degrees with respect to each other. Because of their phase difference, *x* and *y* cannot be added directly. But since they form the two sides of a right-angle triangle, of which *z* is the hypotenuse, they may be added vectorially according to the formula $z = \sqrt{x^2 + y^2}$.

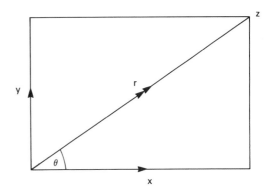

For polar form:

$$z = x + jy = |z|e^{j\theta} = |z|(\cos\theta + j\sin\theta)$$

$$x = r\cos\theta \qquad y = r\sin\theta$$

where:

$$r = |z|$$

For complex arithmetic:

$$z_1 = x_1 + jy_1$$
$$z_2 = x_2 + jy_2$$
$$z_1 \pm z_2 = (x_1 \pm x_2) + j(y_1 \pm y_2)$$
$$z_1 \cdot z_2 = (x_1x_2 - y_1y_2) + j(x_1y_2 + x_2y_1)$$

For conjugate:

$$z^* = x - jy$$
$$z \cdot z^* = x^2 + y^2 = |z|^2$$

For function:
Another complex variable $w = u + jv$ may be related functionally to z by

$$w = u + jv = f(x + jy) = f(z)$$

which implies:

$$u = u(x, y)$$
$$v = v(x, y)$$

For instance:

$$\cosh z = \cosh (x + jy)$$
$$= \cosh x \cosh jy + \sinh x \sinh jy$$
$$= \cosh x \cos y + j \sinh x \sin y$$
$$u = \cosh x \cos y$$
$$v = \sinh x \sin y$$

Composition Resistors *See* Resistors.

Computers All digital computers consist of the elements shown in Figure C-13. See the appropriate entry for an explanation of each:
Central Processing Unit; *see* Microprocessor.
Internal Memory: *see* Memory.
Input/Output: *see* Peripheral Devices
Bulk Storage: *see* Magnetic Storage.

Conductance *See* Resistance.

Conductors *See* Resistance.

Figure C-13 Digital Computers Consist of a CPU and Main Memory.
These are linked by an input/output bus to various peripheral
devices for input and output of data. [3]

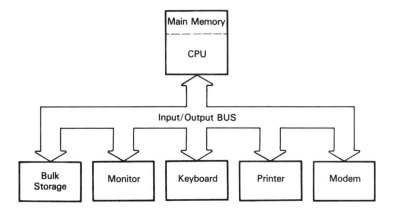

Connectors Coupling devices for joining two cables, or for connecting a
cable to a panel connector on a piece of electronic equipment. Connectors
are male or female according to whether they plug into or receive the
mating connector. A few commonly used connectors are shown in Figure
C-14. Alligator clips and banana plugs are used for temporary connections, such as test leads or patch cords. Banana plugs mate with banana
jacks. Coaxial connectors are mostly used for RF cables. *See* Transmission
Lines.

TABLE C-6   Mathematical and Physical Constants

Mathematical constants		Mathematical constants		Mathematical constants	
π	$= 3.1415927\ldots$	$\dfrac{1}{2\pi}$	$= 0.1591549\ldots$	$\sqrt{3}$	$= 1.7320508\ldots$
π^2	$= 9.8696044\ldots$	$\left(\dfrac{1}{2\pi}\right)^2$	$= 0.0253303\ldots$	$\dfrac{1}{\sqrt{2}}$	$= 0.7071068\ldots$
π^3	$= 31.006277\ldots$	2π	$= 6.2831853\ldots$	$\dfrac{1}{\sqrt{3}}$	$= 0.5773503\ldots$
$\dfrac{1}{\pi}$	$= 0.3183099\ldots$	$(2\pi)^2$	$= 39.478418\ldots$	$\log \pi$	$= 0.4971499\ldots$
$\dfrac{1}{\pi^2}$	$= 0.1013212\ldots$	4π	$= 12.566371\ldots$	$\log \pi^2$	$= 0.9942997\ldots$
$\dfrac{1}{\pi^3}$	$= 0.0322515\ldots$	$\dfrac{\pi}{2}$	$= 1.5707963\ldots$	$\log \sqrt{\pi}$	$= 0.2485749\ldots$
$\sqrt{\pi}$	$= 1.7724539\ldots$	$\sqrt{\dfrac{\pi}{2}}$	$= 1.2533141\ldots$	$\log \dfrac{\pi}{2}$	$= 0.1961199\ldots$
$\dfrac{1}{\sqrt{\pi}}$	$= 0.5641896\ldots$	$\sqrt{2}$	$= 1.4142136\ldots$		

TABLE C-6 (*Cont.*) Physical Constants

Quantity	Symbol	Value		SI Units
Velocity of light	c	2.9979250	$\times 10^8$	m/s
Electron charge	e	1.6021917	$\times 10^{-19}$	C
Planck's constant	h	6.626196	$\times 10^{-34}$	J s
Avogadro's number	N	6.022169	$\times 10^{26}$	1/kmol
Atomic mass unit	amu	1.660531	$\times 10^{-27}$	kg
Electron rest mass	m_e	9.109558	$\times 10^{-31}$	kg
Proton rest mass	M_p	1.672614	$\times 10^{-27}$	kg
Neutron rest mass	M_n	1.674920	$\times 10^{-27}$	kg
Magnetic flux quantum	Φ_0	2.0678538	$\times 10^{-15}$	T m^2
Faraday's constant, Ne	F	9.648670	$\times 10^7$	C/kmol
Rydberg constant	R_∞	1.09737312	$\times 10^7$	1/m
Bohr radius	α_0	5.2917715	$\times 10^{-11}$	m
Classical electron radius	r_0	2.817939	$\times 10^{-15}$	m
Bohr magneton	μ_B	9.274096	$\times 10^{-24}$	J/T
Electron magnetic moment	μ_e	9.284851	$\times 10^{-24}$	J/T
Proton magnetic moment	μ_p	1.4106203	$\times 10^{-26}$	J/T
Nuclear magneton	μ_n	5.050951	$\times 10^{-27}$	J/T
Compton wavelength of electron	λ_C	2.4263096	$\times 10^{-12}$	m
Compton wavelength of proton	$\lambda_{C,p}$	1.3214409	$\times 10^{-15}$	m
Compton wavelength of neutron	$\lambda_{C,n}$	1.3196217	$\times 10^{-15}$	m
Boltzman's constant	k	1.380622	$\times 10^{-23}$	J/K
First radiation constant	c_1	3.741844	$\times 10^{-24}$	J m
Second radiation constant	c_2	1.438833	$\times 10^{-2}$	m K
Gravitational constant	G	6.6732	$\times 10^{-11}$	N m^2/kg^2

Constants Table C-6 lists the values and symbols of mathematical and physical constants.

Conversion Factors Table C-7 gives factors to convert metric unit values to conventional unit values, and vice versa.

Figure C-14 Some connectors in common use. A Alligator clip. B Double banana plug (male). C Single banana plug (male). D Bayonet-type (BNC) coaxial connector (female). E Bayonet-type (BNC) coaxial connector (male). F N-type coaxial connector (female). G N-type coaxial connector (male). H EIA 25-pin interface connector (male), typical of connectors with up to 50 pins used between computers and peripheral equipment. I F-type coaxial connector (female). J F-type coaxial connector (male).

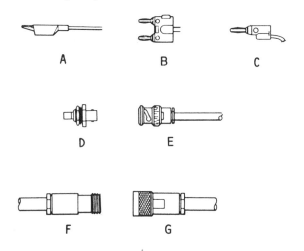

A   B   C

D   E

F   G

H

I   J

Table C-7 Conversion Factors

To convert	to	multiply by	conversely, multiply by
abampere	ampere	1.00 $\times 10^1$	1.00 $\times 10^{-1}$
abcoulomb	coulomb	1.00 $\times 10^1$	1.00 $\times 10^{-1}$
abfarad	farad	1.00 $\times 10^9$	1.00 $\times 10^{-9}$
abhenry	henry	1.00 $\times 10^{-9}$	1.00 $\times 10^9$
abmho	slemens	1.00 $\times 10^7$	1.00 $\times 10^{-9}$
abohm	ohm	1.00 $\times 10^{-7}$	1.00 $\times 10^9$
abvolt	volt	1.00 $\times 10^{-8}$	1.00 $\times 10^3$
ampere (1948)	ampere	9.998 35 $\times 10^{-1}$	1.000 17 $\times 10^0$
angstrom	meter	1.00 $\times 10^{-10}$	1.00 $\times 10^{10}$
atmosphere	pascal	1.013 25 $\times 10^3$	9.869 23 $\times 10^{-6}$
bar	pascal	1.00 $\times 10^3$	1.00 $\times 10^{-5}$
barn	meter^2	1.00 $\times 10^{-21}$	1.00 $\times 10^{22}$
British Thermal Unit (mean)	joule	1.055 87 $\times 10^3$	9.470 86 $\times 10^{-4}$
calorie (thermochemical)	joule	4.184 $\times 10^6$	2.390 $\times 10^{-1}$
calorie (kilogram, thermochemical)	joule	4.184 $\times 10^3$	2.390 $\times 10^{-4}$
circular mil	meter^2	5.067 074 8 $\times 10^{-10}$	1.973 525 2 $\times 10^5$
coulomb (1948)	coulomb	9.998 35 $\times 10^{-1}$	1.000 17 $\times 10^6$
cubic foot	meter^3	2.831 69 $\times 10^{-2}$	3.531 46 $\times 10^1$
cubic inch	meter^3	1.638 71 $\times 10^{-5}$	6.102 36 $\times 10^4$
cubic yard	meter^3	7.645 55 $\times 10^{-3}$	1.307 95 $\times 10^0$
curie	becquerel	3.70 $\times 10^{10}$	2.70 $\times 10^{-11}$
degree	radian	1.745 329 2 $\times 10^{-2}$	5.729 577 9 $\times 10^1$
dyne	newton	1.00 $\times 10^{-5}$	1.00 $\times 10^3$
farad (1948)	farad	9.995 05 $\times 10^{-1}$	1.000 50 $\times 10^0$
faraday (carbon 12)	coulomb	9.648 70 $\times 10^4$	1.036 41 $\times 10^{-5}$
fathom	meter	1.828 8 $\times 10^0$	5.468 07 $\times 10^{-1}$
fermi	meter	1.00 $\times 10^{-15}$	1.00 $\times 10^{15}$
fluid ounce (U.S.)	meter	2.957 353 $\times 10^{-5}$	3.381 402 $\times 10^4$
foot	meter	3.048 $\times 10^{-1}$	3.281 $\times 10^0$
foot-candle	lumen/meter^2	1.076 391 0 $\times 10^1$	9.290 304 3 $\times 10^{-2}$
foot-lambert	candela/meter^2	3.426 259 $\times 10^0$	2.918 635 $\times 10^{-1}$
gal	meter/second^2	1.00 $\times 10^{-2}$	1.00 $\times 10^2$
gallon (U.S. liquid)	meter	3.785 411 8 $\times 10^{-3}$	2.641 172 1 $\times 10^2$
gamma	tesla	1.00 $\times 10^{-9}$	1.00 $\times 10^9$
gauss	tesla	1.00 $\times 10^{-4}$	1.00 $\times 10^4$
gilbert	ampere turn	7.957 747 2 $\times 10^{-1}$	1.256 637 0 $\times 10^6$
grain	kilogram	6.479 891 $\times 10^{-5}$	1.543 236 $\times 10^4$
henry (1948)	henry	1.000 495 $\times 10^0$	9.995 052 $\times 10^{-1}$

TABLE C-7   Conversion Factors (*Cont.*)

To convert	to	multiply by	conversely, multiply by
horsepower (electric)	watt	7.46 $\times 10^2$	1.34 $\times 10^{-3}$
inch	meter	2.54 $\times 10^{-7}$	3.94 $\times 10^1$
inch of mercury (32°F)	pascal	3.386 389 $\times 10^3$	2.952 998 $\times 10^{-4}$
joule (1948)	joule	1.000 165 $\times 10^0$	9.998 350 $\times 10^{-1}$
knot	meter/second	5.144 444 4 $\times 10^{-1}$	1.943 844 5 $\times 10^0$
lambert	candela/meter^2	3.183 098 8 $\times 10^3$	3.141 592 7 $\times 10^{-4}$
liter	meter^3	1.00 $\times 10^{-3}$	1.00 $\times 10^3$
lux	lumen/meter^2	1.00 $\times 10^0$	1.00 $\times 10^0$
maxwell	weber	1.00 $\times 10^{-2}$	1.00 $\times 10^8$
mho	slemens	1.00 $\times 10^0$	1.00 $\times 10^0$
micron	meter	1.00 $\times 10^{-6}$	1.00 $\times 10^6$
mil	meter	2.540 $\times 10^{-3}$	3.937 $\times 10^4$
mile (U.S. statute)	meter	1.609 344 $\times 10^3$	6.213 712
mile (nautical)	meter	1.852 $\times 10^3$	5.400 $\times 10^{-4}$
millibar	pascal	1.00 $\times 10^2$	1.00 $\times 10^{-3}$
millimeter of mercury (0°C)	pascal	1.333 224 $\times 10^2$	7.500 615 $\times 10^{-3}$
neper	decibel	8.686 $\times 10^0$	1.151 $\times 10^{-1}$
newton/meter^2	pascal	1.00 $\times 10^0$	1.00 $\times 10^6$
oersted	ampere/meter	7.957 747 2 $\times 10^1$	1.256 637 0 $\times 10^{-2}$
ohm (1948)	ohm	1.000 495 $\times 10^0$	9.995 052 $\times 10^{-1}$
ounce force (avoirdupois)	newton	2.780 138 5 $\times 10^{-1}$	3.596 943 1 $\times 10^0$
ounce mass (avoirdupois)	kilogram	2.834 952 3 $\times 10^{-2}$	3.215 074 6 $\times 10^1$
pleze	pascal	1.00 $\times 10^3$	1.00 $\times 10^{-3}$
pint (U.S. liquid)	meter^3	4.731 764 7 $\times 10^{-4}$	2.113 376 4 $\times 10^3$
poise	newton second/ meter^2	1.00 $\times 10^{-1}$	1.00 $\times 10^1$
pound force (avoirdupois)	newton	4.448 221 6 $\times 10^0$	2.248 089 4 $\times 10^{-1}$
pound mass (avoirdupois)	kilogram	4.535 923 7 $\times 10^{-1}$	2.204 622 6 $\times 10^5$
poundal	newton	1.382 549 5 $\times 10^{-1}$	7.233 014 0 $\times 10^0$
quart (U.S. liquid)	liter	9.463 529 5 $\times 10^{-1}$	1.056 688 2 $\times 10^0$
quart (U.S. liquid)	meter^3	9.463 529 5 $\times 10^{-4}$	1.056 688 2 $\times 10^3$
rad	joule/kilogram	1.00 $\times 10^{-2}$	1.00 $\times 10^2$
rayleigh	1/second meter^2	1.00 $\times 10^{10}$	1.00 $\times 10^{-10}$

TABLE C-7   Conversion Factors (*Cont.*)

To convert	to	multiply by	conversely, multiply by
roentgen	coulomb/kilogram	$2.579\ 76 \quad \times\ 10^{-4}$	$3.876\ 33 \quad \times\ 10^{3}$
rutherford	becquerel	$1.00 \quad \times\ 10^{6}$	$1.00 \quad \times\ 10^{-6}$
slug	kilogram	$1.459\ 390\ 3 \times 10^{1}$	$6.852\ 176\ 5 \times 10^{-2}$
square inch	meter^2	$6.452 \quad \times\ 10^{-4}$	$1.550 \quad \times\ 10^{3}$
square foot	meter^2	$9.290 \quad \times\ 10^{-2}$	$1.076 \quad \times\ 10^{1}$
square yard	meter^2	$8.361 \quad \times\ 10^{-1}$	$1.196 \quad \times\ 10^{0}$
statampere	ampere	$3.335\ 640 \quad \times\ 10^{-10}$	$2.997\ 925 \quad \times\ 10^{9}$
statcoulomb	coulomb	$3.335\ 640 \quad \times\ 10^{-10}$	$2.997\ 925 \quad \times\ 10^{9}$
statfarad	farad	$1.112\ 650 \quad \times\ 10^{-12}$	$8.987\ 554 \quad \times\ 10^{11}$
stathenry	henry	$8.987\ 554 \quad \times\ 10^{11}$	$1.112\ 650 \quad \times\ 10^{-12}$
statmho	slemens	$1.112\ 650 \quad \times\ 10^{-12}$	$8.987\ 554 \quad \times\ 10^{11}$
statohm	ohm	$8.987\ 554 \quad \times\ 10^{11}$	$1.112\ 650 \quad \times\ 10^{-12}$
statvolt	volt	$2.997\ 925 \quad \times\ 10^{2}$	$3.335\ 640 \quad \times\ 10^{-3}$
stilb	candela/meter^2	$1.00 \quad \times\ 10^{4}$	$1.00 \quad \times\ 10^{-4}$
torr (0°C)	pascal	$1.333\ 22 \quad \times\ 10^{2}$	$7.500\ 64 \quad \times\ 10^{-3}$
unit pole	weber	$1.256\ 637 \quad \times\ 10^{-7}$	$7.957\ 748 \quad \times\ 10^{5}$
volt (1948)	volt	$1.000\ 330 \quad \times\ 10^{0}$	$9.996\ 701 \quad \times\ 10^{-1}$
watt (1948)	watt	$1.00\ 165 \quad \times\ 10^{0}$	$9.998\ 350 \quad \times\ 10^{-1}$
yard	meter	$9.144 \quad \times\ 10^{-1}$	$1.094 \quad \times\ 10^{0}$

Temperature conversion formulas

$$\text{Fahrenheit to Celsius: } t_c = \left(\frac{5}{9}\right)(t_f - 32)$$

$$\text{Celsius to Fahrenheit: } t_f = \frac{9t_c}{5} + 32$$

$$\text{Celsius to Kelvin: } \quad t_k = t_c + 273.15$$

$$\text{Kelvin to Celsius: } \quad t_c = t_k - 273.15$$

Current   *See* Alternating Current, Direct Current.

D

Darlington Amplifier *See* Amplifiers.

Decibels The decibel is the tenth part of a bel (B). The bel is the ratio on a logarithmic scale that two amounts of power bear to each other:

$$B = \log_{10} P_1/P_2$$

where P_1 is the power level being considered, and P_2 is an arbitrary reference level.

Since power is proportional to the square of voltage or current, the ratio on a logarithmic scale that two amounts of voltage bear to each other is given by:

$$B = 2 \log_{10} V_1/V_2$$

where V_1 is the voltage level being considered, and V_2 is an arbitrary reference level.

The same ratio applies to current:

$$B = 2 \log_{10} I_1/I_2$$

It is more convenient to express these ratios in decibels, so these formulas become:

$$dB = 10 \log_{10} P_1/P_2$$

$$dB = 20 \log_{10} V_1/V_2$$

$$dB = 20 \log_{10} I_1/I_2$$

The ratio may be that of output power to input power, output voltage to input voltage, or output current to input current.

The reference level is also commonly 6 millivolts across a 500-ohm impedance, and this should be assumed where no reference is specified. Other reference levels are indicated by adding suffixes to the unit, as follows:

dBj	1 mW
dBk	1 kW
dBm	mW, 600 Ω
dBs	same as dBm (Japanese)
dBw	1 W
dBvg	ratio of voltage gain
dBrap	10^{-16} W of acoustical power

83

Table D-1 gives values in decibels from 0 to 20 for power gain and loss, and voltage/current gain and loss, and can, of course, be used both ways. If the value you want to convert falls between two values given, use the value nearest to it. Table D-2 gives the same for values higher than 20 dB.

TABLE D-1   Decibel Conversion Table (0-20)

dB	Power		Voltage or current	
	Gain	Loss	Gain	Loss
0	1	1	1	1
.1	1.02329	.977237	1.01158	.988553
.2	1.04713	.954992	1.02329	.977237
.3	1.07152	.933254	1.03514	.966051
.4	1.09648	.91201	1.04713	.954992
.5	1.12202	.89125	1.05925	.944061
.6	1.14815	.870963	1.07152	.933254
.7	1.1749	.851137	1.08393	.922571
.8	1.20227	.831763	1.09648	.91201
.9	1.23027	.81283	1.10918	.901571
1	1.25893	.794327	1.12202	.89125
1.1	1.28825	.776246	1.13501	.881048
1.2	1.31826	.758576	1.14815	.870963
1.3	1.34897	.741309	1.16145	.860993
1.4	1.38039	.724434	1.1749	.851137
1.5	1.41254	.707944	1.1885	.841394
1.6	1.44544	.691829	1.20227	.831763
1.7	1.47911	.676081	1.21619	.822242
1.8	1.51357	.660692	1.23027	.81283
1.9	1.54882	.645652	1.24452	.803525
2	1.5849	.630956	1.25893	.794327
2.1	1.62182	.616593	1.27351	.785234
2.2	1.65959	.602558	1.28825	.776246
2.3	1.69825	.588842	1.30317	.76736
2.4	1.73781	.575438	1.31826	.758576
2.5	1.77829	.562339	1.33352	.749893
2.6	1.81971	.549539	1.34897	.741309
2.7	1.86209	.53703	1.36459	.732823
2.8	1.90547	.524805	1.38039	.724435
2.9	1.94985	.512859	1.39637	.716142
3	1.99527	.501185	1.41254	.707944
3.1	2.04175	.489777	1.4289	.699841
3.2	2.08931	.478628	1.44544	.691829
3.3	2.13797	.467733	1.46218	.68391
3.4	2.18777	.457086	1.47911	.676082
3.5	2.23873	.446681	1.49624	.668342
3.6	2.29088	.436514	1.51357	.660692

	Power		Voltage or current	
dB	Gain	Loss	Gain	Loss
3.7	2.34424	.426577	1.53109	.653129
3.8	2.39885	.416867	1.54882	.645653
3.9	2.45472	.407378	1.56676	.638262
4	2.5119	.398105	1.5849	.630956
4.1	2.57041	.389043	1.60325	.623733
4.2	2.63028	.380187	1.62182	.616593
4.3	2.69155	.371533	1.6406	.609535
4.4	2.75425	.363076	1.65959	.602558
4.5	2.8184	.354811	1.67881	.59566
4.6	2.88405	.346735	1.69825	.588842
4.7	2.95123	.338842	1.71791	.582101
4.8	3.01997	.331129	1.73781	.575438
4.9	3.09032	.323591	1.75793	.568851
5	3.1623	.316226	1.77829	.562339
5.1	3.23596	.309027	1.79888	.555902
5.2	3.31134	.301993	1.81971	.549539
5.3	3.38847	.295119	1.84078	.543248
5.4	3.4674	.288401	1.86209	.53703
5.5	3.54816	.281836	1.88366	.530882
5.6	3.63081	.275421	1.90547	.524805
5.7	3.71538	.269151	1.92753	.518798
5.8	3.80193	.263025	1.94985	.512859
5.9	3.89049	.257037	1.97243	.506989
6	3.98111	.251186	1.99527	.501185
6.1	4.07384	.245469	2.01838	.495448
6.2	4.16873	.239881	2.04175	.489777
6.3	4.26584	.234421	2.06539	.48417
6.4	4.3652	.229085	2.08931	.478628
6.5	4.46688	.22387	2.1135	.473149
6.6	4.57093	.218774	2.13797	.467733
6.7	4.6774	.213794	2.16273	.462379
6.8	4.78635	.208928	2.18777	.457086
6.9	4.89784	.204172	2.21311	.451854
7	5.01192	.199524	2.23873	.446681
7.1	5.12867	.194982	2.26466	.441568
7.2	5.24813	.190544	2.29088	.436514
7.3	5.37037	.186207	2.31741	.431517
7.4	5.49547	.181968	2.34424	.426577
7.5	5.62347	.177826	2.37139	.421694
7.6	5.75446	.173778	2.39885	.416867
7.7	5.8885	.169823	2.42662	.412095
7.8	6.02566	.165957	2.45472	.407378
7.9	6.16602	.162179	2.48315	.402715
8	6.30964	.158488	2.5119	.398105
8.1	6.45662	.15488	2.54099	.393548
8.2	6.60701	.151354	2.57041	.389043
8.3	6.76091	.147909	2.60018	.38459

TABLE D-1 (Cont.)

	Power		Voltage or current	
dB	Gain	Loss	Gain	Loss
8.4	6.9184	.144542	2.63028	.380187
8.5	7.07955	.141252	2.66074	.375835
8.6	7.24445	.138037	2.69155	.371533
8.7	7.4132	.134895	2.72272	.36728
8.8	7.58588	.131824	2.75425	.363076
8.9	7.76258	.128823	2.78614	.35892
9	7.94339	.125891	2.8184	.354811
9.1	8.12842	.123025	2.85104	.350749
9.2	8.31776	.120225	2.88405	.346734
9.3	8.5115	.117488	2.91745	.342765
9.4	8.70976	.114814	2.95123	.338842
9.5	8.91264	.1122	2.98541	.334963
9.6	9.12025	.109646	3.01997	.331129
9.7	9.33269	.10715	3.05495	.327338
9.8	9.55008	.104711	3.09032	.323591
9.9	9.77253	.102328	3.1261	.319887
10	10	.1	3.1623	.316225
10.1	10.2331	.0977222	3.19892	.312606
10.2	10.4714	.0954978	3.23596	.309027
10.3	10.7154	.093324	3.27343	.30549
10.4	10.965	.0911996	3.31134	.301993
10.5	11.2204	.0891237	3.34968	.298536
10.6	11.4817	.0870949	3.38847	.295119
10.7	11.7492	.0851124	3.42771	.29174
10.8	12.0228	.083175	3.4674	.288401
10.9	12.3029	.0812817	3.50755	.285099
11	12.5895	.0794314	3.54817	.281836
11.1	12.8827	.0776233	3.58925	.27861
11.2	13.1828	.0758564	3.63081	.27542
11.3	13.4899	.0741297	3.67286	.272268
11.4	13.8041	.0724423	3.71539	.269151
11.5	14.1256	.0707933	3.75841	.26607
11.6	14.4547	.0691818	3.80193	.263024
11.7	14.7914	.067607	3.84595	.260014
11.8	15.1359	.0660681	3.89049	.257037
11.9	15.4885	.0645642	3.93554	.254095
12	15.8492	.0630945	3.98111	.251186
12.1	16.2184	.0616583	4.02721	.248311
12.2	16.5962	.0602547	4.07384	.245468
12.3	16.9828	.0588832	4.12102	.242659
12.4	17.3784	.0575428	4.16874	.239881
12.5	17.7832	.056233	4.21701	.237135
12.6	18.1974	.0549529	4.26584	.23442
12.7	18.6213	.053702	4.31524	.231737
12.8	19.055	.0524796	4.36521	.229084
12.9	19.4989	.051285	4.41575	.226462

dB	Power		Voltage or current	
	Gain	Loss	Gain	Loss
13	19.9531	.0501176	4.46689	.22387
13.1	20.4178	.0489768	4.51861	.221307
13.2	20.8934	.0478619	4.57093	.218774
13.3	21.3801	.0467724	4.62386	.216269
13.4	21.8781	.0457077	4.67741	.213794
13.5	22.3877	.0446673	4.73157	.211346
13.6	22.9092	.0436506	4.78636	.208927
13.7	23.4429	.0426569	4.84178	.206536
13.8	23.9889	.0416859	4.89785	.204171
13.9	24.5477	.040737	4.95456	.201834
14	25.1195	.0398097	5.01193	.199524
14.1	25.7046	.0389036	5.06997	.19724
14.2	26.3033	.038018	5.12868	.194982
14.3	26.916	.0371526	5.18807	.19275
14.4	27.543	.0363069	5.24814	.190544
14.5	28.1846	.0354804	5.30891	.188362
14.6	28.8411	.0346728	5.37039	.186206
14.7	29.5129	.0338835	5.43258	.184075
14.8	30.2003	.0331122	5.49548	.181968
14.9	30.9038	.0323585	5.55912	.179885
15	31.6236	.0316219	5.62349	.177826
15.1	32.3601	.0309023	5.68859	.17579
15.2	33.1139	.0301988	5.75447	.173778
15.3	33.8852	.0295114	5.8211	.171789
15.4	34.6745	.0288396	5.88851	.169822
15.5	35.4822	.0281832	5.95669	.167878
15.6	36.3087	.0275416	6.02567	.165957
15.7	37.1544	.0269147	6.09544	.164057
15.8	38.0199	.026302	6.16603	.162179
15.9	38.9055	.0257033	6.23743	.160323
16	39.8117	.0251182	6.30965	.158487
16.1	40.7391	.0245465	6.38272	.156673
16.2	41.688	.0239877	6.45663	.15488
16.3	42.659	.0234417	6.53139	.153107
16.4	43.6527	.0229081	6.60702	.151354
16.5	44.6695	.0223866	6.68353	.149622
16.6	45.71	.021877	6.76092	.147909
16.7	46.7748	.0213791	6.83921	.146216
16.8	47.8643	.0208924	6.9184	.144542
16.9	48.9792	.0204168	6.99852	.142887
17	50.1201	.0199521	7.07956	.141252
17.1	51.2876	.0194979	7.16153	.139635
17.2	52.4822	.0190541	7.24446	.138037
17.3	53.7047	.0186204	7.32835	.136456
17.4	54.9556	.0181965	7.41321	.134894
17.5	56.2357	.0177823	7.49905	.13335

dB	Power Gain	Power Loss	Voltage or current Gain	Voltage or current Loss
17.6	57.5457	.0173775	7.58589	.131824
17.7	58.8861	.0169819	7.67373	.130315
17.8	60.2577	.0165954	7.76258	.128823
17.9	61.6613	.0162176	7.85247	.127348
18	63.0976	.0158485	7.9434	.125891
18.1	64.5674	.0154877	8.03538	.12445
18.2	66.0713	.0151352	8.12843	.123025
18.3	67.6104	.0147906	8.22255	.121617
18.4	69.1852	.014454	8.31777	.120225
18.5	70.7968	.0141249	8.41408	.118848
18.6	72.4459	.0138034	8.51151	.117488
18.7	74.1334	.0134892	8.61007	.116143
18.8	75.8602	.0131821	8.70977	.114814
18.9	77.6272	.0128821	8.81063	.113499
19	79.4354	.0125889	8.91265	.1122
19.1	81.2857	.0123023	9.01586	.110916
19.2	83.1791	.0120223	9.12026	.109646
19.3	85.1166	.0117486	9.22587	.108391
19.4	87.0992	.0114812	9.3327	.10715
19.5	89.1281	.0112198	9.44077	.105924
19.6	91.2041	.0109644	9.55009	.104711
19.7	93.3286	.0107148	9.66067	.103512
19.8	95.5025	.0104709	9.77254	.102328
19.9	97.7271	.0102326	9.8857	.101156
20	100	.01	10	.1

TABLE D-2   Decibel Conversion Table (20-100)

dB	Power Gain	Power Loss	Voltage or current Gain	Voltage or current Loss
20	10^2	10^{-2}	10^1	10^{-1}
40	10^3	10^{-3}	10^2	10^{-2}
60	10^4	10^{-4}	10^3	10^{-3}
80	10^5	10^{-5}	10^4	10^{-4}
100	10^6	10^{-6}	10^5	10^{-5}

Figure D-1 is a computer program in BASIC for converting power, voltage, or current ratios to decibels, and vice versa. Figure D-2 is a sample run as it would appear on your monitor. If this is an application that you might require often, you could save it for future use.

Figure D-1 BASIC Program For Decibel Conversion

```
10 PRINT:PRINT"PROGRAM TO CONVERT POWER/VOLTAGE/CURRENT"
20 PRINT"RATIOS TO DECIBELS, AND VICE VERSA."
30 PRINT:PRINT"DO YOU WANT TO CONVERT:"
40 PRINT"1. POWER RATIO TO DB?"
50 PRINT"2. VOLTAGE OR CURRENT RATIO TO DB?"
60 PRINT"3. DB TO POWER RATIO?"
70 PRINT"4. DB TO VOLTAGE OR CURRENT RATIO?"
80 PRINT:PRINT"ENTER CHOICE (1, 2, 3, OR 4)."
90 INPUT A
100 IF A=1 THEN 140
110 IF A=2 THEN 220
120 IF A=3 THEN 300
130 IF A=4 THEN 350
140 PRINT:PRINT"ENTER REFERENCE VALUE (IF NONE ENTER 1)."
150 INPUT P1
160 PRINT:PRINT"ENTER RATIO VALUE TO BE CONVERTED TO DB."
170 INPUT P2
180 LET P=P2/P1
190 LET D=10*(LOG(P)/LOG(10))
200 PRINT:PRINT"POWER RATIO IN DB = ";D
210 GOTO 390
220 PRINT:PRINT"ENTER REFERENCE VALUE (IF NONE ENTER 1)."
230 INPUT V1
240 PRINT:PRINT"ENTER RATIO VALUE TO BE CONVERTED TO DB."
250 INPUT V2
260 LET V=V2/V1
270 LET D=20*(LOG(V)/LOG(10))
280 PRINT:PRINT"VOLTAGE OR CURRENT IN DB = ";D
290 GOTO 390
300 PRINT:PRINT"ENTER POWER RATIO IN DB."
310 INPUT D
320 LET N=EXP(2.3026*(D/10))
330 PRINT:PRINT"POWER RATIO = ";N
340 GOTO 390
350 PRINT:PRINT"ENTER VOLTAGE OR CURRENT RATIO IN DB."
360 INPUT M
370 LET M=EXP(2.3026*(M/20))
380 PRINT:PRINT"VOLTAGE OR CURRENT RATIO = ";M
390 PRINT:PRINT"TYPE Y TO CONTINUE, Q TO QUIT."
400 INPUT X$
410 IF X$="Y" THEN 30
420 END
```

Figure D-2 Sample Run of Program in Figure D-1

```
PROGRAM TO CONVERT POWER/VOLTAGE/CURRENT
RATIOS TO DECIBELS, AND VICE VERSA.

DO YOU WANT TO CONVERT:
1. POWER RATIO TO DB?
2. VOLTAGE OR CURRENT RATIO TO DB?
3. DB TO POWER RATIO?
4. DB TO VOLTAGE OR CURRENT RATIO?

ENTER CHOICE (1, 2, 3, OR 4).
? 1

ENTER REFERENCE VALUE (IF NONE ENTER 1).
? 1

ENTER RATIO VALUE TO BE CONVERTED TO DB.
? 15

POWER RATIO IN DB = 11.7609

TYPE Y TO CONTINUE, Q TO QUIT.
? Q
```

Decimal Number System *See* Number Systems.

Delay Line *See* Transmission Lines.

Delta Network *See* Tee or Wye Network.

Derivative *See* Calculus.

Diac *See* Diodes.

Dielectric Materials and Components *See* Capacitors.

Differential *See* Calculus.

Differential Amplifier *See* Amplifiers.

Differentiator The basic differentiator circuit in Figure D-3 consists of a series capacitor and a shunt resistor. Since a capacitor cannot pass DC, this circuit can only pass the transitions of a square wave, not the level portion, in accordance with:

$$v_o = -RC(\Delta v_i / \Delta t)$$

where:

v_o = output voltage.

R = shunt resistance.

C = series capacitance.

Δv_i = change in input voltage.

Δt = change in time (i.e., time taken for the input voltage to change).

Figure D-3 Differentiator Circuit

The output of a differentiator is proportional to the rate of change of the input; consequently, when a square wave is applied to the input, an output results only during transitions. The slope is caused by the decay of the charge on the capacitor and depends on the *RC* constant of the capacitor and resistor. A differentiator is found in almost every TV receiver. Its purpose is to change the vertical synchronizing pulses into sharp triggering pulses to maintain horizontal synchronization during the period between fields when these extrawide pulses are being received. [6]

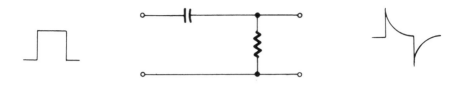

A differentiator using an operational amplifier is shown in Figure D-4.

Figure D-4 An Operational Amplifier Connected as a Differentiator
    Note that the series capacitor is in the input so that the op-amp is capacitor coupled to the previous stage. The resistor is in the feedback path. The input is a square wave with a pulse-repetition rate of 1 kHz. It has positive-going and negative-going transitions spaced at 0.5-ms intervals. Since only the transitions are passed by C, the output consists of alternating positive- and negative-going spikes at 0.5-ms intervals. Their phase is reversed with respect to that of the input since the op-amp inverting input is used.

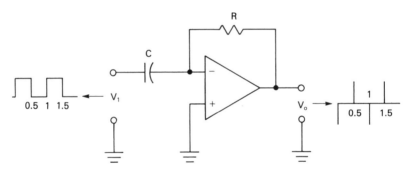

Digital Circuits *See* Logic Circuits.

DIODES

Numbering System

Junction diodes are numbered by either the JEDEC (Joint Electron Device Engineering Council) system or by the manufacturer's type number. JEDEC-registered diodes have numbers consisting of N preceded by a digit (e.g., 1N914, 1N4001, etc.). Manufacturers' numbers vary with the manufacturer (e.g., S1S11, 15108046, etc.). The parameters of JEDEC-registered devices are standardized, and they may be available from more than one manufacturer.

Types of Diodes

The types of diodes covered here are:

Rectifier diodes

Zener diodes

Light-emitting diodes (LEDs)

Voltage-variable capacitance diodes (varactors)

Microwave diodes

Small-signal diodes

Silicon-controlled rectifier diodes

Triacs and diacs

Rectifier Diodes

Parameters given in specifications are explained in Table D-3.

TABLE D-3 Commonly Used Parameters of Rectifier Diodes

Parameter	Symbol	Meaning
DC forward voltage	V_F	Voltage across a forward-biased diode.
DC forward current	I_F	Current flowing in a forward-biased diode.
DC reverse voltage	V_R	Voltage across a reverse-biased diode.
DC reverse current	I_R	Leakage current flowing in a reverse-biased diode.
Reverse breakdown voltage	V_{br} B_V PRV PIV	Maximum reverse voltage across diode before it breaks down.
Power dissipation	P_D	Maximum power that may be dissipated in a diode.
Operating junction temperature	T_j	Temperature of the junction.
Capacitance	C	Capacitance across diode biased either way.
Reverse recovery time	t_{rr}	Time required for reverse current or voltage to reach a specified value after switching diode from forward to reverse bias.
Forward recovery time	t_{fr}	Time required for forward voltage or current to reach a specified value after switching diode from reverse to forward bias.
Noise figure	NF_o	Ratio of RMS output noise power of receiver in which diode is used to that of an ideal receiver of same gain and bandwidth.
Conversion loss	L_C	Power lost in mixer diode when converting an RF signal to an IF signal.
Video resistance	R_v	Low-level impedance of a detector diode.

The key parameters for a rectifier diode are V_R and V_s:

$$V_R = 1.4142V_s - 0.7 \text{ V}$$

where:

V_s = RMS voltage across secondary of power transformer.

0.7 V = approximate voltage drop across diode when conducting.

With a capacitor-input filter, surge current also must be considered. In such a case, I_F should be derated 50 percent.

Zener Diodes

Parameters given in specifications are explained in Table D-4.

TABLE D-4   Commonly Used Parameters of Zener Diodes

Parameter	Symbol	Meaning
Zener voltage	V_Z	Nominal regulating voltage of diode.
Knee current	I_{ZK}	Minimum current for operation.
Maximum zener current	I_{ZM}	Maximum current that can flow in diode.
Zener impedance	Z_Z	Change in zener voltage for small change in zener current with respect to specified test current I_{ZT}.

For a zener diode connected in series with a dropping resistor, the value for the resistor should be such that the maximum current in the diode does not exceed $0.9I_{ZM}$.

A typical shunt regulator using a zener diode is shown in Figure D-5. In this circuit:

$$I_Z = (V_i - V_o)/R_1 - V_o/R_L$$

$$\Delta V_o = \Delta I_Z Z_Z$$

$$\Delta I_Z \cong \Delta V_i/R_1$$

$$\Delta V_o \cong Z_Z(\Delta V_i/R_1)$$

Light-Emitting Diodes

Parameters given in specifications are explained in Table D-5. An LED driving circuit is shown in Figure D-6.

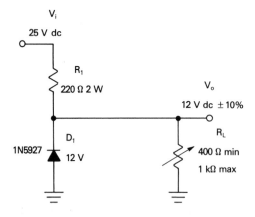

Figure D-5 Zener Diode Used as a Shunt Regulator

The diode is reverse-biased and allows no current to flow through it up to the zener voltage, which is 12 V. As a result, the input voltage of 25 V becomes an unvarying output voltage of 12 V. R_L is adjusted for a precise voltage.

TABLE D-5   Commonly Used Parameters of Light-Emitting Diodes

Parameter	Symbol	Meaning
Forward voltage	V_F	Forward voltage across LED.
Candlepower (cd)	CP	Measure of luminous intensity of emitted light.
Radiant power output	P_o	Light power (brightness) of LED.
Peak spectral emission	λ_{peak}	Wavelength of brightest emitted color.
Spectral bandwidth	BW	Bandwidth of emitted color.

In the circuit in Figure D-6:

$$I_F = (V_{CC} - V_F)/R_1$$

where:

$$V_{CC} \text{ is the supply voltage.}$$

Voltage-Variable Capacitance Diodes (Varactors)

Parameters given in specifications are explained in Table D-6. Typical varactor ratings are given in Table D-7.

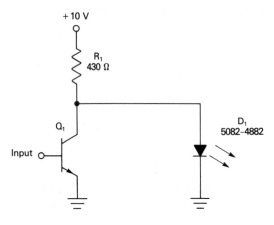

Figure D-6 LED Driving Circuit

When $Q1$ is conducting, its collector voltage is almost zero, insufficient to forward-bias $D1$, which therefore does not light. However, when $Q1$ does not conduct, its collector voltage rises toward that of the supply voltage. $D1$ becomes forward-biased and lights. If $V_F = 1.6$ V, the current is given by:

$$I_F = \frac{10 \text{ V} - 1.6 \text{ V}}{430 \text{ ohms}} = 19.5 \text{ mA}$$

TABLE D-6   Commonly Used Parameters of Voltage-Variable Capacitance Diodes (Varactors)

Parameter	Symbol	Meaning
Series inductance	L_S	Inductance (mostly of the leads) which is in series with the diode capacitance.
Capacitance temperature coefficient	TC_C	Change in capacitance caused by temperature change.
Figure of merit	Q	Ratio of capacitive reactance to effective series resistance.
Tuning ratio	TR	Ratio of low to high capacitance at specified reverse voltage

In Figure D-7, the resonant frequency is given by:

$$f = 1/[2\pi\sqrt{L_1(C_D + C_S)}]$$

Figure D-7 Voltage-Variable Capacitance Diode Circuit
This parallel-resonant circuit consists of L1 and D1 (a voltage-variable capacitance diode). C_S represents the stray capacitance in the circuit. C1 is there to block DC. As it is large, compared to C_S and D1, it acts as a short circuit for AC, so does not affect the tuning. L1 is slug tuned. Its inductance can be varied from 6.5 H to 9.5 H. The diode's capacitance can be varied from 9 to 11 pF, according to the voltage applied to it. Circuits such as this, and also those with RC resonant circuits, are used in electronic tuning.

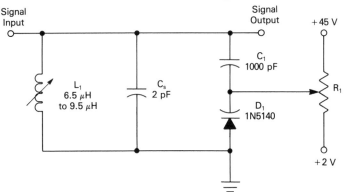

Capacitance C_D is given by:

$$C_D = 1/(4\pi^2f^2L_1) - C_S$$

Inductance L_1 is given by:

$$L_1 = 1/[4\pi^2f^2(C_D + C_S)]$$

Figure of merit Q is given by:

$$Q = (Q_LQ_C)/(Q_L + Q_C)$$

TABLE D-7 Typical Silicon Varactor Characteristics ($T_C = 25°C$)

Rating	Symbol	Value	Unit
Reverse voltage	V_R	60	V DC
Forward current	I_F	250	mA DC
RF power input[1]	P_{in}	5.0	W
Dissipation[2]	P_D	400	mW
Dissipation[3]	P_C	2.0	W
Junction temperature	T_J	$+175$	°C
Storage temperature	T_{stg}	-65 to $+200$	°C
Reverse breakdown voltage	B_{VR}	70	V DC
Reverse voltage leakage current	I_R	0.02 max	μA DC
Series inductance	L_S	5.0	nH
Case capacitance	C_C	0.25	pF
Capacitance temperature coefficient	TC_C	200	ppm/°C

[1]With adequate heat sink, if required.
[2]At ambient temperature of 25°C; derate 2.67 mW/°C above 25°C.
[3]At case temperature of 25°C; derate 13.3 mW/°C above 25°C.

Microwave Diodes

Schottky and PIN diodes are used in microwave applications as detectors, switches, and mixers. Their parameters, as given in manufacturer's specifications, are explained in Table D-8.

TABLE D-8 Schottky and PIN Diode Parameters

Parameter	Symbol	Meaning
Carrier lifetime	τ	Average life of carrier after crossing forward-biased junction (indication of switching speed).
Standing-wave ratio	SWR	Amount of transmission line impedance mismatch caused by diode.
IF impedance	Z_{IF}	Diode impedance at the *IF* specified when used as a mixer.
Isolation	—	Attenuation in dB between input and output caused by PIN switch biased to isolate signal.
Insertion loss	—	Attenuation in dB of signal caused by PIN switch biased for continuity.

Silicon-Controlled Rectifiers (SCRs)

SCRs are often used for motor control, in which a triggering circuit provides a pulse with a varying delay from the start of the positive half-cycle of the motor AC. With no delay, triggering is immediate, and the SCR conducts for the full half-cycle. If delayed, it conducts for only a portion of the half-cycle so that power to the motor is reduced. Their parameters, as given in manufacturer's specifications, are explained in Table D-9.

TABLE D-9 Commonly Used Parameters of *SCRs*

Parameter	Symbol	Meaning
Forward breakdown voltage	$V_{(br)F}$ V_{BO}	Forward voltage at which volt-device fires
Reverse breakdown voltage	$V_{(br)R}$	Maximum reverse voltage causing SCR to go into avalanche
On-state voltage	V_T, V_F	Voltage across SCR when it is conducting
On-state current	I_T, I_F	Current through SCR when it is conducting
Holding current	I_H	Minimum current through SCR when it is conducting
Latching current	I_L	Minimum current that maintains SCR in conducting state with trigger removed
Gate-trigger current	I_{GT}	Minimum gate current required to turn SCR on
Gate-trigger voltage	V_{GT}	Gate voltage required to produce gate trigger current
Gate turn-on time	t_{on}	Time for SCR to turn on
Commutated turn-off time	t_{off}, t_q	Time for SCR to turn off
Critical rate-of-rise	dv/dt	Rate of change of voltage applied to nonconducting SCR anode that may switch SCR on if exceeded

I_{GT} is determined from:

$$I_{GT} = (v_T - V_{GT})/R_S$$

where:

v_T = trigger voltage.

R_S = series resistor through which v_T is applied.

RMS current flowing through SCR is given by:

$$I_{A,\mathrm{RMS}} = (\sqrt{2}/4)I_{A,\mathrm{peak}}$$

where:

$I_{A,\mathrm{peak}}$ = maximum current through SCR. (It should be remembered that SCR conducts only on alternate half-cycles.)

Maximum junction temperature is given by:

$$T_J = P_D(\theta_{JC} + \theta_{CA}) + t_A$$

where:

θ_{JC} = junction-to-case thermal resistance of SCR.

θ_{CA} = case-to-ambient thermal resistance of heat sink

T_A = ambient temperature.

Diacs and Triacs

A diac is a bidirectional breakdown diode which conducts only when its specified breakdown voltage is exceeded. This is called the "breakover voltage." Conduction is in both directions, so the diode can be used as an AC switch.

A triac has a third lead. A gating voltage is applied to this lead to turn it on. The triac then conducts in both directions like a diac (but unlike an SCR, which only conducts in one direction).

Because it is a bidirectional device, a triac has no cathode or anode. The terminals for the main conductive path are called Main Terminal 1 (MT1) and Main Terminal 2 (MT2). Gate voltages and polarities are referenced to MT1.

Parameters for triacs are the same as for SCRs. *See also* Transistors.

DIP Abbreviation for dual inline package. *See* integrated circuits.

Displays A display is any device that conveys information by visual means. This would therefore include pilot lights and other components that exhibit the information by a simple on-off condition. For these, *see* Lamps, and Diodes (LEDs).

More comprehensive information is conveyed by alpha and numeric displays. Seven-segment character displays are used extensively in calculators and similar equipment. The display, as shown in Figure D-8, consists of seven segments that are activated by digital circuitry to show numeric characters 0 through 9, and certain alpha characters (such as A, C, E, F, H, I, J, L, O, P, S, and U). However, if a complete alphabet of alpha characters is required, a star-shaped or dot-matrix display must be used. The segments may be bar-shaped LEDs or liquid crystal electrodes.

Bar-shaped segments are also found in bargraph displays that meter some quantity. Many of these are used as dashboard instruments in automobiles.

Since all these are digital displays, in which the component segments are either on or off, they cannot reproduce anything with a gray scale, such as a halftone illustration. Only video displays can do that. *See* Vacuum Tubes (cathode-ray tube).

Figure D-8 A Seven-Segment LED Display

This display has seven LEDs, lettered a through g. When an LED is forward-biased, the segment lights. In this example, each cathode is connected to a different pin (1, 2, 7, 8, 10, 11, 13), but all the anodes are connected to two common pins (3, 14). Pins 4, 5, 6, 9, and 12 are not used and are usually not provided. Only one of the two anode pins needs to be connected to the supply voltage. The segment pins require a resistor between each and ground, and switching circuitry to turn them on and off as necessary. This type of display may have common cathodes instead, with the segments being the anodes. [9]

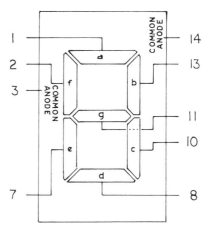

E

Earphone *See* Transducers.

Effective Voltage *See* Alternating Current.

Efficiency *See* under specific device.

ELECTRIC CIRCUIT THEORY

Electric circuit theory involves network or mesh analysis. Figure E-1 explains conventions used in this connection. The following laws are given in terms of DC circuits. (In DC circuits, resistors are the only passive elements.) However, they are equally valid for AC circuits in a steady state (in which capacitors and inductors are also passive elements), except that impedance values (Z), which take reactance into account as well

Figure E-1 Conventions Used in Analyzing an Electric Circuit

N = node (where two or more elements are joined).

J = junction (node where three or more elements are joined); sometimes called a major node.

Element extends from one node to another.

Branch extends from one junction to another (may consist of more than one element.

Loop is a single closed path for current.

Source is a source of energy (active element). It can be a voltage source or a current source; it can also be dependent (controlled), such as a transistor; or independent (such as a battery).

Passive elements are resistors, capacitors, inductors, etc.

Current direction is conventional (opposite to electron flow).

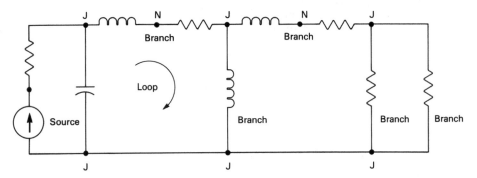

as resistance, must be used for the latter. (*See also* Alternating Current, Capacitance, Inductance, and Resistance.)

Kirchhoff's Current Law

At any node or junction of a circuit, the algebraic sum of the entering currents I_{ent} is zero:

$$\sum I_{ent} = 0$$

The exiting currents I_{exit} are treated as negative entering currents:

$$\sum I_{ent} = \sum I_{exit}$$

Kirchhoff's Voltage Law

Around any closed pathway in either a clockwise or counter-clockwise direction, the algebraic sum of the voltage drops V_{drop} is zero:

$$\sum V_{drop} = 0$$

A drop occurs when current passes through an element from $+$ to $-$; a rise occurs when it passes from $-$ to $+$. A voltage rise V_{rise} is treated as a negative drop.

$$\sum V_{drop} = \sum V_{rise}$$

Voltage Divider

A voltage divider consists of two or more resistors in series. The voltage V_n across a particular resistor R_n in a voltage divider is given by:

$$V_n = V_{tot}(R_n/R_{tot})$$

where:

V_{tot} = the applied voltage, in volts.

R_{tot} = the sum of the resistances, in ohms.

Current Divider

A current divider consists of two or more resistors in parallel. The current I_n in a particular resistor R_n in a current divider is given by:

$$I_n = I_{tot}(R_{EQ}/R_n)$$

where:

I_{tot} = the applied current, in amperes.

R_{EQ} = the equivalent resistance of all the resistors in parallel.

Thévenin and Norton Theorems

A linear circuit, regardless of its complexity, can be replaced by a Thévenin equivalent circuit consisting of an independent voltage source V_{TH} in series with a resistor R_{TH}.

The same circuit can be replaced with a Norton equivalent circuit consisting of an independent current source I_N in parallel with a conductance $G_N(G = 1/R)$.

The Thévenin and Norton equivalent circuits are related to each other as follows:

$$V_{TH} = R_{TH}I_N$$

$$I_N = G_N V_{TH}$$

In an AC circuit, G is replaced with Y (admittance).

Electron Tubes *See* Vacuum Tubes.

F

FEEDBACK

Feedback is used with amplifiers to modify their operating characteristics. A portion of the output signal is fed back to the input.

In most cases, it is subtracted from the input signal. This is called negative or degenerative feedback. It can, however, be added to the input signal, in which case the feedback is called positive or regenerative.

Negative feedback stabilizes amplifier gain, increases the bandwidth, and reduces noise and distortion. It is an important feature of operational amplifiers. Positive feedback has just the opposite effect. It is seldom used for amplifiers, its primary use being in oscillators.

Feedback also affects the input and output impedances of amplifiers. The manner in which these change depends upon the type of feedback.

Figure F-1 is a block diagram of an amplifier with feedback. Without the feedback network, the amplifier has an open-loop gain.

Figure F-1 Block Diagram of Amplifier with Feedback—[6]

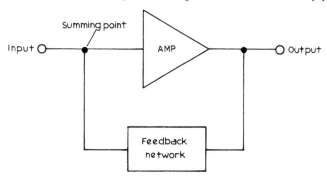

Voltage gain is given by:

$$A_v = \frac{v_o}{v_i}$$

where A_v is voltage gain, v_o is output voltage, and v_i is input voltage.

Similarly, current gain is given by:

$$A_i = \frac{i_o}{i_i}$$

where A_i is current gain, i_o is output current, and i_i is input current.

However, with a feedback loop giving negative feedback, the gain of the amplifier is reduced and is called closed-loop gain. The fraction of the output that is fed back to the input is called the feedback transfer ratio, or B. The new gain formulas are now:

$$A_{vf} = \frac{A_v}{1 - A_v B}$$

$$A_{if} = \frac{A_i}{1 - A_i B}$$

where A_{vf} and A_{if} are voltage gain and current gain, respectively, with feedback. B is negative for negative feedback, positive for positive feedback.

For example, suppose the amplifier has an open-loop voltage gain of 200, and 15 percent of the output is fed back to the input. The closed-loop gain is obtained from:

$$A_{vf} = \frac{200}{1 - (200 \times -0.15)} = 6.45$$

Feedback is *series* or *shunt*. Figure F-2 shows a common-emitter circuit with series feedback. This is derived from the emitter resistor R_E,

Figure F-2 Common-Emitter Amplifier with Series Feedback—[6]

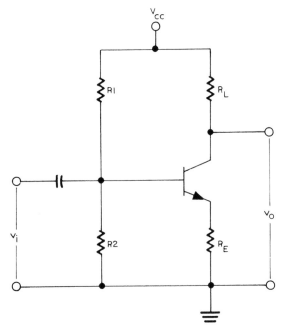

since it is common to both the input and the output and also is unby-passed. The emitter current is approximately equal to the output current, so:

$$B = \frac{R_E}{R_E + R_L}$$

as long as $R_E > h_{ie}$, and R1 and R2 are large, which is generally the case. Otherwise, the equivalent resistance R_B of the voltage divider R1 and R2 is given by:

$$R_B = \frac{R_1 R_2}{R_1 + R_2}$$

The input resistance to the transistor R'_i is given by:

$$R'_i = h_{ie} + R_E$$

and the input resistance (= impedance) of the complete circuit R_i is given by:

$$R_i = \frac{R_B R'_i}{R_B + R'_i}$$

Current gain is given by:

$$A_{if} = -\beta \frac{R_B}{R_B + h_{ie} + \beta R_E}$$

and voltage gain by:

$$A_{vf} = A_{if}\left(\frac{R_L}{R_i}\right)$$

Output impedance R_o is given by:

$$R_o = \frac{h_{fe}}{h_{oe}} \frac{R_E}{h_{ie} + R_E + R'_s}$$

where:

$$R'_s = \frac{R_s R_B}{R_s + R_B}$$

and where R_s is the source resistance.

Series feedback is also called current feedback.

Shunt feedback is illustrated in Figure F-3. Feedback is via R_F.

The input impedance is given by:

$$Z_i = \frac{Z_F}{1 + A_v}$$

Figure F-3 Common-Emitter Amplifier with Shunt Feedback—[6]

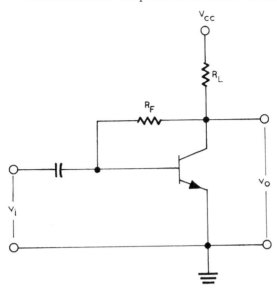

When R_F is purely resistive, $Z_i = R_i'$, so the input resistance of the complete circuit is given by:

$$R_i = \frac{R_i' h_{ie}}{R_i' + h_{ie}}$$

and the current gain (where R_F is very much greater than h_{ie}) is given by:

$$A_{if} = \frac{-\beta}{1 + \beta(R_L/R_F)}$$

Voltage gain is given by:

$$A_{vf} = A_{if} \left(\frac{R_L}{R_i}\right)$$

Output impedance is given by:

$$R_o = \frac{R_{om}}{h_{oe}R_{om} + 1}$$

where:

$$R_{om} = \frac{A_v R_F}{A_v - 1}$$

Shunt feedback is also called voltage feedback. (*See also* Amplifiers: Operational Amplifiers.)

Field-Effect Transistor (FET) *See* Transistors.

FILTERS

The main types of filters are as follows, and are used in the frequency ranges shown:

Inductance-capacitance-resistance:	100 Hz–300 MHz
Active	0.01 Hz–500 kHz
Monolithic	0.01 Hz–>500 kHz
Crystal	1 kHz–100 MHz
Surface Acoustic-Wave	1 MHz–2 GHz
Microwave	225 MHz–100 GHz

Filters covered here are classified as:

Low-pass
High-pass
Band-pass
Band-stop

Inductance-Capacitance-Resistance (LCR) Filters

These filters consist of networks of passive components (inductors, capacitors, or resistors) that offer little opposition to a selected frequency, or band of frequencies, but severely attenuate others.

General configurations of simple LCR filters (called image-parameter constant-k filters) are shown in Figure F-4. At A is a basic half-section, often called an L-section. It consists of two impedances. When $Z1$ is inductive and $Z2$ is capacitive, $Z1$ offers negligible opposition to all frequencies below a certain cut-off frequency, while $Z2$ offers a high impedance up to the cut-off frequency. Above this frequency, $Z1$ attenuates the signal more and more as the frequency increases, while $Z2$ shunts an increasing proportion of it to ground. It is therefore called a low-pass filter.

If the impedances are transposed, so that $Z1$ is now capacitive and $Z2$ is inductive, $Z1$ offers a high impedance to lower frequencies, but passes higher frequencies easily. $Z2$, however, offers little opposition to lower frequencies, but offers more and more as the frequency increases. This configuration is therefore called a high-pass filter.

As you might expect, the increase or decrease of attenuation with frequency is rather gradual. An L half-section does not exhibit a very sharp transition from its pass band to its nonpass band. The full sections shown at B and C are designed to improve this.

Figure F-4 All Filters Are Built with These Sections

  A is a half-section, often called an *L*-section. *B* is a full section, called a T-section. It really consists of two half-sections back to back, with the $Z2$ impedances merged. *C* is a full section, called a pi section. It also consists of two half-sections, but facing the other way, so that the two $Z1$ impedances are merged.

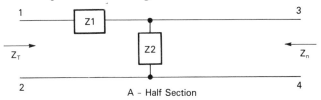

A – Half Section

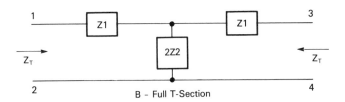

B – Full T-Section

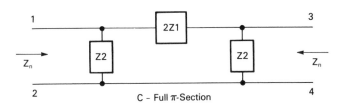

C – Full π-Section

  When using either of these, the value of inductance or capacitance has to be doubled where shown. For instance, in a full T-section, $Z2$ is twice the value calculated for $Z2$ in the *L* half-section. Similarly, in the full pi section, $Z1$ is twice the value calculated for its value in the *L* half-section.

  In band-pass and band-stop filters, $Z1$ and $Z2$ consist of series or parallel LC resonant circuits. A series resonant circuit offers little opposition to the frequency at which it is resonant, but blocks others. A parallel resonant circuit works in the opposite way, passing all frequencies except that at which it is resonant.

  Figures F-5 through F-12 show half-sections for each of these pass bands, together with their response curves and formulas for calculating

Figure F-5 Low-Pass Filter—[6]

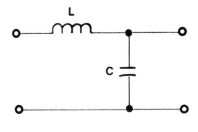

Figure F-6 Low-Pass Filter Response Curve—[6]

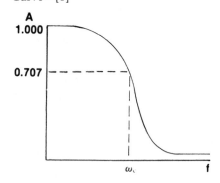

Figure F-7 High-Pass Filter—[6]

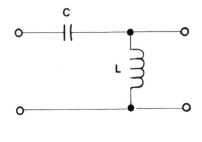

Figure F-8 High-Pass Filter Response Curve—[6]

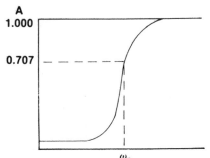

Figure F-9 Band-Pass Filter—[6]

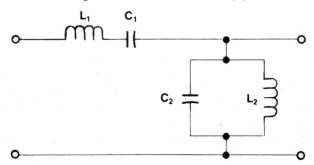

Figure F-10 Band-Pass Filter Response Curve—[6]

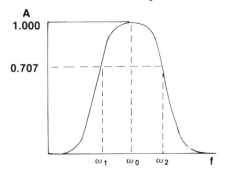

Figure F-11 Band-Stop Filter—[6]

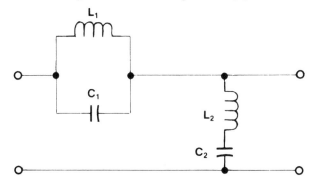

Figure F-12 Band-Stop Filter Response Curve—[6]

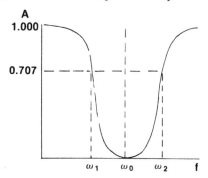

component values. The L-sections may be converted to T- or pi-sections as explained above.

Low-Pass and High-Pass Filters

The low-pass filter is shown in Figure F-5, and its response curve in Figure F-6. The high-pass filter and its response curve are shown in Figures F-7 and F-8. Values of C and L are calculated from the following formulas:

$$C = 1/\omega_c R \qquad L = R/\omega_c$$

where:

C = capacitance in farads.

L = inductance in henries.

R = nominal terminating resistance ($= \sqrt{L/C}$).

ω_c = cut-off frequency $\times$ 6.28.

Band-Pass Filter

The band-pass filter is shown in Figure F-9, and its response curve in Figure F-10. Values of C_1, C_2, L_1, and L_2 are calculated from the following formulas:

$$C_1 = (\omega_2 - \omega_2)/R\omega_0^2 \qquad L_1 = R/(\omega_2 - \omega_1)$$

$$C_2 = 1/R(\omega_2 - \omega_1) \qquad L_2 = R(\omega_2 - \omega_1)\omega_0^2$$

where:

C_1 = series capacitance in farads.

C_2 = shunt capacitance in farads.

L_1 = series inductance in henries.

L_2 = shunt inductance in henries.

R = nominal terminating resistance ($= \sqrt{L_1/C_2} = \sqrt{L_2/C_1}$).

ω_0 = midband frequency $\times$ 6.28 ($= \sqrt{\omega_1\omega_2}$).

ω_1 = lower cut-off frequency $\times$ 6.28.

ω_2 = upper cut-off frequency $\times$ 6.28.

Band-Stop Filter

The band-stop filter is shown in Figure F-11 and its response curve in Figure F-12. Values of C_1, C_2, L_1, and L_2 are calculated from the following formulas:

$$C_1 = 1/R(\omega_2 - \omega_1) \qquad L_1 = R(\omega_2 - \omega_1)/\omega_1\omega_2$$

$$C_2 = (\omega_2 - \omega_1)\omega_1\omega_2 R \qquad L_2 = R/(\omega_2 - \omega_1)$$

where:

ω_0 = midband frequency $\times$ 6.28.

$$= \sqrt{\omega_1 \omega_2} = 1/\sqrt{L_1 C_1} = 1/\sqrt{L_2 C_2}.$$

All other expressions are the same as for high-pass filters.

Constant-k low-pass and high-pass filters can be improved by converting them to *series-m* filters. In the case of a low-pass filter, this is done by adding a shunt inductor ($L2$) in series with the shunt capacitor shown in Figure F-5. The values obtained for the constant-k filter are then adjusted by multiplying them by a factor m. This is a number between 0 and 1 and need not be calculated, since for nearly all practical purposes 0.6 is satisfactory.

$$L1 = mL_k$$
$$L2 = [(1 - m^2)/m]L_k$$
$$C = mC_k$$

where:

$L1$ = new series inductance.

L_k = constant-k series inductance.

L_2 = new shunt inductance.

C = new shunt capacitance.

C_k = constant-k shunt capacitance.

m = 0.6.

In the case of a high-pass filter, a shunt capacitor is added to the shunt arm in series with the inductor shown in Figure F-7. The constant-k values are then adjusted as follows:

$$C1 = C_k/m$$
$$C2 = [m/(1 - m^2)]C_k$$
$$L = L_k/m$$

where:

$C1$ = new series capacitance.

C_k = constant-k series capacitance.

$C2$ = new shunt capacitance.

L = new shunt inductance.

L_k = constant-k shunt inductance.

m = 0.6.

Constant-k band-pass and band-stop filters can be changed to m-derived configurations also, but the improvement is less noticeable and hardly worth the additional calculation and cost of extra components. If a sharper response is needed, it is better to employ filter synthesis.

Filter synthesis uses complex polynomials to define the transfer function. Many publications now exist with comprehensive look-up tables for designing modern synthesis filters, such as the Butterworth,* Chebyshev,* elliptic, and Bessel types.

Figure F-13 gives a computer program for designing constant-k and m-derived filters.

Active Filters*

Because inductors for frequencies below 30 kHz are expensive, a new class of filters was designed using operational amplifiers. The latter have high input impedance and very low output impedance so that any number can be cascaded. In these networks, only resistors and capacitors are used in addition to operational amplifiers.

*For information on the design of these, see John Douglas-Young, *Illustrated Encyclopedic Dictionary of Electronics*, 2nd edn., Prentice Hall (1987).

Figure F13 Program for Designing Image
Parameter Filters

```
10 PRINT:PRINT"DESIGN DATA FOR IMAGE PARAMETER FILTERS"
20 PRINT:PRINT"ENTER 1,2,3, OR 4 FOR REQUIRED PASSBAND:"
30 PRINT TAB(10);"1. LOW PASS"
40 PRINT TAB(10);"2. HIGH PASS"
50 PRINT TAB(10);"3. BAND PASS"
60 PRINT TAB(10);"4. BAND STOP"
70 INPUT A
80 PRINT:PRINT"LOW-PASS AND HIGH-PASS FILTERS CAN BE"
90 PRINT"CONSTANT-K OR SERIES-M. ENTER K OR M"
100 INPUT A$
110 IF A=1 THEN 150
120 IF A=2 THEN 170
130 IF A=3 THEN 190
140 IF A=4 THEN 210
150 IF A$="K"THEN 380
160 IF A$="M"THEN 910
170 IF A$="K"THEN 510
180 IF A$="M"THEN 1000
190 IF A$="M"THEN 230
200 IF A$="K"THEN 610
210 IF A$="M" THEN 260
220 IF A$="K"THEN 760
230 PRINT:PRINT"THIS PROGRAM DOES NOT CALCULATE FOR"
240 PRINT"M-DERIVED BANDPASS FILTERS"
250 GOTO 280
260 PRINT:PRINT"THIS PROGRAM DOES NOT CALCULATE FOR"
270 PRINT"M-DERIVED BANDSTOP FILTERS"
280 N=0
290 IF N>500 THEN 320
```

```
300 N=N+1
310 GOTO 290
320 IF A=3 THEN 610
330 IF A=4 THEN 760
340 PRINT:PRINT"TYPE Y TO CONTINUE, Q TO QUIT"
350 INPUT Y$
360 IF Y$="Y"THEN 10
370 END
380 PRINT:PRINT"CONSTANT-K LOW-PASS L SECTION"
390 PRINT:PRINT"ENTER CUT-OFF FREQUENCY (-3 DB) IN HERTZ"
400 INPUT F
410 PRINT:PRINT"ENTER OUTPUT RESISTANCE IN OHMS"
420 INPUT R
430 L=R/(6.2831854*F)
440 C=1/(6.2831854*F*R)
450 IF A$="M"THEN 490
460 PRINT:PRINT"SERIES INDUCTANCE=";L;"H"
470 PRINT"SHUNT CAPACITANCE=";C;"F"
480 GOTO 340
490 IF A=1 THEN 930
500 IF A=2 THEN 1020
510 PRINT:PRINT"HIGH-PASS CONSTANT-K L SECTION"
520 PRINT:PRINT"ENTER CUT-OFF FREQUENCY (-3 DB) IN HERTZ"
530 INPUT F
540 PRINT:PRINT"ENTER OUTPUT LOAD RESISTANCE IN OHMS"
550 INPUT R
560 L=R/(6.2831854*F)
570 C=1/(6.2831854*F*R)
580 PRINT:PRINT"SERIES CAPACITANCE=";C;"F"
590 PRINT"SHUNT INDUCTANCE=";L;"H"
600 GOTO 340
610 PRINT:PRINT"BANDPASS CONSTANT-K L SECTION"
620 PRINT:PRINT"ENTER LOWER, UPPER CUT-OFF FREQUENCIES"
630 PRINT"(-3 DB) IN HERTZ (F1,F2)"
640 INPUT F1,F2
650 PRINT:PRINT"ENTER OUTPUT LOAD RESISTANCE IN OHMS"
660 INPUT R
670 L1=R/(3.1415927*(F2-F1))
680 L2=R*(F2-F1)/(12.5663708*F1*F2)
690 C1=(F2-F1)/(12.5663708*F1*F2*R)
700 C2=1/(3.1415927*(F2-F1)*R)
710 PRINT:PRINT"SERIES INDUCTANCE (L1)=";L1;"H"
720 PRINT"SHUNT INDUCTANCE (L2)=";L2;"H"
730 PRINT"SERIES CAPACITANCE (C1)=";C1;"F"
740 PRINT"SHUNT CAPACITANCE (C2)=";C2;"F"
750 GOTO 340
760 PRINT:PRINT"BANDSTOP CONSTANT-K L SECTION"
770 PRINT:PRINT"ENTER LOWER, UPPER CUT-OFF FREQUENCIES"
780 PRINT"(-3 DB) IN HERTZ (F1,F2)"
790 INPUT F1,F2
800 PRINT:PRINT"ENTER OUTPUT LOAD RESISTANCE IN OHMS"
810 INPUT R
820 L1=(F2-F1)*R/(3.1415927*F1*F2)
830 L2=R/(12.5663708*(F2-F1))
840 C1=1/(12.5663708*(F2-F1)*R)
850 C2=(F2-F1)/(3.1415927*F1*F2*R)
860 PRINT:PRINT"SERIES INDUCTANCE (L1)=";L1;"H"
870 PRINT"SHUNT INDUCTANCE (L2)=";L2;"H"
880 PRINT"SERIES CAPACITANCE (C1)=";C1;"F"
890 PRINT"SHUNT CAPACITANCE (C2)=";C2;"F"
900 GOTO 340
```

```
910 PRINT:PRINT"M-DERIVED LOW-PASS L SECTION"
920 GOTO 390
930 L1=.6*L
940 L2=1.066667*L
950 C=.6*C
960 PRINT:PRINT"SERIES INDUCTANCE (L1)=";L1;"H"
970 PRINT"SHUNT INDUCTANCE (L2)=";L2;"H"
980 PRINT"SHUNT CAPACITANCE (C)=";C;"F"
990 GOTO 340
1000 PRINT:PRINT"M-DERIVED HIGH-PASS L SECTION"
1010 GOTO 390
1020 L=L/.6
1030 C1=C/.6
1040 C2=.9375*C
1050 PRINT:PRINT"SHUNT INDUCTANCE=";L;"H"
1060 PRINT"SERIES CAPACITANCE (C1)=";C1;"F"
1070 PRINT"SHUNT CAPACITANCE (C2)=";C2;"F"
1080 GOTO 340
```

Monolithic Filters

These are filters in the form of integrated circuits, based upon switched capacitances or charge coupled devices.

Crystal Filters

These employ quartz crystals cut in either the X or the Y group, as in Table F-1.

TABLE F-1   Crystal Filters

Cut	Group	Frequency (kHz)
X		40–20,000
5°X	X	0.9–500
MT		50–100
NT		4–50
Y		1000–20,000
AT		500–10,000
BT		1000–75,000
CT		300–1100
DT	Y	60–500
ET		600–1800
FT		150–1500
GT		100–550

Surface Acoustic-Wave Filters

Surface acoustic-wave (SAW) band-pass filters consist of a piezoelectric substrate with interdigital transducers, as shown in Figure F-14. The geometry of the transducers determines the center frequency of the response. SAW filter parameters are given in Table F-2.

Figure F-14 The Principle of the Surface Acoustic Wave Filter

On the polished surface of a piezoelectric substrate, a metal pattern is deposited and etched as in the manufacture of integrated circuits. The input signal causes mechanical vibrations (seismic waves) to travel on the surface of the substrate from the input transducer to the output transducer. Here the vibrations are reconverted to an electrical signal. The period (distance between fingers) of the interdigital electrode structure equals one surface acoustic wavelength at the center frequency of the response. — [6]

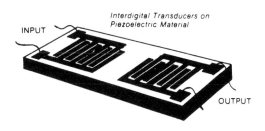

TABLE F-2   SAW Filter Parameters

Parameter	Band-pass data
Center frequency f_o	1 MHz–2 GHz
3-dB bandwidth	20 kHz–0.8 f_o
Minimum loss	1.5 dB
Minimum shape factor*	1.2
Minimum transition width (band-pass to band-stop)	20 kHz
Sidelobe rejection	65 dB
Ultimate rejection	80 dB
Band-pass ripple	0.2 dB
Linear phase deviation	2°

*Ratio of band-pass width at 3 dB and 40 dB.

SAW filters are commonly used in modern television receivers as intermediate-frequency filters.

Microwave Filters

Microwave filters are made of sections of transmission lines (stubs), strip lines, coupled lines, and various waveguide structures. *See* Transmission Lines and Waveguides.

Fixed Resistors *See* Resistors.

Flat Pack *See* Integrated Circuits.

FM *See* Frequency Modulation.

FREQUENCY

Frequency and Wavelength

Frequency is related to wavelength as follows:

$$f = c/\lambda$$

where:

f = frequency, in hertz.

c = velocity of propagation ($\approx 3 \times 10^8 \text{ m s}^{-1}$).

λ = wavelength, in meters.

Frequency Spectrum

This is the entire distribution of electromagnetic waves, according to their frequency or wavelength, from long radio waves to gamma rays, as shown in Figure F-15.

Radio Frequency Spectrum Data

Internationally-agreed frequency allocations are shown in Figure F-16, the bands into which they are divided being those designated in Figure F-15.

Broadcast Frequencies

See Broadcasting.

Citizen's Band

Citizen's Band Channels are shown in Figure F-17.

Audio Frequency Spectrum

Frequencies of sounds within the range of human ear sensitivity are given in Figure F-18.

Standard-Frequency Broadcasts

The standard-frequency and time stations of the National Bureau of Standards are WWV, WWVB, and WWVL at Fort Collins, Colorado, and WWVH at Kekaha, Kauai, Hawaii. WWV and WWVH broadcast continuously on 5, 10, 15, 20, and 25 MHz, giving time signals in Coordinated Universal Time, radio propagation forecasts, and geophysical alerts. WWVB broadcasts time signals in binary code on a frequency of 60 kHz. WWVL is an experimental VLF station whose frequency and schedule are variable.

Figure F-15 Frequency Spectrum—[6]

Frequency (hertz)		Wavelength (meters)		Radioactive and Radio Waves	Ultraviolet, Visible, Infrared and Audio Waves
100 EHz	$(\times 10^{18})$	3 pm	$(\times 10^{-12})$	Gamma rays	
10 EHz	"	30 pm	"	(hard)	
1 EHz	"	300 pm	"	X rays	
100 PHz	$(\times 10^{15})$	3 nm	$(\times 10^{-9})$	(soft)	Ultraviolet rays
10 PHz	"	30 nm	"		
1 PHz	"	300 nm	"		
100 THz	$(\times 10^{12})$	3 μm	$(\times 10^{-6})$		Visible light rays
10 THz	"	30 μm	"		Infrared rays
1 THz	"	300 μm	"	12	
100 GHz	$(\times 10^{9})$	3 mm	$(\times 10^{-3})$	EHF - 11	
10 GHz	"	30 mm	"	SHF - 10	
1 GHz	"	300 mm	"	UHF - 9	
100 MHz	$(\times 10^{6})$	3 m	$(\times 10^{0})$	VHF - 8	
10 MHz	"	30 m	"	HF - 7	
1 MHz	"	300 m	"	MF - 6	
100 kHz	$(\times 10^{3})$	3 km	$(\times 10^{3})$	LF - 5	
10 kHz	"	30 km	"	VLF - 4	
1 kHz	"	300 km	"	VF - 3	
100 Hz	$(\times 10^{0})$	3 Mm	$(\times 10^{6})$	ELF - 2	Audio waves
10 Hz	"	30 Mm	"		
1 Hz	"	300 Mm	"		

Figure F-16 Radio Frequency Spectrum—[6]

Band No. 12:	300 gigahertz to 3 terahertz: no frequency allocated
Band No. 11:	30 to 300 gigahertz (millimetric waves), extremely high frequency (EHF)

GHz	Allocated for:
275	Amateur radio
250–275	Satellites, space research, radio astronomy
240–250	Amateur radio
220–240	Satellites, space research, radio astronomy
200–220	Amateur radio
170–200	Satellites, space research, radio astronomy
152–170	Amateur radio

Figure F-16 (continued)

Band No. 12: Band No. 11: GHz	300 gigahertz to 3 terahertz: no frequency allocated 30 to 300 gigahertz (millimetric waves), extremely high frequency (EHF) Allocated for:
84–152	Satellites, space research, radio astronomy
71–84	Amateur radio
50–71	Satellites, space research
48–50	Amateur
40–48	Satellites
36–40	Mobile
35.2–36.0	Radio location
34.2–35.2	Radio location, space research
33.4–34.2	Radio location
32.3–33.4	Radio navigation
31.8–32.3	Radio navigation, space research
31.5–31.8	Space research
31.3–31.5	Radio astronomy
31.0–31.3	Fixed, mobile, space research

Band No. 10: GHz	3 to 30 gigahertz (centimetric waves), superhigh frequency (SHF) Allocated for:
29.50–31.00	Fixed satellite (Earth to space)
27.50–29.50	Fixed satellite (Earth to space), fixed, mobile
25.25–27.50	Fixed, mobile
24.25–25.25	Radio navigation
24.05–24.25	Radio location, amateur radio
24.00–24.05	Amateur radio
23.60–24.00	Radio astronomy
22.00–23.60	Fixed, mobile
21.20–22.00	Earth exploration satellite (space to Earth), fixed, mobile
19.70–21.20	Fixed satellite (space to Earth)
17.70–19.70	Fixed satellite (space to Earth), fixed, mobile
15.70–17.70	Radio location
15.40–15.70	Aeronautical radio navigation
15.35–15.40	Radio astronomy
14.50–15.35	Fixed, mobile
14.40–14.50	Fixed satellite (Earth to space), fixed, mobile
14.30–14.40	Fixed satellite (Earth to space), radio navigation satellite
14.00–14.30	Fixed satellite (Earth to space), radio navigation
13.40–14.00	Radio location
13.25–13.40	Aeronautical radio navigation
12.75–13.25	Fixed, mobile
12.50–12.75	Fixed satellite (Earth to space), fixed, mobile (except aeronautical)
12.20–12.50	Broadcasting, fixed, mobile (except aeronautical)
11.70–12.20	Broadcasting, broadcasting satellite, fixed, fixed satellite (space to Earth) mobile, (except aeronautical)
11.45–11.70	Fixed satellite (space to Earth), fixed, mobile

Figure F-16 (continued)

Band No. 10:	3 to 30 gigahertz (centimetric waves), superhigh frequency (SHF)
GHz	Allocated for:
11.20–11.45	Fixed, mobile
10.95–11.20	Fixed satellite (space to Earth), fixed, mobile
10.70–10.95	Fixed, mobile
10.68–10.70	Radio astronomy
10.60–10.68	Radio astronomy, fixed, mobile, radio location
10.55–10.60	Fixed, mobile, radio location
10.50–10.55	Radio location (CW only)
10.00–10.50	Radio location, amateur radio
9.80–10.00	Radio location, fixed
9.50–9.80	Radio location
9.30–9.50	Radio navigation, radio location
9.20–9.30	Radio location
9.00–9.20	Aeronautical radio navigation (ground-based radar), radio location
8.85–9.00	Radio location
8.75–8.85	Radio location, aeronautical radio navigation (doppler radar)
8.50–8.75	Radio location
8.40–8.50	Space research (space to Earth), fixed, mobile
5.925–8.400	Satellites, fixed, mobile
5.725–5.925	Radio location, amateur radio
5.670–5.725	Radio location, amateur radio, deep space research
5.650–5.670	Radio location, amateur radio
5.470–5.650	Maritime radio navigation, radio location
5.460–5.470	Radio navigation, radio location
5.350–5.460	Aeronautical radio navigation, radio location
5.255–5.350	Radio location
5.250–5.255	Radio location, space research
5.000–5.250	Aeronautical radio navigation
4.990–5.000	Radio astronomy
4.700–4.990	Fixed, mobile
4.400–4.700	Fixed satellite (Earth to space), fixed, mobile
4.200–4.400	Aeronautical radio navigation
3.700–4.200	Fixed satellite (space to Earth), fixed, mobile
3.500–3.700	Fixed satellite (space to Earth), fixed mobile, radio location
3.400–3.500	Fixed satellite (space to Earth), radio location, amateur
3.300–3.400	Radio location, amateur radio
3.100–3.300	Radio location

Band No. 9:	300 to 3000 megahertz (decimetric waves), ultra-high frequency (UHF)
MHz	Allocated for:
2900-3100	Radio navigation (ground-based radar), radio location
2700-2900	Aeronautical radio navigation
2690-2700	Radio astronomy

Figure F-16 (continued)

Band No. 9:	300 to 3000 megahertz (decimetric waves), ultra-high frequency (UHF)
MHz	Allocated for:
2500-2690	Satellites, fixed, mobile (except aeronautical)
2300-2500	Radio location, fixed, mobile, amateur radio (2300-2450 MHz)
2290-2300	Space research (space to Earth), fixed, mobile
1790-2290	Fixed, mobile
1770-1790	Meteorological satellite, fixed, mobile
1710-1770	Fixed, mobile
1700-1710	Space research (space to Earth), fixed, mobile
1690-1700	Meteorological satellite (space to Earth), meteorological aids
1670-1690	Meteorological satellite (space to Earth), meteorological aids, fixed
1660-1670	Meteorological aids, radio astronomy
1645-1660	Aeronautical mobile satellite
1644-1645	Aeronautical mobile satellite, maritime mobile satellite
1636.5-1644	Maritime mobile satellite
1558.5-1636.5	Aeronautical radio navigation
1543.5-1558.5	Aeronautical mobile satellite
1542.5-1543.5	Aeronautical mobile satellite, maritime mobile satellite
1535-1542.5	Maritime mobile satellite
1525-1535	Space operations (telemetering), Earth exploration satellite, fixed, mobile
1429-1525	Fixed, mobile
1427-1429	Space operations (telecommand), fixed, mobile (except aeronautical)
1400-1427	Radio astronomy
1350-1400	Radio location
1300-1350	Aeronautical radio navigation, radio location
1215-1300	Radio location, amateur radio
960.0-1215	Aeronautical radio navigation
928.0-960.0	Fixed
902.0-928.0	Amateur radio
890.0-902.0	Radio location, fixed
470.0-890.0	Broadcasting (television)
460.0-470.0	Meteorological satellite, fixed, mobile (Citizens Band: 462.5375-462.7375 MHz and 467 MHz)
450.0-460.0	Fixed, mobile
420.0-450.0	Radio location, amateur radio
410.0-420.0	Fixed, mobile (except aeronautical)
406.1-410.0	Radio astronomy, fixed, mobile (except aeronautical)
406.0-406.1	Mobile satellite (Earth to space)
403.0-406.0	Meteorological aids, fixed, mobile (except aeronautical)
402.0-403.0	Meteorological aids, meteorological satellite (Earth to space), fixed, mobile (except aeronautical)
401.0-402.0	Space operations (telemetering), meteorological aids, meteorological satellite (Earth to space), fixed, mobile (except aeronautical)

Figure F-16 (continued)

Band No. 9:	300 to 3000 megahertz (decimetric waves), ultra-high frequency (UHF)
MHz	Allocated for:
400.15-401.0	Space research (telemetering and tracking), meteorological satellite (maintenance telemetering), meteorological aids
400.05-400.15	Standard frequency satellite
399.9-400.05	Radio navigation satellite
335.4-399.9	Fixed, mobile
328.6-335.4	Aeronautical radio navigation (glide-path systems)

Band No. 8:	30 to 300 megahertz (metric waves), very high frequency (VHF)
MHz	Allocated for:
273.0-328.6	Fixed, mobile
267.0-273.0	Space operations (telemetering), fixed, mobile
225.0-267.0	Fixed, mobile (survival craft and equipment 243.0 MHz)
220.0-225.0	Radio location, amateur radio
216.0-220.0	Radio location, fixed, mobile
174.0-216.0	Broadcasting (television), fixed, mobile
150.05-174.0	Fixed, mobile (distress and calling-telephone-156.8 MHz)
149.9-150.05	Radio navigation satellite
148.0-149.9	Fixed, mobile
144.0-148.0	Amateur radio
138.0-144.0	Space research (space to Earth), radio location, fixed, mobile
137.0-138.0	Space research (space to Earth), space operations (telemetering and tracking), meteorological satellite
136.0-137.0	Space research (space to Earth)
117.975-136.0	Aeronautical mobile
108.0-117.975	Aeronautical radio navigation
88.0-108.0	Broadcasting (FM radio)
75.4-88.0	Broadcasting (television), fixed, mobile
74.6-75.4	Aeronautical radio navigation
73.0-74.6	Radio astronomy
54.0-73.0	Broadcasting (television), fixed, mobile
50.0-54.0	Amateur radio
38.25-50.0	Fixed, mobile
37.75-38.25	Radio astronomy, fixed, mobile
30.01-37.75	Fixed, mobile
30.005-30.01	Space operations (satellite identification), fixed, mobile

Band No. 7:	3 to 30 megahertz (decametric waves), high frequency (HF)
MHz	Allocated for:
29.70-30.005	Fixed, mobile
28.00-29.70	Amateur radio

Figure F-16 (continued)

Band No. 7:	3 to 30 megahertz (decametric waves), high frequency (HF)
MHz	**Allocated for:**

MHz	Allocated for:
27.50-28.00	Meteorological aids, fixed, mobile
26.10-27.50	Fixed, mobile (except aeronautical) (Citizens Band: 26.96-27.23 MHz)
25.60-26.10	Broadcasting (international AM radio)
25.11-25.60	Fixed, mobile (except aeronautical)
25.07-25.11	Maritime mobile
25.01-25.07	Fixed, mobile (except aeronautical)
24.99-25.01	Standard frequency (WWV/WWVH)
24.89-24.99	Amateur radio
23.35-24.89	Fixed, land mobile
23.20-23.35	Aeronautical fixed and mobile
22.72-23.20	Fixed
22.00-22.72	Maritime mobile
21.87-22.00	Aeronautical fixed and mobile
21.85-21.87	Radio astronomy
21.75-21.85	Fixed
21.45-21.75	Broadcasting (international AM radio)
21.00-21.45	Amateur radio
20.01-21.00	Fixed
19.99-20.01	Standard frequency (WWV/WWVH)
18.068-19.99	Fixed
18.052-18.068	Fixed, space research
18.03-18.052	Fixed
17.90-18.03	Aeronautical mobile
17.70-17.90	Broadcasting (international AM radio)
17.36-17.70	Fixed
16.46-17.36	Maritime mobile
15.45-16.46	Fixed
15.10-15.45	Broadcasting (international AM radio)
15.01-15.10	Aeronautical mobile
14.99-15.01	Standard frequency (WWV/WWVH)
14.35-14.99	Fixed
14.00-14.35	Amateur radio
13.36-14.00	Fixed
13.20-13.36	Aeronautical mobile
12.33-13.20	Maritime mobile
11.975-12.33	Fixed
11.70-11.975	Broadcasting (international AM radio)
11.40-11.70	Fixed
11.175-11.40	Aeronautical mobile
10.10-11.175	Fixed
10.10-10.15	Amateur radio
10.005-10.10	Aeronautical mobile
9.995-10.005	Standard frequency (WWV/WWVH)
9.775-9.995	Fixed
9.500-9.775	Broadcasting (international AM radio)
9.040-9.500	Fixed
8.815-9.040	Aeronautical mobile

Figure F-16 (continued)

Band No. 7:	3 to 30 megahertz (decametric waves), high frequency (HF)
MHz	Allocated for:
8.195-8.815	Maritime mobile
7.300-8.195	Fixed
7.000-7.300	Amateur radio
6.765-7.000	Fixed
6.525-6.765	Aeronautical mobile
6.200-6.525	Maritime mobile
5.950-6.200	Broadcasting (international AM radio)
5.730-5.950	Fixed
5.450-5.730	Aeronautical mobile
5.250-5.450	Fixed, land mobile
5.060-5.250	Fixed
5.005-5.060	Fixed, broadcasting (international AM radio)
4.995-5.005	Standard frequency (WWV/WWVH)
4.850-4.995	Fixed, land mobile, broadcasting (international AM radio)
4.750-4.850	Fixed, broadcasting (international AM radio)
4.650-4.750	Aeronautical mobile
4.438-4.650	Fixed, mobile (except aeronautical)
4.063-4.438	Maritime mobile
4.000-4.063	Fixed
3.500-4.000	Amateur radio
3.400-3.500	Aeronautical mobile
3.200-3.400	Fixed, mobile (except aeronautical), broadcasting (international AM radio)
3.155-3.200	Fixed, mobile (except aeronautical)
3.025-3.155	Aeronautical mobile

Band No. 6:	300 to 3000 kilohertz (hectometric waves), medium frequency (MF)
kHz	Allocated for:
2850-3025	Aeronautical mobile
2505-2850	Fixed, mobile
2495-2505	Standard frequency (WWV/WWHV)
2300-2495	Fixed, mobile, broadcasting (international AM radio)
2194-2300	Fixed, mobile
2170-2194	Mobile (distress and calling-telephone-2182 kHz)
2107-2170	Fixed, mobile
2065-2107	Maritime mobile
2000-2065	Fixed, mobile
1800-2000	Fixed, mobile (except aeronautical), radio navigation amateur radio
1605-1800	Fixed, mobile, aeronautical radio navigation, radio location
535-1605	Broadcasting (domestic AM radio)
525-535	Mobile, broadcasting, aeronautical radio navigation
510-525	Mobile, aeronautical radio navigation
490-510	Mobile (distress and calling-telegraph-500 kHz)

Figure F-16 (continued)

| Band No. 6: | 300 to 3000 kilohertz (hectometric waves), medium frequency (MF) |
| kHz | Allocated for: |

kHz	Allocated for:
415-490	Maritime mobile (radiotelegraphy only)
405-415	Maritime radio navigation (radio direction-finding), aeronautical radio navigation
325-405	Aeronautical radio navigation, aeronautical mobile

| Band No. 5: | 30 to 300 kilohertz (kilometric waves), low frequency (LF) |
| kHz | Allocated for: |

kHz	Allocated for:
285-325	Maritime radio navigation (radio beacons), aeronautical radio navigation
200-285	Aeronautical radio navigation, aeronautical mobile
160-200	Fixed
130-160	Fixed, maritime mobile
70-130	Fixed, maritime mobile, radio navigation, radio location

| Band No. 4: | 3 to 30 kilohertz (myriametric waves), very-low frequency (VLF) |
| kHz | Allocated for: |

kHz	Allocated for:
20.05-70.00	Fixed, maritime mobile (WWVB at 60 kHz)
19.95-20.05	Standard frequency (WWV/WWVH)
14.00-19.95	Fixed, maritime mobile
10.00-14.00	Radio navigation, radio location
10.00	No allocations
Band No. 3:	300 to 3000 hertz: no frequencies allocated
Band No. 2:	30 to 300 hertz: no frequencies allocated

Figure F-17 Citizen's Band Frequencies and Tolerances

Channel	Assigned frequency (MHz)	Lower limit (MHz)	Upper limit (MHz)
1	26.965	26.9637	26.9663
2	26.975	26.9737	26.9764
3	26.985	26.9837	26.9864
4	27.005	27.0037	27.0064
5	27.015	27.0137	27.0164
6	27.025	27.0237	27.0264
7	27.035	27.0337	27.0364
8	27.055	27.0537	27.0564
9	27.065	27.0637	27.0664
10	27.075	27.0736	27.0764

Figure F-17 (continued)

==

Channel	Assigned frequency (MHz)	Lower Limit (MHz)	Upper Limit (MHz)
11	27.085	27.0836	27.0864
12	27.105	27.1036	27.1064
13	27.115	27.1136	27.1164
14	27.125	27.1236	27.1264
15	27.135	27.1336	27.1364
16	27.155	27.1536	27.1564
17	27.165	27.1636	27.1664
18	27.175	27.1736	27.1764
19	27.185	27.1836	27.1864
20	27.205	27.2036	27.2064
21	27.215	27.2136	27.2164
22	27.225	27.2236	27.2264
23	27.255	27.2536	27.2564
24	27.235	27.2336	27.2364
25	27.245	27.2436	27.2464
26	27.265	27.2636	27.2664
27	27.275	27.2736	27.2764
28	27.285	27.2836	27.2864
29	27.295	27.2936	27.2964
30	27.305	27.3036	27.3064
31	27.315	27.3136	27.3164
32	27.325	27.3236	27.3264
33	27.335	27.3336	27.3364
34	27.345	27.3436	27.3464
35	27.355	27.3536	27.3564
36	27.365	27.3636	27.3664
37	27.375	27.3736	27.3764
38	27.385	27.3836	27.3864
39	27.395	27.3936	27.3964
40	27.405	27.4036	27.4064

==

Coordinated Universal Time (UTC) is based on the time kept by an atomic clock which has an accuracy of one part in 10^{12}. Owing to variations in the speed of rotation of the Earth, International Atomic Time (TAI) and Ephemeris Time (ET) do not always agree exactly, so UTC has to be corrected occasionally by adding or subtracting a "leap second." This keeps the difference to not more than -0.7 second. These adjustments are made at the end of the last minute of December 31 or June 30, as required, so these minutes may contain 59 or 61 seconds according to the sign of the adjustment.

The WWV/WWVH broadcasts consist of a pulse sent out at each second, starting with the first in the minute and accompanied by a continuous audio tone. This goes on for 45 seconds, when the tone ceases and the seconds are marked by ticks. The WWVH station then announces

Figure F-18 Audio Frequency Spectrum—[6]

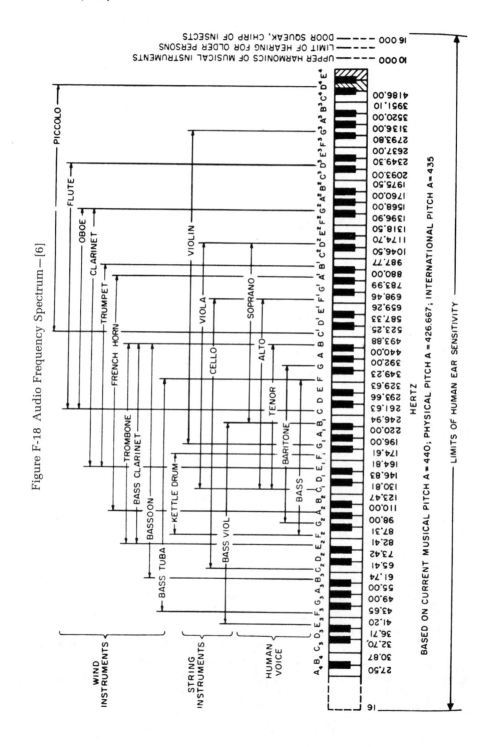

what the UTC time will be at the end of the minute; the WWV station does the same, but 7.5 seconds later. Precisely on the 60th second, WWVH transmits a 1200-hertz tone for 0.8 second and simultaneously WWV transmits a 1000-hertz tone for 0.8 second. The audio tone is then resumed unless an announcement is to be made (propagation forecast or geophysical alert). The audio tone alternates between 600 and 500 hertz in successive minutes, and the 29th and 59th second pulses are always omitted. Both stations identify the beginning of each hour with a 1500-hertz tone for 0.8 second.

FREQUENCY MODULATION

In frequency modulation, the carrier *frequency* is made to vary in accordance with the *amplitude* of the modulating frequency. The modulated wave can be resolved into its carrier and sideband components, the amplitudes of which vary as Bessel functions of the modulation index m, which is given by:

$$m = \Delta F/f$$

where:

ΔF = peak deviation, in hertz.

f = modulating frequency, in hertz.

From the above, the modulating frequency f required for a given modulation index is:

$$f = \Delta F/m$$

The overall energy of an FM signal does not change. It is divided between the carrier and the sidebands, but the total remains the same. Therefore, whenever the carrier wave crosses the zero axis, all the energy is in the sidebands. The values of the modulation index m necessary to produce successive carrier nulls are as follows:

Null	Value of m
1st	2.4
2nd	5.52
3rd	8.65
4th	11.79

So, assuming that $\Delta F = \pm 15$ kHz for 100% modulation, f must be 15 kHz/2.4 = 6.25 kHz for 100% modulation; if $\Delta F = \pm 75$ kHz, f must be 75/2.4 = 31.25 kHz; and so on. However, in the second example, 31.25

kHz is not a practical value, because it would be outside the pass band of the audio system; therefore, the second null should be used, which gives $75/5.52 = 13.587$ kHz; or even the third, which gives $75/8.65 = 8.67$ kHz.

Full-Wave Rectifier Power Supply
See Power Sources.

Fuses and Circuit Breakers *Fuses* are rated (see Table F-3) as to maximum current, voltage, and type. The current is the maximum that the fuse can withstand before blowing. The voltage indicated is that which is a safe fire hazard. To use a fuse rated for 32 V in a circuit where the voltage is 250 V is dangerous, regardless of its current rating, because of the possibility of arcing or short circuit. The type means whether the fuse is slow (S), medium-to-fast acting (MF), or very fast acting (VF). See Figure F-19.

Figure F-19 Fast- and Slow-Blow Fuses.
    A fast-blow fuse consists of a thin strip of metal that will melt instantly when heated by a current in excess of its rated value. A slow-blow fuse has a composition element that an excessive current destroys by burning; as it does not melt, its charred remains are pulled apart by a spring. The ends of the fusible element are connected to the metal ferrules on each end of the glass or ceramic tube that forms the body. Metal spring clips in the fuse holder hold the ferrules and provide the means for the electrical connection of the fuse in the circuit. —[6]

fast-blow   **slow-blow**

TABLE F-3 Fuse Data

Identification code		Current (A)	Voltage (V)	Type	Dimensions (in.)	Packaging: body/terminals
ABC	(3AB)	1/8–30	32	MF	1/4 × 1 1/4	ceramic/ferrules
AGA	(1AG)	1/16–30	32/125	MF	1/4 × 5/8, 7/8	glass/ferrules
AGC	(3AG)	1/500–30	32/250	MF	1/4 × 1 1/4	glass/ferrules
AGU	(5AG)	1–30	250	MF	13/32 × 1 1/2	glass/ferrules
AGW	(7AG)	1/4–30	32	MF	1/4 × 7/8	glass/ferrules
AGX	(8AG) (MJB) (MJW)	1/500–30	32/125/ 250	MF	1/4 × 1	glass/ferrules
ANN		10–800	130	VF		(flat body)
BAF		1/2–30	125/250	MF	13/32 × 1 1/2	laminated/ferrules
BAN	(5AB)	2/10–30	250	MF	13/32 × 1 1/2	fiber/ferrules
FBP		1–100	200/250/ 500/700	VF	9/16 × 2	ceramic/ferrules
FNM	(5AB)	1/10–30	32/125/ 250	S	13/32 × 1 1/2	fiber/ferrules
FNQ		1/10–30	500	S	13/32 × 1 1/2	fiber/ferrules
FWP		15–30	200/250/ 500/700	VF	9/16 × 2	ceramic/ferrules
GBB	(3AB)	1/4–30	60	VF	1/4 × 1 1/4	ceramic/ferrules
GDA		0.05–7.00	250	MF	0.205 × 0.787	ceramic/ferrules
GDB		0.03–10.00	250	MF	0.205 × 0.787	glass/ferrules
GDC		0.03–7.00	250	S	0.205 × 0.787	glass/ferrules
GFA		1/200–15	32/125	MF	0.145 × 0.30	glass/axial leads
GJV		1/16–10	250	MF	1/4 × 1 1/4	glass/radial leads
GLH	(3AG)	7–10	125	MF	1/4 × 1 1/4	glass/ferrules
GLN		1/200–15	32/125	MF	0.145 × 0.30	glass/radial leads
GLK		15/100–5	125	MF	0.145 × 0.30	glass/radial leads
GMA	(GJU)	1/32–15	125/250	MF	0.197 × 0.769	glass/ferrules
KAA		1/2–30	130	VF	13/32 × 1 1/2	melamine/ferrules
KAB + KAX		1/2–30	250	VF	9/16 × 2	melamine/ferrules
KAC		1–30	600	VF	9/16 diam.	melamine/studs
KAW		1–30	130	VF	13/32 × 1 1/2	melamine/ferrules
KBC		1–30	600	VF	13/16 × 5	melamine/ferrules
KTK		1/10–30	600	MF	13/32 × 1 1/2	melamine/ferrules
MDA	(3AB)	1/100–30	125/250	S	1/4 × 1 1/4	ceramic/ferrules
MDL	(3AG)	1/100–30	125/250	S	1/4 × 1 1/4	glass/ferrules
MDQ	(3AG)	1 1/4–10	250	S	1/4 × 1 1/4	glass/ferrules
MDV	(3AG)	1/11–10	125/250	S	1/4 diam.	glass/radial leads
MDX	(3AG)	1 1/4–10	125/250	S	1/4 × 1 1/4	glass/ferrules
MGB	(3AG)	1/16 or 1/8	250	MF	1/4 × 1 1/4	glass/ferrules
MKB	(8AG)	1/16 or 1/8	250	MF	1/4 × 1	glass/ferrules
MTH	(3AG)	4–6	250	MF	1/4 × 1 1/4	glass/ferrules
SFE		4–30	32	MF	1/4 × 5/8, 1 7/8	glass/ferrules

Circuit breakers are automatic switches that are normally closed, but open when the current exceeds a predetermined value (generally 20–30% above the rated current). The familiar type shown in Figure F-20 is reset manually, but there is also an automatic-reset type that restores the circuit after 10 seconds, provided a minimum holding current is present.

Manual-reset circuit breakers are available with a large number of current ratings, and with voltage ratings of 125 V. Automatic-resetting types typically range from 0.65 A to 7.00 A, with voltage ratings from 6V to 24 V.

Figure F-20 A Manual Reset Circuit Breaker.

When the circuit breaker is "on," current flows along the dark-gray path (diagram (a)). But an overload current will cause the bimetallic element (diagram (b)) to heat so that it bends and presses the yoke down. This releases the trip lever, and the upper spring opens the contacts. However, this is a relatively slow process. If a very heavy current (as in a dead short) flows through the circuit breaker, fast action is required to prevent the circuit wiring from catching fire. In this case, the high current creates a strong magnetic force in the magnetic plate, pulling the yoke down instantly.

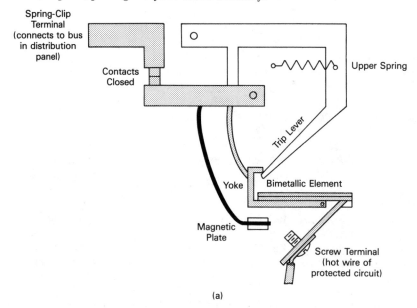

(a)

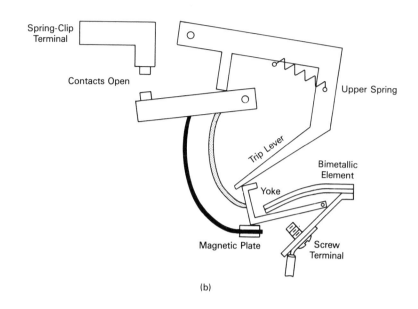

Spring-Clip Terminal

Contacts Open

Upper Spring

Trip Lever

Bimetallic Element

Yoke

Magnetic Plate

Screw Terminal

(b)

G

Gain *See* Amplifiers.

Gate *See* Logic Circuits.

Generators *See* Oscillators.

GRAPHIC SYMBOLS

Figure G-1 shows the symbols used in schematic diagrams to indicate the components in a circuit and their interconnections. A graphic symbol is not an illustration of a part, but a representation of its function.

Figure G-1 Graphic Symbols—[6]

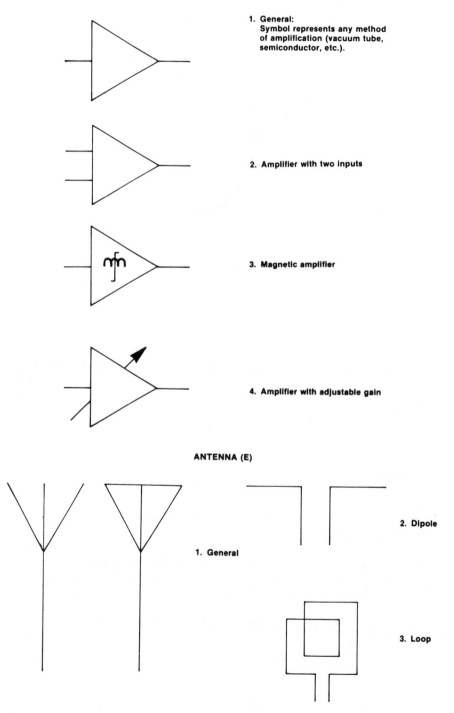

AMPLIFIER (A)

1. General:
   Symbol represents any method of amplification (vacuum tube, semiconductor, etc.).

2. Amplifier with two inputs

3. Magnetic amplifier

4. Amplifier with adjustable gain

ANTENNA (E)

1. General

2. Dipole

3. Loop

Figure G-1 (continued)

AUDIBLE SIGNALING DEVICE

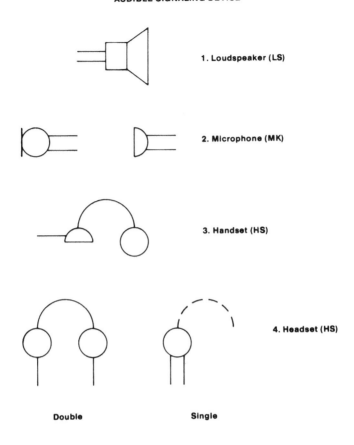

1. Loudspeaker (LS)

2. Microphone (MK)

3. Handset (HS)

4. Headset (HS)

Double

Single

BATTERY (BT)

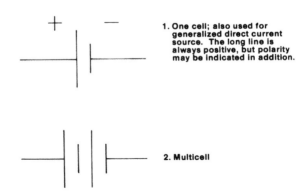

1. One cell; also used for generalized direct current source. The long line is always positive, but polarity may be indicated in addition.

2. Multicell

Figure G-1 (continued)

CABLE, CONDUCTOR, WIRING (W)

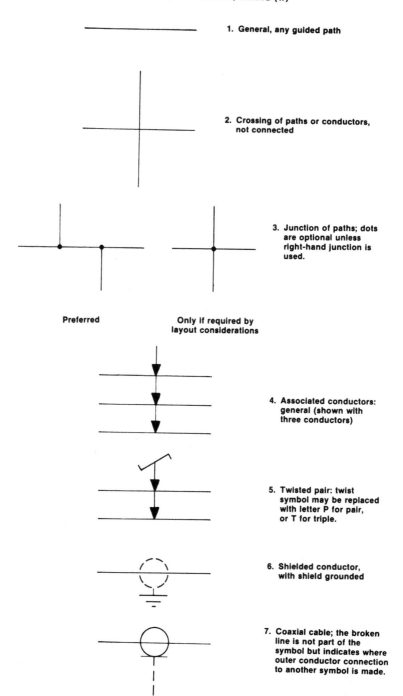

1. General, any guided path

2. Crossing of paths or conductors, not connected

3. Junction of paths; dots are optional unless right-hand junction is used.

Preferred   Only if required by layout considerations

4. Associated conductors: general (shown with three conductors)

5. Twisted pair: twist symbol may be replaced with letter P for pair, or T for triple.

6. Shielded conductor, with shield grounded

7. Coaxial cable; the broken line is not part of the symbol but indicates where outer conductor connection to another symbol is made.

8. Circular waveguide

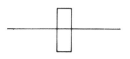

9. Rectangular waveguide

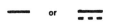 or

10. Kind of current symbol, placed beside conductor to indicate direct current. Used only if necessary for clarity.

11. Kind of current symbol, placed beside conductor to indicate alternating current: one symbol for power; two for audio; three for RF. Used only if necessary for clarity.

12. Kind of current symbol, placed beside conductor to indicate direct *or* alternating current (universal). Used only if necessary for clarity.

13. Kind of current symbol, placed beside conductor to indicate undulating or rectified current. Used only if necessary for clarity.

CAPACITOR (C)

Style 1   Style 2

1. Capacitor; the curved or modified electrode indicates the outside, low potential or movable element.

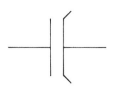

Style 1 modified
to identify electrode

135

Figure G-1 (continued)

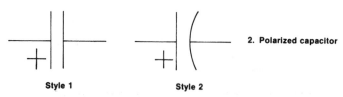

2. Polarized capacitor

Style 1   **Style 2**

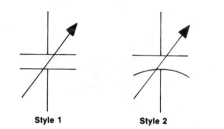

3. Adjustable or variable capacitor. If mechanical linkage of more than one unit is to be shown, the tails of the arrows are joined by a dashed line.

Style 1   **Style 2**

CIRCUIT BREAKER (CB)

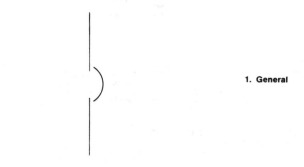

1. General

CONNECTOR: FEMALE (J), MALE (P)

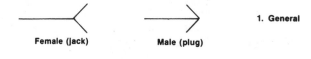

1. General

Female (jack)   **Male (plug)**

2. Male and female connectors engaged

Figure G-1 (continued)

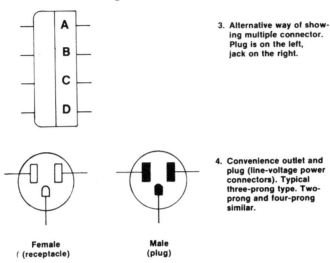

3. Alternative way of showing multiple connector.
   Plug is on the left,
   jack on the right.

4. Convenience outlet and
   plug (line-voltage power
   connectors). Typical
   three-prong type. Two-
   prong and four-prong
   similar.

Female
((receptacle)

Male
(plug)

CRYSTAL UNIT, PIEZOELECTRIC (Y)

1. Piezoelectric crystal
   unit, including quartz
   crystal.

FUSE (F)

1. General: all three
   symbols are used.

GROUND, CIRCUIT RETURN (no class letter)

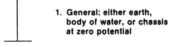

1. General: either earth,
   body of water, or chassis
   at zero potential

2. Chassis ground: may be at
   substantial potential with
   respect to earth ground.

Figure G-1 (continued)

INDUCTOR (L)

   or

1. General: right-hand symbol is deprecated and should not be used on new schematics.

2. Magnetic core inductor

3. Tapped inductor

4. Adjustable inductor

INTEGRATED CIRCUIT (U)

1. General: unused pin connections need not be shown.

    The asterisk is not part of the symbol. It indicates where the type number is placed.

LAMP (DS)

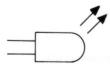

1. General; light source, general

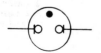

2. Glow lamp, neon lamp (a.c. type)

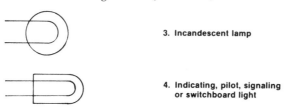

3. Incandescent lamp

4. Indicating, pilot, signaling
   or switchboard light

METER (M)

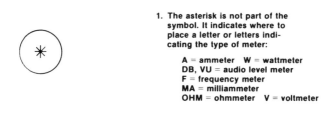

1. The asterisk is not part of the
   symbol. It indicates where to
   place a letter or letters indicating the type of meter:

   A = ammeter   W = wattmeter
   DB, VU = audio level meter
   F = frequency meter
   MA = milliammeter
   OHM = ohmmeter   V = voltmeter

RELAY (K)

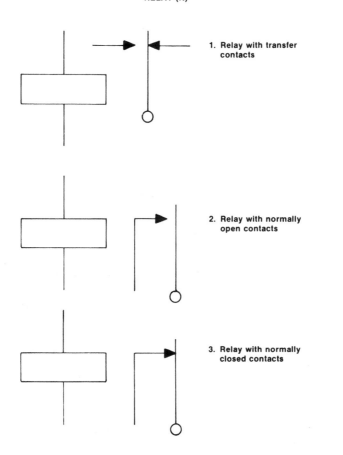

1. Relay with transfer
   contacts

2. Relay with normally
   open contacts

3. Relay with normally
   closed contacts

Figure G-1 (continued)

RESISTOR (R)

1. General

2. Tapped resistor

3. Resistor with adjustable contact (potentiometer)

4. Continuously adjustable resistor (rheostat)

5. Thermistor

6. Photoconductive transducer (e.g., cadmium-sulfide photocell)

SEMICONDUCTOR DEVICE DIODE (D OR CR)

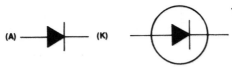

1. Semiconductor diode; enclosure symbol may be omitted where confusion would not be caused.

   A = anode, K = cathode. The letters are not part of the symbol.

2. Breakdown diode (zener diode)

3. Tunnel diode

Figure G-1 (continued)

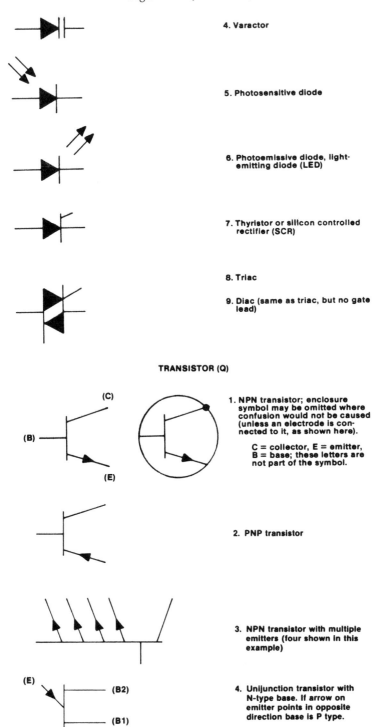

4. Varactor

5. Photosensitive diode

6. Photoemissive diode, light-emitting diode (LED)

7. Thyristor or silicon controlled rectifier (SCR)

8. Triac

9. Diac (same as triac, but no gate lead)

TRANSISTOR (Q)

(C)
(B)
(E)

1. NPN transistor; enclosure symbol may be omitted where confusion would not be caused (unless an electrode is connected to it, as shown here).

   C = collector, E = emitter, B = base; these letters are not part of the symbol.

2. PNP transistor

3. NPN transistor with multiple emitters (four shown in this example)

(E)
(B2)
(B1)

4. Unijunction transistor with N-type base. If arrow on emitter points in opposite direction base is P type.

141

Figure G-1 (continued)

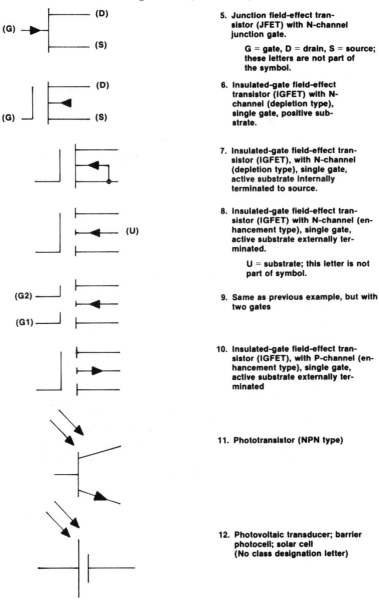

5. Junction field-effect transistor (JFET) with N-channel junction gate.

   G = gate, D = drain, S = source; these letters are not part of the symbol.

6. Insulated-gate field-effect transistor (IGFET) with N-channel (depletion type), single gate, positive substrate.

7. Insulated-gate field-effect transistor (IGFET), with N-channel (depletion type), single gate, active substrate internally terminated to source.

8. Insulated-gate field-effect transistor (IGFET) with N-channel (enhancement type), single gate, active substrate externally terminated.

   U = substrate; this letter is not part of symbol.

9. Same as previous example, but with two gates

10. Insulated-gate field-effect transistor (IGFET), with P-channel (enhancement type), single gate, active substrate externally terminated

11. Phototransistor (NPN type)

12. Photovoltaic transducer; barrier photocell; solar cell (No class designation letter)

SWITCH (S)

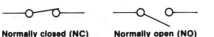

Normally closed (NC)   Normally open (NO)

1. Single-throw switch; terminals are necessary for clarity in an NC switch, but may be omitted in an NO switch.

Figure G-1 (continued)

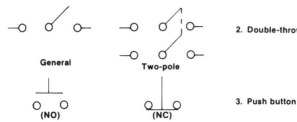

General   Two-pole

2. Double-throw switch

(NO)   (NC)

3. Push button

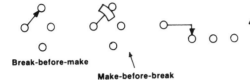

Break-before-make   Make-before-break

4. Selector or multiposition; any number of transmission paths may be shown

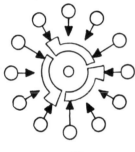

OR

5. Rotary or wafer-type switch. Viewed from end opposite control knob. For more than one section the first is the one nearest the control knob. With contacts on both sides front contacts are nearest control knob.

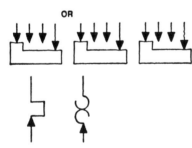

6. Flasher; self-interrupting switch

SYNCHRO (B)

1. General: if identification is required, add appropriate letter combination from following list adjacent to symbol:

CDX	control-differential transmitter
CT	control transformer
CX	control transmitter
TDR	torque-differential receiver
TDX	torque-differential transmitter
TR	torque receiver
TX	torque transmitter
RS	resolver

Figure G-1 (continued)

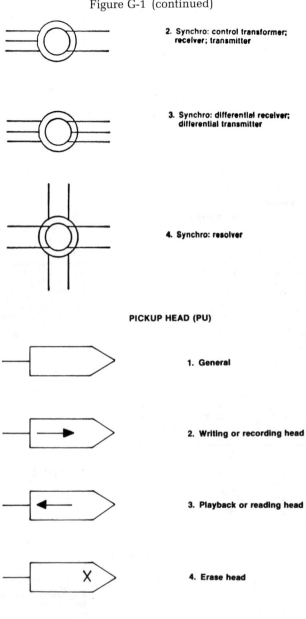

2. Synchro: control transformer; receiver; transmitter

3. Synchro: differential receiver; differential transmitter

4. Synchro: resolver

PICKUP HEAD (PU)

1. General

2. Writing or recording head

3. Playback or reading head

4. Erase head

5. Stereo head

TRANSFORMER (T)

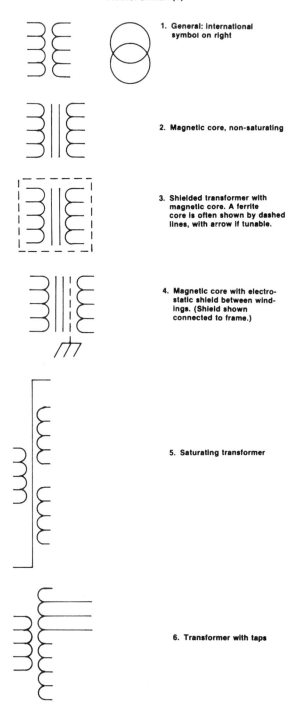

1. General: international symbol on right

2. Magnetic core, non-saturating

3. Shielded transformer with magnetic core. A ferrite core is often shown by dashed lines, with arrow if tunable.

4. Magnetic core with electro-static shield between wind-ings. (Shield shown connected to frame.)

5. Saturating transformer

6. Transformer with taps

Figure G-1 (continued)

Fixed

Adjustable

7. Autotransformer

**8. Transformer with
instantaneous polarity
marks. Instantaneous
polarities of voltage or
current correspond at points
indicated. To be used only
when it is necessary to show
the relative polarity of the
windings.**

VACUUM TUBE (V)

**1. Triode with directly-heated
filamentary cathode**

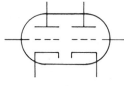

**2. Triode with indirectly-heated
cathode (heater included)**

**3. Twin triode with indirectly-
heated cathode (heater omitted)**

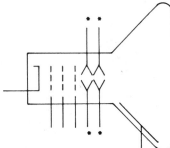

**4. Pentode with indirectly-heated
cathode (heater omitted)**

**5. Cathode-ray tube (CRT) with
deflection plates (*).
Same symbol without deflection
plates is used for monochrome
picture tube (single electron
gun, magnetic deflection).**

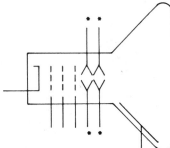

Figure G-1 (continued)

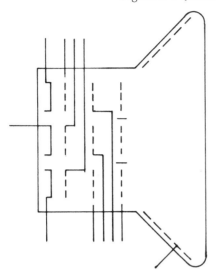

6. **Color picture tube with three electron guns and electromagnetic deflection**

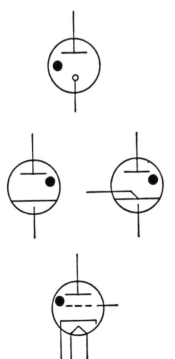

7. **Cold-cathode gas-filled tube**

8. **Mercury-pool vapor-rectifier tubes; right-hand tube has ignitor.**

9. **Thyratron with indirectly-heated cathode (heater shown)**

Figure G-1 (continued)

LOGIC SYMBOLS

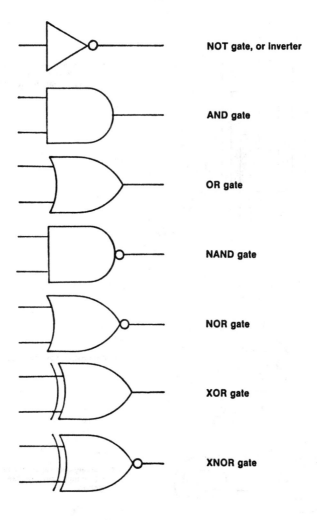

NOT gate, or inverter

AND gate

OR gate

NAND gate

NOR gate

XOR gate

XNOR gate

H

Half-Wave Antenna *See* Antennas.

Half-Wave Rectifier Power Supply *See* Power Sources.

Heterodyne *See* Intermediate Frequency.

Horsepower *See* Conversion Tables.

***h* Parameters** *See* Transistors.

I

IF *See* Intermediate Frequency.

IGFET (Insulated-Gate Field-Effect Transistor), *See* Transistors.

Impedance *See* Capacitance, Inductance, or Resistance, as appropriate.

Inductance When an electric current flows in a conductor, an associated magnetic field also exists. Any change in the current causes a corresponding change in the magnetic field. A change in the magnetic field causes a voltage to appear in the conductor which causes a current to flow that opposes the original current change. As a result, the current does not reach its new value until it has overcome this opposition. This property is called self-inductance, more usually inductance.

Inductance (L) is measured in henries (H). It is an intrinsic property of any conductor, but is most pronounced in wire coils. In these it increases with the number of turns and the cross-sectional area of the coil. It also depends upon the permeability of the material forming the path for the magnetic field. *See* Inductors.

INDUCTORS

An inductor is also called a coil or a choke. Coil is the general term: a choke is a coil designed to offer a high impedance to (block) frequencies above a chosen range. A coil may consist of wire wound around a magnetic material, such as iron, or it may have air for a core. Since iron is a preferred path for magnetic flux, iron-core coils have much more inductance than air-core coils.

When AC is applied to an inductor, it encounters *reactance*, given by:

$$X_L = 2\pi f L$$

where:

X_L = reactance, in ohms.

π = 3.1416 . . .

f = frequency, in hertz.

L = inductance, in henries.

Design of Small Air-Core Coils

A *single-layer coil*, as shown in Figure I-1(a), is often called a solenoid.

Figure I-1 Design of Small Air-Core Coils
(a) Single layer, or solenoid. (b) Multilayer.

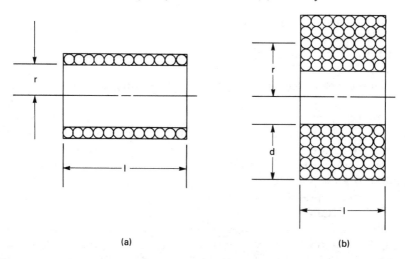

(a)   (b)

Where its length is more than 2/3 of its radius, its inductance is calculated as follows:

$$L = (0.394r^2N^2)/(9r + 10l)$$

Where the length is less than 2/3 of the radius, a single-layer coil's inductance is given by:

$$L = (0.394r^2N^2)/[\{9 - (r/5l)\}r + 10l]$$

When a *single-layer coil* is tight-wound, the length of the coil is given by:

$$l = N/p$$

where:

p = the number of turns per unit length.

The number of turns is given by:

$$N = (12.7L/pr^2)[1 + \sqrt{1 + (0.14r^3p^2)/L}]$$

The numbers of turns per inch and turns per centimeter for enameled copper wire are given in Table I-1.

The inductance of a *multi-layer coil*, as shown in Figure I-1(b), is given by:

$$L = (0.315r^2N^2)/(6r + 9l + 10d)$$

where:

L = inductance, in microhenries (H).

r = internal radius, in centimeters.

N = number of turns.

l = length, in centimeters.

d = winding depth, in centimeters.

The inductance of *universal-wound coils* (see Figure I-2) can be cal-

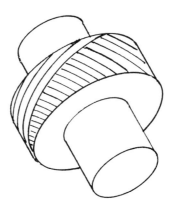

Figure I-2 Universal Winding

Table I-1   Enameled Copper Wire for Coils (Magnet Wire).—[6]

ENAMELED COPPER WIRE TABLE

Gage (AWG/BS)	Nominal Diameter (in)	Nominal Diameter (mm)	Turns/inch	Turns/cm	Ohms/1000'	Ohms/100 m
10	0.1019	2.588	9.6	3.8	0.9989	0.3277
11	0.09074	2.305	10.7	4.2	1.260	0.4134
12	0.08081	2.053	12.0	4.7	1.588	0.5210
13	0.07196	1.828	13.5	5.3	2.003	0.6572
14	0.06408	1.628	15.0	5.9	2.525	0.8284
15	0.05707	1.450	16.8	6.6	3.184	1.045
16	0.05082	1.291	18.9	7.4	4.016	1.318
17	0.04526	1.150	21.2	8.3	5.064	1.661
18	0.04030	1.024	23.6	9.3	6.385	2.095
19	0.03589	0.9116	26.4	10.4	8.051	2.641
20	0.03196	0.8118	29.4	11.8	10.15	3.330
21	0.02846	0.7229	33.1	13.03	12.80	4.200
22	0.02535	0.6439	37.0	14.6	16.14	5.300
23	0.02257	0.5733	41.3	16.3	20.36	6.680
24	0.02010	0.5105	46.3	18.2	25.67	8.422
25	0.01790	0.4547	51.7	20.4	32.37	10.62
26	0.01594	0.4049	58.0	22.8	40.81	13.39
27	0.01420	0.3607	64.9	25.6	51.47	16.89
28	0.01264	0.3211	72.7	28.7	64.90	21.29
29	0.01126	0.2860	81.6	32.1	81.83	26.88
30	0.01003	0.2548	90.5	35.6	103.2	33.86
31	0.008928	0.2268	101	39.8	130.1	42.68
32	0.007950	0.2019	113	44.5	164.1	53.84
33	0.007080	0.1798	127	50.0	206.9	67.88
34	0.006305	0.1601	143	56.3	260.9	85.60
35	0.005615	0.1426	158	62.2	329.0	107.9
36	0.005000	0.1270	175	68.9	414.8	136.1
37	0.004453	0.1131	198	78.0	523.1	171.6
38	0.003965	0.1007	224	88.2	659.6	216.4
39	0.003531	0.08969	248	97.6	831.8	272.9
40	0.003145	0.07988	282	111.0	1049.0	344.2

culated in the same way as for multilayer coils, but the inductance will be approximately 10 percent higher.

Inductance in a straight wire may become important at high frequencies and is given by:

$$L = 0.0021[2.3 \log (4l/d - 0.75)]$$

(provided the diameter is very much smaller than the length)

where:

$$l = \text{length of wire, in centimeters.}$$

$$d = \text{diameter of wire, in centimeters.}$$

Mutual inductance (M) occurs when two coils are close enough so that when a current flows in one coil its magnetic field encompasses the other coil also. Then, if the current in the first coil changes, it will induce a voltage in the second coil. It makes no difference in which coil the current flows. The mutual inductance is the same either way.

The degree of closeness of the magnetic coupling between the two coils is called the *coefficient of coupling (K)*. If all the flux from the first coil links with the second coil, so that there is no leakage, $K = 1$. This can be approached in iron-core coils, but is very much lower in air-core coils.

A widely used method for measuring M is by means of an inductance bridge. The two coils are first connected in series, so that their mutual inductance aids the total inductance, and the latter is measured. Then the connections of the second coil are reversed, so that the mutual inductance opposes the total inductance, and the new total inductance is measured. The mutual inductance is given by:

$$M = (L_A - L_O)/4$$

where:

$$M = \text{mutual inductance, in henries.}$$

$$L_A = \text{total } L \text{ with } M \text{ aiding, in henries.}$$

$$L_O = \text{total } L \text{ with } M \text{ opposing, in henries.}$$

The coefficient of coupling is given by:

$$K = M/\sqrt{L_1 L_2}$$

where:

$$M = \text{mutual inductance, in henries.}$$

$$L_1 = \text{inductance of first coil, in henries.}$$

$$L_2 = \text{inductance of second coil, in henries.}$$

 M and K can be calculated without much difficulty from the physical dimensions of coils, provided that they are only single-layer solenoids. In the case of a continuous winding with a tap, and with no gap between the parts of the winding on either side of the tap, the mutual inductance is calculated as follows:

$$M = (L_T - L_1 - L_2)/2$$

where:

L_T = L of whole coil, determined from physical dimensions, in henries.

L_1 = L of part on one side of the tap, determined from physical dimensions, in henries.

L_2 = L of part on other side of the tap, determined from physical dimensions, in henries.

The total coil inductance, including mutual inductance, is given by:

$$L = L_1 + L_2 + 2M$$

Where there is a gap in the winding of the single-layer solenoid, the gap is assumed to be filled by an imaginary winding (L_i) continuous with the two real windings. The mutual inductance is given by:

$$M = (L_{1+i+2} + L_i - L_{1+i} - L_{i+2})/2$$

where:

L_{1+i+2} = inductance of $L_1 + L_i + L_2$.

L_{1+i} = inductance of $L_1 + L_i$.

L_{i+2} = inductance of $L_i + L_2$.

 If two single-layer solenoids are connected in parallel, with M aiding, the total inductance is given by:

$$L = 1/[1/(L_1 + M) + 1/(L_2 + M)]$$

If M is opposing, the total inductance is given by:

$$L = 1/[1/(L_1 - M) + 1/(L_2 - M)]$$

The *figure of merit (Q)* of a coil is given by:

$$Q = X_L/R_s$$

where:

X_L = the reactance of the coil, in ohms.

R_s = the series resistance of the coil, in ohms.

Where a coil is shunted by a resistance, the parallel resistance is converted to a series resistance by dividing it into X_L^2. It is then added to the series resistance. Q is obtained by dividing X_L by the total R_s, as above.

Iron-Core Coils

The relative permeability (μ_r) of air is 1, but for coils wound on cores of magnetic materials, it is very much higher. The inductance of simple single-layer coils is given by:

$$L = N^2 \mu A/l$$

where:

L = inductance, in henries.

N = number of turns.

μ = permeability, in ampere turns per meter.

A = cross-sectional area of core.

l = length of core.

Maximum relative permeability of some materials used for cores:

Cast iron	500	Silicon steel	7,000
Cast steel	1,500	Pure iron	180,000
Cold-rolled steel	2,000	Permalloy*	25,000
Iron	5,000	Parmalloy*	100,000
Low-carbon steel	2,500	Supermalloy*	800,000

Inductor Types

Inductors may be of the types already diagrammed (solenoid, multilayer, universal), or of other types designed to minimize undesirable features in certain applications. One of the most popular among low-frequency types is the toroidal type illustrated in Figure I-3. This coil is wound on

Figure I-3 Toroidal Coil
    The core may be of iron or ferrite.

*These are alloys containing 79% nickel.

an iron doughnut-shaped core, which ensures that all the magnetic flux is confined within it. Leakage is virtually nil.

Insulation for windings in close-wound coils should be as thin as possible, consistent with the voltage and current it is required to handle. Fine enameled-copper wire is generally used. On the other hand, coils designed for high frequencies need far fewer turns. Consequently, they are usually made of coarser gauge bare wire, with the turns separated from each other, and with air cores. In between these and iron-core coils used at low frequencies are close-wound coils with ferrite cores. Ferrite consists of iron oxide and other metallic oxides combined with ceramic to make a core that is not subject to the losses due to eddy currents induced in an iron core at higher frequencies. *See* Transformers.

Figure I-4 gives a computer program for coil calculations. A sample run of a typical coil calculation is shown in Figure I-5.

Figure I-4 Computer program for coil calculations.

```
10 PRINT"DESIGN OF SMALL AIR-CORE COILS"
20 PRINT:PRINT"ENTER ITEM NUMBER FROM MENU:"
30 PRINT TAB(10);"1.INDUCTANCE"
40 PRINT TAB(10);"2.NUMBER OF TURNS"
50 PRINT TAB(10);"3.M AND K FROM PHYSICAL"
60 PRINT TAB(12);"DIMENSIONS"
70 INPUT A
80 IF A=2 THEN 490
90 IF A=3 THEN 640
100 PRINT:PRINT"ENTER ITEM NUMBER FROM MENU:"
110 PRINT TAB(10);"1.SINGLE-LAYER"
120 PRINT TAB(10);"2.MULTILAYER"
130 PRINT TAB(10);"3.STRAIGHT WIRE"
140 INPUT B
150 IF B=1 THEN 180
160 IF B=2 THEN 340
170 GOTO 1220
180 PRINT:PRINT"INDUCTANCE OF SINGLE-LAYER INDUCTOR"
190 PRINT:PRINT"ENTER INTERNAL RADIUS IN CM"
200 INPUT R
210 PRINT"ENTER LENGTH IN CM"
220 INPUT L
230 PRINT"ENTER NUMBER OF TURNS"
240 INPUT N
250 IF L>.667*R THEN 280
260 I=(.394*R^2*N^2)/(R*(9-(R/(5*L)))+10*L)
270 GOTO 290
280 I=(.394*R^2*N^2)/(9*R+10*L)
290 PRINT:PRINT"INDUCTANCE =";I;"MICROHENRIES"
300 PRINT:PRINT"ENTER Y TO CONTINUE, Q TO QUIT"
310 INPUT Y$
320 IF Y$="Y"THEN 20
330 END
```

Figure I-4 continued.

```
340 PRINT:PRINT"INDUCTANCE OF MULTILAYER INDUCTOR"
350 PRINT:PRINT"ENTER MEAN RADIUS IN CM"
360 INPUT R
370 PRINT"ENTER LENGTH IN CM"
380 INPUT L
390 PRINT"ENTER WINDING DEPTH IN CM"
400 INPUT D
410 PRINT"ENTER NUMBER OF TURNS"
420 INPUT N
430 I=(.315*R^2*N^2)/((6*R)+(9*L)+(10*D))
440 PRINT:PRINT"INDUCTANCE =";I;"MICROHENRIES"
450 PRINT:PRINT"ENTER Y TO CONTINUE, Q TO QUIT"
460 INPUT Y$
470 IF Y$="Y"THEN 20
480 END
490 PRINT:PRINT"NUMBER OF TURNS, SINGLE-LAYER INDUCTOR"
500 PRINT:PRINT"ENTER NUMBER OF TURNS PER CM FROM TABLE"
510 INPUT P
520 PRINT"ENTER INTERNAL RADIUS IN CM"
530 INPUT R
540 PRINT"ENTER INDUCTANCE IN MICROHENRIES"
550 INPUT I
560 N=((12.7*I)/(P*R^2))*(1+SQR(1+((.14*R^3*P^2)/I)))
570 L=N/P
580 PRINT:PRINT"NUMBER OF TURNS REQUIRED =";N
590 PRINT"LENGTH OF COIL =";L;"CM"
600 PRINT:PRINT"ENTER Y TO CONTINUE, Q TO QUIT"
610 INPUT Y$
620 IF Y$="Y"THEN 20
630 END
640 PRINT:PRINT"MUTUAL INDUCTANCE (M) AND"
650 PRINT"COEFFICIENT OF COUPLING (K)"
660 PRINT"FROM PHYSICAL DIMENSIONS"
670 PRINT"(SINGLE-LAYER SOLENOID ONLY)"
680 PRINT:PRINT"ENTER ITEM NUMBER FROM MENU:"
690 PRINT TAB(10);"1.CONTINUOUS WINDING WITH TAP"
700 PRINT TAB(10);"2.WOUND SAME WAY, WITH GAP"
710 INPUT C
720 IF C=2 THEN 930
730 PRINT:PRINT"ENTER TOTAL NUMBER OF TURNS"
740 INPUT N
750 PRINT"ENTER NUMBER OF TURNS FROM"
760 PRINT"WINDING TO TAP (SHORTEST WAY)"
770 INPUT N2
780 N1=N-N2
790 PRINT"ENTER INTERNAL RADIUS IN CM"
800 INPUT R
810 PRINT"ENTER TOTAL LENGTH IN CM"
820 INPUT L
830 L1=L*N1/N
840 L2=L-L1
850 I=(.394*R^2*N^2)/(9*R+10*L)
860 I1=(.394*R^2*N1^2)/(9*R+10*L1)
870 I2=(.394*R^2*N2^2)/(9*R+10*L2)
```

Figure I-4 continued.

```
880 M=.5*(I-I1-I2)
890 K=M/SQR(I1*I2)
900 PRINT:PRINT"MUTUAL INDUCTANCE =";M;"MICROHENRIES"
910 PRINT"COEFFICIENT OF COUPLING =";K
920 GOTO 1180
930 PRINT"ENTER OVERALL LENGTH IN CM"
940 INPUT L
950 PRINT"ENTER LENGTH OF FIRST WINDING IN CM"
960 INPUT L1
970 PRINT"ENTER LENGTH OF SECOND WINDING IN CM"
980 INPUT L2
990 L3=L-(L1+L2)
1000 PRINT"ENTER TURNS PER CM FROM TABLE"
1010 INPUT P
1020 N=P*L
1030 N1=P*L1
1040 N2=P*L2
1050 N3=P*L3
1060 PRINT"ENTER INTERNAL RADIUS IN CM"
1070 INPUT R
1080 I=(.394*R^2*N^2)/(9*R+10*L)
1090 I1=(.394*R^2*(N1+N3)^2)/(9*R+10*(L1+L3))
1100 I2=(.394*R^2*N3^2)/(9*R+10*L3)
1110 I3=(.394*R^2*(N3+N2)^2)/(9*R+10*(L3+L2))
1120 M=.5*(I+I2-I1-I3)
1130 I4=(.394*R^2*N1^2)/(9*R+10*L1)
1140 I5=(.394*R^2*N2^2)/(9*R+10*L1)
1150 K=M/SQR(I4*I5)
1160 PRINT:PRINT"MUTUAL INDUCTANCE =";M;"MICROHENRIES"
1170 PRINT"COEFFICIENT OF COUPLING =";K
1180 PRINT:PRINT"ENTER Y TO CONTINUE, Q TO QUIT"
1190 INPUT Y$
1200 IF Y$="Y"THEN 20
1210 END
1220 PRINT:PRINT"INDUCTANCE OF STRAIGHT WIRE"
1230 PRINT:PRINT"ENTER LENGTH IN CM"
1240 INPUT L
1250 PRINT"ENTER DIAMETER IN CM"
1260 INPUT D
1270 PRINT"ENTER FREQUENCY IN MHZ"
1280 INPUT F
1290 I=.002*L*(2.3*LOG((4*L)/D-.75)/LOG(10))
1300 X=2*3.1415927*F*I
1310 PRINT:PRINT"INDUCTANCE =";I;"MICROHENRIES"
1320 PRINT"REACTANCE AT";F;"MHZ =";X;"OHMS"
1330 PRINT:PRINT"ENTER Y TO CONTINUE, Q TO QUIT"
1340 INPUT Y$
1350 IF Y$="Y"THEN 20
1360 END
```

Figure I-5 Sample Run of Program
in Figure I-4.

```
DESIGN OF SMALL AIR-CORE COILS


ENTER ITEM NUMBER FROM MENU:

        1.INDUCTANCE

        2.NUMBER OF TURNS

        3.M AND K FROM PHYSICAL

          DIMENSIONS


? 2


NUMBER OF TURNS, SINGLE LAYER INDUCTOR


ENTER NUMBER OF TURNS PER CM FROM TABLE
? 14.6
ENTER INTERNAL RADIUS IN CM
? 1.25
ENTER INDUCTANCE IN MICROHENRIES
? 120


NUMBER OF TURNS REQUIRED = 148.235
LENGTH OF COIL = 10.1531 CM


ENTER Y TO CONTINUE, Q TO QUIT
? Q
```

Inductors in Parallel

The total inductance of inductors connected in parallel with no mutual inductance is given by:

$$L_T = \cfrac{1}{\cfrac{1}{L_1} + \cfrac{1}{L_2} + \cfrac{1}{L_3} + \cdots}$$

The total inductance of *two* inductors connected in parallel with no mutual inductance is given by:

$$L_T = \frac{L_1 \times L_2}{L_1 + L_2}$$

Inductors in Series

The total inductance of inductors in series with no mutual inductance is given by:

$$L_T = L_1 + L_2 + L_3 + \cdots$$

Industrial Wiring Insulation Color Code

Wiring installed in buildings is required to have insulation that conforms to the colors specified in Table I-2.

TABLE I-2   Industrial Wiring Insulation Color Code

Color	Abbreviation	Circuit function
Black	Bk	Line voltage conductor (120 V RMS)*
White	W	Neutral conductor
Green	Gn	Ground conductor
Bare	—	Ground conductor
Red	R	Line voltage conductor (120 V RMS)* (also for AC control)
Yellow	Y	Ground conductor (also for interlock panel control)
Blue	Bl	DC control

*Two black conductors, or a black and a red conductor, used for 240 V RMS.

Infrared Radiation IR wavelengths are subdivided into *near* (750–1500 nm), *middle* (1600–6000 nm), *far* (6100–40,000 nm), and *far-far* (4.1×10^4–10^6 nm).

Input Impedance *See* Operational Amplifier, Transistor.

Instantaneous Current, Voltage *See* Alternating Current.

Instruments *See* Measurement.

INTEGRATED CIRCUITS

An integrated circuit (IC) is an interconnected array of active and passive elements integrated with a single semiconductor substrate, or deposited on the substrate by a continuous series of compatible processes, and capable of performing at least one complete electronic circuit function. The principal types of IC are as follows:

Hybrid Integrated Circuit (HIC)

This is manufactured by combining a number of techniques, such as diffused monolithic portions, thin-film elements, and discrete devices.

Film Integrated Circuit

This is made up of elements that are films all formed in place upon an insulating substrate. A *thick-film* IC consists of a ceramic substrate upon which the passive circuit elements are produced by silk-screening specially formulated pastes. The active elements are added as discrete chips. A *thin-film* IC has a passive substrate on which the various passive elements are deposited in a vacuum in the form of thin patterned films of conductive or nonconductive material. Active components are added as discrete chips or packages.

Monolithic Integrated Circuit (MIC)

This is formed upon or within a semiconductor substrate with at least one of the elements formed within the substrate, and contains no thin film or discrete components. The majority of ICs are of this type. They are classified according to their component density as follows:

Small-scale integration	(SSI)	≤12 components
Medium-scale integration	(MSI)	12–100 components
Large-scale integration	(LSI)	100–1000 components
Very large-scale integration	(VLSI)	>1000 components

The term *gates* is used instead of components in digital ICs.

ICs are also classified as bipolar or metal-oxide semiconductor (MOS) according to which type of active device is employed. (*See* Transistors for explanation of these terms).

Packaging

The packaging of ICs varies according to the number of pins, as shown in Figure I-6. Small ICs, with few pins, are usually supplied in metal cans

Figure I-6 Types of IC Packaging
Some VLSI circuits may have as many as 64 pins. — [8]

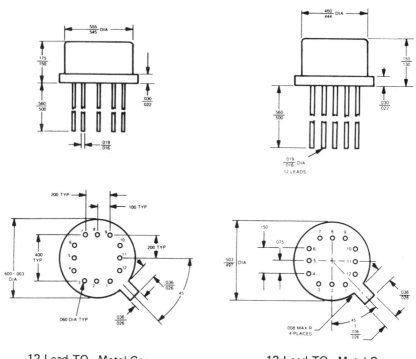

12 Lead TO - Metal Can   12 Lead TO - Metal Can

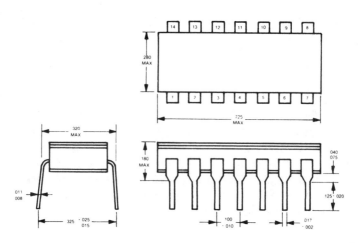

14 Lead Cavity DIP

Figure I-6 (continued)

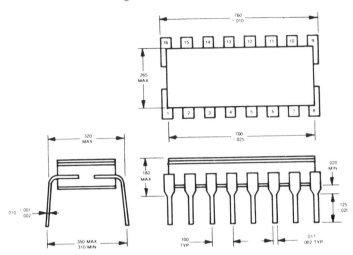

16 Lead Cavity DIP

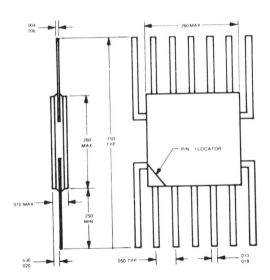

14 Lead Flat Package

similar to those used by transistors. Larger ICs are encapsulated in dual in-line packages (DIPs). Some smaller ICs are also provided in the form of flat packs, which may have either leads or "bumps" (metal protrusions for attachment to a printed circuit).

Coding

Unfortunately, there is no standard code for identifying ICs. Each manufacturer uses his own. It is necessary to use semiconductor reference guides for identification and specifications. However, some U.S. manufacturers use the following preferred code:

XXAANNNNBCD

where:

XX = manufacturer identification (MC for Motorola, for instance).

AA = device family:

AD = analog-to-digital;
AH = analog hybrid;
AM = analog monolithic;
CD = CMOS digital;
DA = digital-to-analog;
DM = digital monolithic;
LF = linear FET;
LH = linear hybrid;
LM = linear monolithic;
LX = transducer;
MM = MOS monolithic.

NNNN = device number.

B = device number suffix (if any).

C = package style:

D = glass/metal DIP;
F = glass/metal flat pack;
H = small metal can (T05, etc.);
J = glass/ceramic DIP;
K = large metal can (T03);
L = small multipin metal can;
N = plastic DIP;

P = can with heat sink;
S = power DIP;
T = can with heat sink;
W = flat pack;
Z = small plastic can.

D = temperature data.

Integration *See* Calculus.

Integrator The circuit, as shown in Figure I-7, has output proportionate to the integral of the input signal, in which:

$$V_O = -1/T \int_0^t V_I \, dt$$

where:

$$T = RC.$$

Figure I-7 Integrator
    Some integrators include an operational amplifier. This circuit is used in TV receivers to integrate the six vertical sync pulses that come at the end of each field into a single large pulse that triggers the vertical oscillator.—[1]

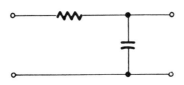 

Interference *See* Noise.

Intermediate Frequency (IF) Radio and television receivers, and practically all others, use a local oscillator that is tuned in step with the RF tuner so that the oscillator frequency always differs by the same amount from that of the selected incoming frequency. *Heterodyning*, or mixing, these two frequencies results in the generation of two more signals with frequencies that equal the sum and difference of the first two. Consequently, there are four signals in the output of the tuner. A tuned circuit or other device then filters out three of them, leaving the fixed difference frequency to be amplified by the *intermediate-frequency amplifier*.
    With a fixed and favorably chosen intermediate frequency (which is still an RF signal), much greater selectivity and amplification are possible

than would be the case with signals of various frequencies. Intermediate frequencies in common use are:

AM radio receivers	455 kHz
FM radio receivers	10.7 MHz
TV receivers, video	43–45 MHz*
TV receivers, audio	4.5 MHz

Double heterodyning, as its name implies, is used in some high-frequency receivers to change the incoming RF signal to a first IF value for preliminary amplification and filtering, after which it is heterodyned again to obtain a second IF signal, which is then processed in a second IF amplifier. This gives higher gain without instability, and provides greater suppression of undesired signal frequencies.

Ionosphere *See* Propagation.

Iron-Core Inductor *See* Inductors, Transformers.

*The gain of a TV intermediate-frequency amplifier is essentially constant from 43 to 45 MHz. Above 45 MHz, the response curve slopes down; at 45.75 MHz (the picture carrier frequency), it is 50 percent. This slope is required to compensate for the vestigial sideband in the transmitted signal. (*See* Broadcasting.)

J

Jacks and Plugs Jacks are sockets that accept plugs. They may be panel-mounted for connecting leads or cables to inputs or outputs of electronic equipment, or inline for connecting leads or cables to each other. (*See* Figure J-1.) Most jacks and plugs simply push together and pull apart, unlike connectors, which have screw-threaded fittings as a rule. *See* Connectors.

JFET Junction Field-Effect Transistor. *See* Transistors.

Junction *See* Transistors.

Junction Field-Effect Transistor *See* Transistors.

Figure J-1 Jacks and Plugs.

A. Typical single-conductor panel jack.

B. ¼" 2-conductor phone plug and panel jack.

C. ¼" 3-conductor phone plug and panel jack.

D. Phono (RCA-type) panel jacks and plugs.

E. ¼" 2-conductor inline phone jack and plug.

Phone jacks and plugs are made in ⅛" and ³⁄₃₂" diameter also.

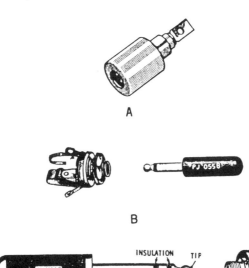

A

B

C

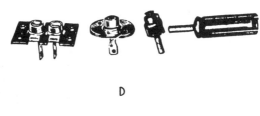

D

E

Kirchoff's Laws *See* Electric Circuit Theory.

Lamps Miniature incandescent lamps used for pilot lights and other similar lamp-types are shown in Figure L-1. Neon-glow lamps are given in Figure L-2.

Figure L-1 Incandescent Lamps—[5]

S-6 Bulb
CANDELABRA SCREW
Base

S-6 Bulb
BAYONET BASE
Double Contact

| DESIGNATION ◄ | RATINGS | | | DESIGNATION ► |
	WATTS	VOLTS	HOURS	
6S6—6V	6	6	1500	6S6DC—6V
6S6—12V	6	12	1500	6S6DC—12V
6S6—24V	6	24	1500	6S6DC—24V
6S6—30V	6	30	1500	6S6DC—30V
6S6—48V	6	48	1500	6S6DC—48V
6S6—75V	6	75	1500	6S6DC—75V
6S6—125V	6	125	1500	6S6DC—125V
6S6—135V	6	135	1500	6S6DC—135V
6S6—145V	6	145	1500	6S6DC—145V
10S6—230V	10	230	1500	10S6DC—230V
10S6—250V	10	250	1500	10S6DC—250V

C-7 Bulb
BAYONET BASE
Double Contact

10C7/DC
10 watts
120 volts
6000 hours

C-7 Bulb
BAYONET BASE
Double Contact

10C7/1DC
10 watts
120 volts
6000 hours

C-7 Bulb
CANDELABRA SCREW
Base

10C7/5DC
10 watts
120 volts
6000 hours

C-7 Bulb
CANDELABRA SCREW
Base

7C7—120V
7 watts
120 volts
1500 hours

10C7/5—120V
10 watts
120 volts
6000 hours

T-4½ Bulb
CANDELABRA
SCREW Base

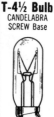

6T 4½/1
6 watts
125 volts
1500 hours

S-6 Bulb
INTERMEDIATE
SCREW Base

6S6/7
125 volts

10S6/13
230 V.; 250 V.

Figure L-1 (continued)

T-3¼ Bulb, MINIATURE BAYONET Base

NO.	Manufacturer's Rating VOLTS	AMPS	HOURS	VOLTS for 6000 hours	NO.	Manufacturer's Rating VOLTS	AMPS	HOURS	VOLTS for 6000 hours
49	2.0	.06	1000	1.7	1815	14	.20	3000	13.3
45	3.2	.35	3000	2.9	1826	18	.15	250	14.0
47	6.3	.15	3000	6.0	1819	28	.04	1000	24.0
1847	6.3	.15	Long	6.3	1829	28	.07	1000	24.0
44	6.3	.25	3000	6.0	1820	28	.10	1000	24.0
1891	14	.24	500	12.0	313	28	.17	500	21.7
1488	14	.15	200	10.5	1828	37.5	.05	Long	37.5
1813	14.4	.10	3000	12.5	1835	55	.05	Long	55.0

T-3¼ Bulb, MINIATURE SCREW Base

NO.	Manufacturer's Rating VOLTS	AMPS	HOURS	VOLTS for 6000 hours
48	2.0	.06	1000	1.7
42	3.2	.35	3000	3.0
40	6.3	.15	3000	6.0
46	6.3	.25	3000	6.0
1481	14	.15	200	10.5
1487	14	.20	3000	13.3
1827	18	.15	250	14.5
1821	28	.17	1000	24.2
1832	37.5	.05	*(L)	37.5

G-3½ Bulb—MINIATURE BAYONET Base—G-4½ Bulb

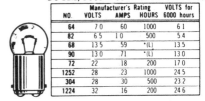

NO.	Manufacturer's Rating VOLTS	AMPS	HOURS	VOLTS for 6000 hours
51	7.5	.21	1000	6.6
53	14.4	.12	1000	13.5
1445	18	.15	250	13.5
*356	28	.17	500	23.0
*for intermittent service only				
55	7	.40	500	5.8
57	14	.24	500	11.5

G-3½

G-4½

T-2 Bulb, TELEPHONE SLIDE Base

NO.	Manufacturer's Rating VOLTS	Min. (AMPS) Max		LIFE
6A	6	0.12	0.16	
12C	12		0.17	
24A	24	0.025	0.035	Indefinite long life— over 6000 hours
24E	24	0.032	0.038	
48B	48	0.09	0.0110	
48C	48	0.032	0.038	
55C	55	0.045	0.055	

*(L)—Indefinite long life, over 6000 hours

G-6 Bulb, DOUBLE CONTACT BAYONET Base

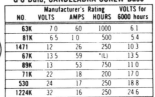

NO.	Manufacturer's Rating VOLTS	AMPS	HOURS	VOLTS for 6000 hours
64	7.0	.60	1000	6.1
82	6.5	1.0	500	5.4
68	13.5	.59	*(L)	13.5
90	13.0	.71	*(L)	13.0
72	22	.18	200	17.0
1252	28	.23	1000	24.5
304	28	.30	500	23.2
1224	32	.16	200	24.6

G-6 Bulb, CANDELABRA SCREW Base

NO.	Manufacturer's Rating VOLTS	AMPS	HOURS	VOLTS for 6000 hours
63K	7.0	.60	1000	6.1
81K	6.5	1.0	500	5.4
1471	12	.26	250	10.3
67K	13.5	.59	*(L)	13.5
89K	13	.53	750	11.0
71K	22	.18	200	17.0
530	24	.17	250	18.8
1224K	32	.16	250	24.6

T-1¾ Bulb, MIDGET FLANGE Base

NO.	Manufacturer's Rating VOLTS	AMPS	HOURS
331	1.3	.06	500
343	2.5	.40	30
338	2.7	.06	500
328	6.0	.20	500
345	6.0	.04	1000
330	14.0	.08	750
327	28.0	.04	1000

Figure L-2 Neon-Glow Lamps—[5]

T-3¼ Bulb, ⅓ Watt, MINIATURE BAYONET Base
Types NE-51 and NE-51H (High brightness)

Recommended Resistance Values (Ohms) For NE-51		
Applied Volts	**105-125**	**210-250**
Best Light	56,000	180,000
Medium Life	100,000	270,000
Long Life	220,000	680,000

for NE51-H		
Applied Volts	**105-125**	**210-250**
Best Light	18,000	56,000
Medium Light	33,000	120,000
Long Life	82,000	220,000

T-4¼ Bulb, ¼ Watt, DOUBLE CONTACT BAYONET Base
Types NE-48, NE-16, and NE-17

Recommended Resistance Values (Ohms)		
Applied Volts	**105-125**	**210-250**
Best Light	16,400	44,000
Long Life	30,000	94,000

T-4½ Bulb, ¼ and ½ Watt, CANDELABRA
SCREW Base
Types NE-45 and NE-57 (¼ W),
and NE-58 (½ W)

T-2 Bulb, 1/25 Watt, TELEPHONE SLIDE Base
Type NE-3

Recommended Resistance Values (Ohms)	
Applied Volts	**105-125**
Best Light	56,000
Medium Life	100,000
Long Life	220,000

S-7 Bulb, 1 Watt, DOUBLE CONTACT BAYONET Base
Type NE-79

Recommended Resistance Values (Ohms)		
Applied Volts	**105-125**	**210-250**
Best Light	3,000	9,400
Long Life	6,000	60,000

T-2 Bulb, MIDGET FLANGE Base
Types NE-2D and NE-2J

Recommended Resistance Values (Ohms) For NE-2D	
Applied Voltage	**105-125 AC or DC**
Best Light	56,000
Medium Life	100,000
Long Life	220,000

For NE-2J (High Brightness)	
Applied Volts	**105-125 AC only**
Best Light	18,000
Medium Life	33,000
Long Life	82,000

LIGHT

Visible light is that section of the electromagnetic spectrum with wavelengths between 380 and 720 nanometers. The visible light spectrum is
shown in Figure L-3.

Figure L-4 Response to Light of Average Human Eye
The human eye does not respond equally to all wavelengths. At
normal light levels, its response is called *photopic* (solid curve). This
curve peaks at 555 nm. At normal light levels, the eye distinguishes
colors, but obviously it takes much more violet light to produce the
same visibility effect as green-yellow. At low light levels, the response
is called *scotopic* (dashed curve). This curve peaks at 507 nm. The
eye cannot distinguish colors at low light levels, but is much more
sensitive to the presence of light.—[6]   ⟶

Figure L-3 Visible Light Spectrum

Wavelengths in nanometers are used rather than frequencies (400–789 THz), because they are easily interchangeable with other units:

$$1 \text{ nm} = 10 \text{ angstroms } (\mathring{A})$$

$$1 \text{ nm} = 0.001 \text{ micron } (\mu m)$$

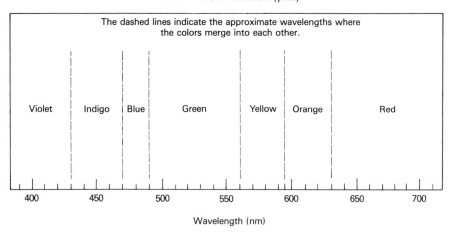

The response of the average human eye as established by the Commission Internationale de l'Éclairage (CIE) is shown in Figure L-4.

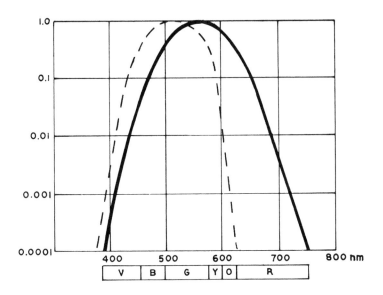

Table L-1 summarizes radiometric and photometric terms and units.

TABLE L-1 Summary of Radiometric and Photometric Terms*—[6]

Term	Symbol	Metric unit	Alternative unit
Radiant flux	Φ_e	W	
Luminous flux	Φ_v	lm	
Irradiance	E_e	W cm^{-2}	
Illuminance	E_v	lm cm^{-2}	phot
		lm m^{-2}	lux
		lm ft^{-2}	footcandle
Radiant intensity	I_e	W sr^{-1}	
Luminous intensity	I_v	lm sr^{-1}	candela
Radiant exitance	M_e	W cm^{-2}	
Luminous exitance	M_v	lm cm^{-2}	
Radiance	L_e	W cm^{-2}	
Luminance	L_v	sr^{-1}	
		lm cm^{-2}	
		sr^{-1}	
		cd cm^{-2}	stilb
		$1/\pi$ cd cm^{-2}	lambert
		$1/\pi$ cd ft^{-2}	footlambert

*Radiometric values are those measured by a scientific instrument; photometric values are radiometric values converted to reflect human eye response.

Table L-2 gives approximate levels of brightness of various sources of light. Table L-3 gives approximate levels of illumination from various natural sources.

TABLE L-2 Comparative Luminance (=apparent brightness) of Various Sources

Source	Luminance (cd m^{-2})
Nuclear explosion fireball	2.00×10^{12}
Lightning	6.80×10^{10}
Welder's carbon arc	1.60×10^{7}
Tungsten lamp	8.90×10^{5}
Sun at midday	1.60×10^{4}
Blue sky, no clouds	7.90×10^{3}
Fluorescent lamp	6.85×10^{3}
Moon, full	2.50×10^{3}

TABLE L-3   Comparative Illuminance
of (= light falling on) Natural Scene
from Various Sources

Source	Illumination (lm m^{-2})
Direct sunlight	10^5
Full daylight, out of sunlight	10^4
Bright overcast	10^3
Dark overcast	10^2
Twilight	10
Dusk	1
Full moon, clear sky	10^{-1}
Quarter moon, clear sky	10^{-2}
Starlight, clear sky	10^{-3}
Starlight, overcast	10^{-4}

Light-Emitting Diode (LED) *See* Diodes.

Logarithms *See* Mathematical Tables.

LOGIC CIRCUITS

Classification

Logic circuits are classified by *function* and *technology*. Figure L-5 illustrates the three basic logic functions, using *bipolar* technology.

Other functions are derived from the three basic functions by the addition of inverters, as shown in Figure L-6.

Bipolar Technology

Bipolar technology involves the use of the *bipolar junction transistor* (BJT). The most popular configuration is the NAND gate shown in Figure L-7. This uses a multi-emitter transistor instead of separate transistors as in earlier circuits, and is called *transistor-transistor logic* (TTL). The NAND gates can be converted to other gates by various combinations, as shown in Figure L-8.

These circuits are saturating circuits. The transistors operate either in the off mode or fully saturated. A bipolar transistor is off when its input voltage is below 0.8 V, and on when the voltage is over 2 V. The supply voltage is generally 5 V.

Figure L-5 Basic Logic Functions

Function	Symbol	Basic Circuit	Truth Table

NOT Gate (inverter)

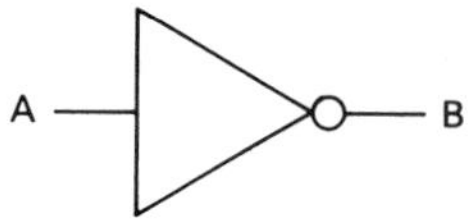

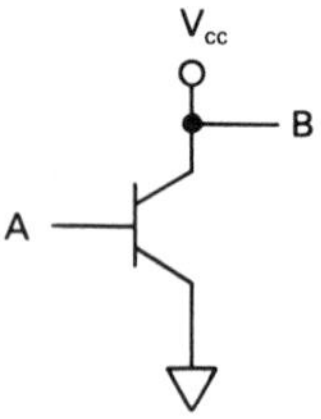

A	B
0	1
1	0

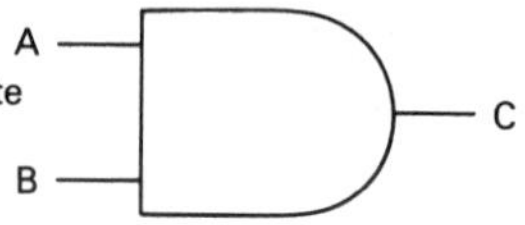

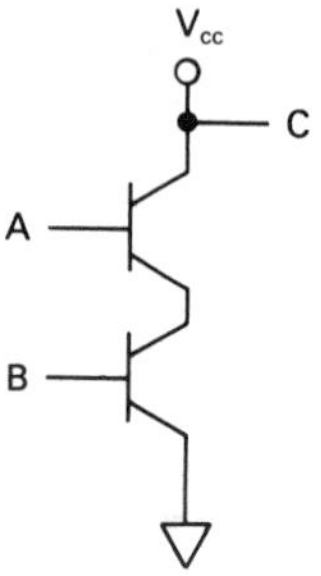

AND Gate

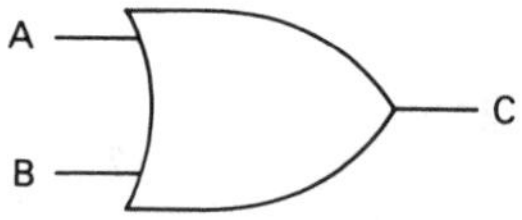

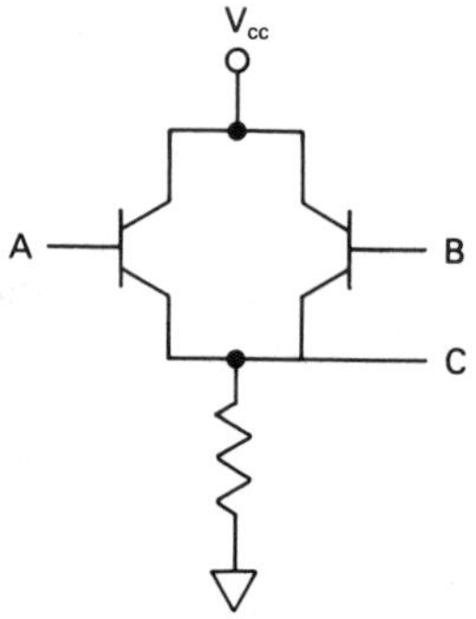

A	B	C
0	0	0
0	1	0
1	0	0
1	1	1

OR Gate

A	B	C
0	0	0
0	1	1
1	0	1
1	1	1

Figure L-6 NOR and NAND Gates

NOR and NAND gates are OR and AND gates with added inversion (the small circles indicate inversion). An exclusive-OR (XOR) gate is an OR gate altered so that it gives a false output when both inputs are true, instead of a true output, as shown in the OR truth table in Fig. L-5. An exclusive-NOR (XNOR) gate is the inverse of an XOR gate.

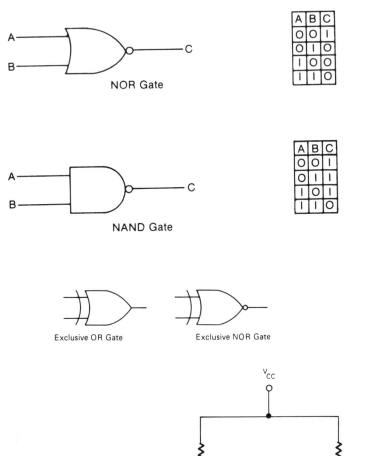

NOR Gate

A	B	C
O	O	I
O	I	O
I	O	O
I	I	O

NAND Gate

A	B	C
O	O	I
O	I	I
I	O	I
I	I	O

Exclusive OR Gate

Exclusive NOR Gate

Figure L-7 A TTL NAND Gate
This gate uses a multi-emitter transistor that can have up to eight emitters. Q1 operates in the same way as an AND gate, but the inverter Q2 makes it into a NAND gate.—[3]

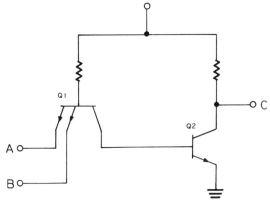

A	B	C
O	O	I
I	O	I
O	I	I
I	I	O

Figure L-8 How Two-Input NAND Gates Can Be Combined to Make Other Gates—[3]

The pin numbers are those of a 7400 Quad 2-Input NAND Gate IC.

(a) By shorting its inputs, a NAND gate becomes a NOT gate (inverter).

(b) An AND gate is obtained by adding a NAND gate connected as an inverter.

(c) An OR gate is obtained by adding two NAND gates connected as inverters.

(d) A NOR gate is obtained by adding three NAND gates connected as inverters.

(e) An XOR gate is obtained by connecting four NAND gates as shown.

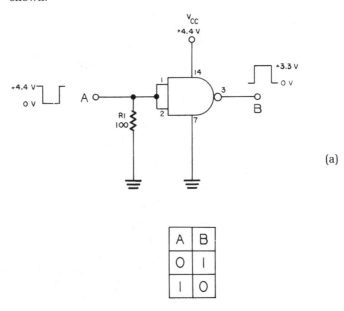

(a)

A	B
0	1
1	0

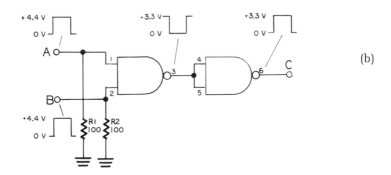

(b)

A	B	C
0	0	0
1	0	0
0	1	0
1	1	1

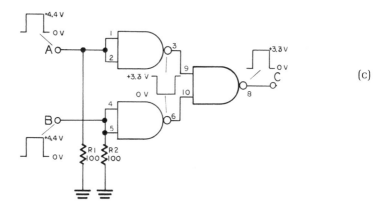

(c)

A	B	C
0	0	0
1	0	1
0	1	1
1	1	1

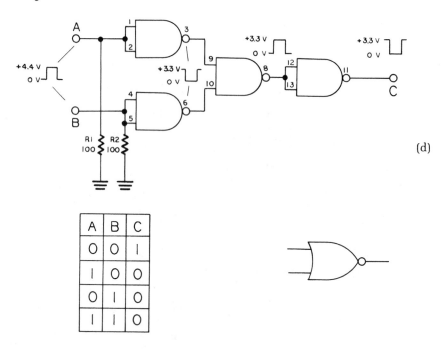

(d)

A	B	C
0	0	1
1	0	0
0	1	0
1	1	0

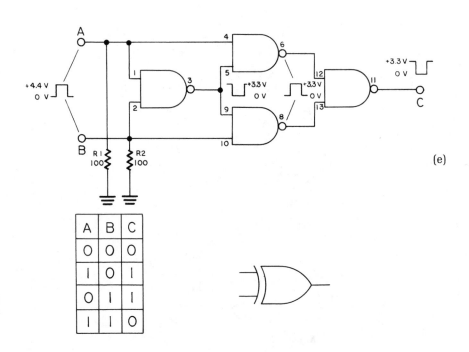

(e)

A	B	C
0	0	0
1	0	1
0	1	1
1	1	0

Earlier logic families, which are seldom used now, are:

RTL   resistor-transistor logic;
RCTL   resistor-capacitor-transistor logic;
DTL   diode-transistor logic.

These are slower and noisier than TTL.

If the transistor is prevented from saturating, hole storage effects are reduced so that operating speed is increased. TTL gate speed can be increased by using Schottky transistors, which do not saturate even when fully on. However, the Schottky junction can increase capacitance, so careful selection of circuit components is required. This family is known as TTL-S.

The fastest bipolar logic family is *emitter-coupled logic* (ECL), which is also nonsaturating (see Figure L-9).

Figure L-9 An ECL Gate
    If output $C1$ is used, it is a NOR gate; if output $C2$ is used, it is an OR gate. —[3]

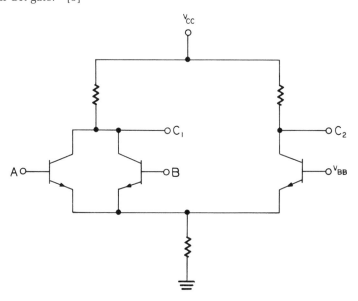

Another nonsaturating bipolar gate is *integrated-injection logic (I^2L)*. (*See* Figure L-10.) In this system, the transistors are merged, and only the collectors are separate. Current is injected into the bases of the output transistors, and their noise immunity and speed are improved at higher current levels. However, if very high speed is not required, the power dissipation is low, and the small size of the device makes it suitable for LSI.

Figure L-10 An I^2L NOR Gate—[3]

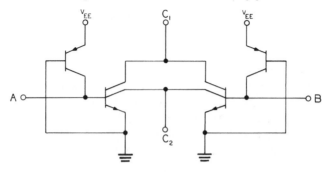

Unipolar Logic Circuits

On the whole, unipolar circuits are better suited to LSI than bipolar, since they are smaller, and so provide higher circuit density.

Complementary metal-oxide-semiconductor (CMOS) logic has found widespread use in SSI and MSI. Figure L-11 shows the arrangement for a NAND gate.

Figure L-11 A CMOS NAND Gate—[3]

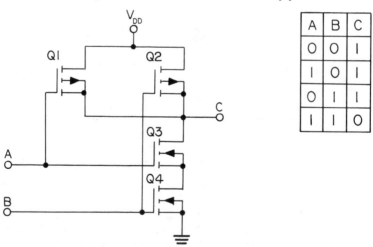

A	B	C
0	0	1
1	0	1
0	1	1
1	1	0

CMOS logic can operate over a wide range of supply voltages. Figure L-12 shows that noise immunity is high and that it increases with higher supply voltages.

CMOS logic is not used for LSI, where even smaller devices are required. Figure L-13 shows a typical NAND gate for LSI.

Figure L-12 CMOS Noise Immunity
     Increasing the supply voltage (V_{DD}) for a CMOS device increases the width of the noise-immunity bands.

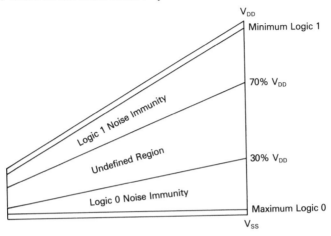

Figure L-13 A MOS NAND Gate (*n* or *p*) Used in LSI

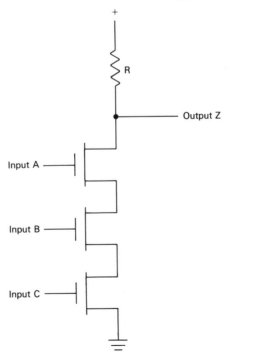

Comparison of Logic Families

No one logic family is best in all respects. For instance, CMOS, which is number one in power economy, fan-out, and noise immunity, is also the slowest. Table L-4 compares the six principal families on a scale of 1 to 6 (best to worst).

Condensed Truth Table

Table L-5 gives a truth table for all five logic gates. By tabulating their inputs and outputs together, we have made it easy for you to compare them, and even to memorize them without much difficulty.

TABLE L-4   Comparison of Logic Families (1 = best, 6 = worst)

Logic family	Speed	Power dissipation	Fan-out	Noise immunity	Noise generation
DTL	4	4	3	4	2
TTL	3	4	3	3	3
TTL-S	2	5	3	3	3
ECL	1	6	2	3	1
NMOS	5	2	2	2	2
CMOS	6	1	1	1	2

TABLE L-5   Combined Truth Table for All Logic Gates

Inputs		Outputs (*C*)				
A	*B*	AND	NAND	OR	NOR	XOR
0	0	0	1	0	1	0
0	1	0	1	1	0	1
1	0	0	1	1	0	1
1	1	1	0	1	0	0

Flip-Flops

A flip-flop is basically a bistable multivibrator. It has two states. When triggered by an input voltage, it changes state. It will remain in that state until triggered again.

   This capability is made use of in a computer central processing unit. A set of flip-flops comprises a register. When a group of binary digits ("bits") is applied to the register, each flip-flop alters state according to whether the bit applied to it was a 0 or 1 bit. The group of bits has now been stored since the flip-flops will hold their states until changed by another input.

Flip-flops are also used in this way in counters and other digital devices.

Figure L-14 shows *SR*, *D*, and *J-K* flip-flops made from NAND gates and their truth tables. The *D* and *J-K* flip-flops require a clock input.

Figure L-14 Widely Used Flip-Flops

(a) An *S-R* flip-flop using two 2-input NAND gates. Data are applied at the *S* input; a pulse at the *R* input resets the flip-flop to zero. The term "latch" is used for this type of flip-flop which does not use a clock; however, technically the term "latch" belongs to the two feedback loops. (The pin numbers are those for two of the gates in a 7400 Quad 2-Input NAND Gate IC.)

(b) The operation of a *D* flip-flop using four 2-input NAND gates and an inverter is controlled by clock pulses applied to the *C* input; data are applied at the *D* input. The timing diagram (*right*) shows how the output *Q* can change only on the *leading* edge of a clock pulse; and how edge-triggering, as it is called, discriminates against random glitches such as that marked *G*. (The pin numbers are those of a 7400 Quad 2-Input NAND Gate IC.)

(c) This *J-K* flip-flop uses 3-input NAND gates. It operates only on the *trailing* edge of each clock pulse. On each clock pulse: when the *J* and *K* inputs are both false, nothing happens; when *J* only is true, *Q* will go true; when *K* only is true, *Q̄* will go true; when *J* and *K* are both true, the outputs toggle (switch oppositely). (The pin numbers are those of one of the flip-flops in a 7476 Dual *J-K* Master-Slave Flip-Flop IC.)—[3]

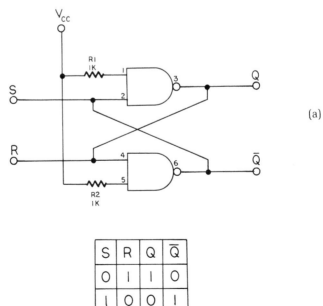

(a)

S	R	Q	Q̄
0	1	1	0
1	0	0	1

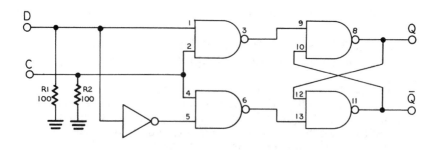

(b)

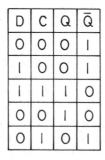

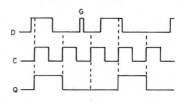

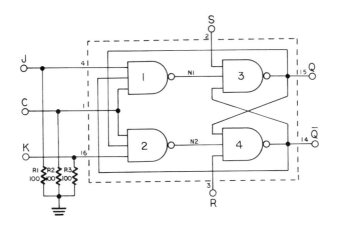

(c)

J	K	C	Q	$\overline{Q}$
0	0	0	1	0
0	0	1	1	0
1	0	0	1	0
1	0	1	1	0
0	1	0	1	0
0	1	1	0	1
1	1	0	0	1
1	1	1	1	0

Shift Registers

When the stored data are moved sequentially along a chain of flip-flops, the system is called a shift register. An example of one is shown in Figure L-15.

Figure L-15 Shift Register
This is a 4-bit serial-in, parallel-out (SIPO) shift register, using four D flip-flops. If the output were taken from the Q output of FF4 instead of from all four flip-flops at once, it would be a serial-in, serial-out (SISO) shift register. Shift registers can also be parallel-in, parallel-out (PIPO); parallel-in, serial-out (PISO); and shift in either direction. —[3]

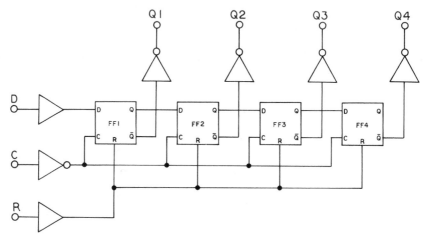

Counters

Flip-flops are also connected together to form counters. There are two types: asynchronous and synchronous. In the first-named, the output from each stage "clocks" the next stage, so the input pulse "ripples" through the flip-flops. In the synchronous type, an external clock pulse is used.

For most purposes, a decimal count (0 through 9) is required, so a BCD counting circuit is used, as shown in Figure L-16. In this circuit, the J and K inputs of flip-flops A, C, and D do not have signal connections. They are connected to a positive voltage source, so are in a 1 condition at all times. These flip-flops will switch on the clock pulse alone. The J and K inputs of B are connected to the $\overline{Q}$ output of D. As long as this is 1, the B flip-flop will be enabled. The action of the counter is explained in the timing diagram.

This counter can also be used as a frequency divider.

Loudspeaker *See* Transducers.

Figure L-16 BCD Counting Unit

(a) BCD counter using four *J-K* flip-flops and two NAND gates. The outputs labeled *A, B, C, D* are connected to a RESET push-button, which enables you to reset all the flip-flops to zero at any time.

(b) Each flip-flop changes state from 1 to 0 or from 0 to 1 on the trailing edge of the input pulse. The timing diagram shows this counter could also be used as a frequency divider.—[8]

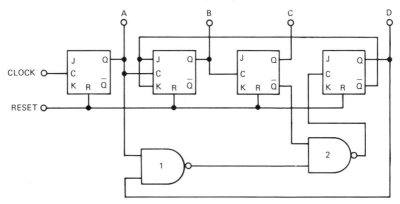

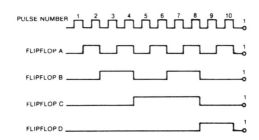

Magnetic Amplifiers The basic circuit for a magnetic amplifier (also known as a transductor, saturable-core inductor, or saturable-core reactor) is shown in Figure M-1. It consists of two windings on the same core. The winding with five scallops is the control winding; the one with three scallops is the power winding. The saturable properties symbol superimposed on them indicates that they are magnetically coupled by a saturable core.

Figure M-1 Schematic Symbol for Magnetic Amplifier—[6]

In the absence of a control signal, the core does not saturate. The flux induced in the core rises toward the saturation level with each peak of the alternating current in the power winding, but does not reach it. The power winding therefore offers a continuous high impedance to the power supply so that essentially all the power supply potential is dropped across the power winding, and none across a load in series with it, as in Figure M-2(a).

If a current is now made to flow in the control winding, it will induce additional flux in the core. When the currents in the control winding and the power winding are flowing in directions that cause the flux due to each winding to add, the total flux drives the core into saturation when it reaches the saturation level. When this happens, the power winding becomes a very low impedance, and practically all of the supply voltage appears across the load, as in Figures M-2(b) and M-2(c).

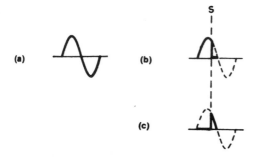

Figure M-2 How a Magnetic Amplifier Works

(a) AC voltage across power winding with no control signal.

(b) AC voltage across power winding with control signal that causes core to saturate at S.

(c) Resultant AC voltage across load.—[6]

The exact moment when the core saturates will depend upon the current level in the control winding. The flux induced by the power winding rises on each half cycle until saturation occurs, and this will be early or late in the half cycle according to the level of flux induced by the control winding. This enables the duration of the power applied to the load during each half cycle to be set as desired.

However, power can flow in the load only on every other half cycle since the core cannot saturate when the fluxes subtract. Consequently, full-wave power utilization requires that *two* saturable core inductors be provided with their power windings connected oppositely, as shown in Figure M-3.

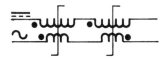

Figure M-3 Full-Wave Magnetic Amplifier—[6]

This also enables the saturated core to be reset to nonsaturation in time for the next cycle that saturates it. As the other core saturates, the current pulse in its power winding induces a current pulse in its control winding. Since both control windings are in series, the pulse also appears in the other control winding, providing the necessary coercive force to reduce the induction to zero.

Magnetic Materials *See* Properties of Materials.

MAGNETIC STORAGE

Magnetic disk storage is widely used for computers of all sizes, and magnetic tape storage is also used by computers, and by video and audio recording devices.

The recording medium used is magnetic iron oxide in a binder, coating a mylar or other material disk or tape. Disks are of the following types:

Type	Used in	Diameter	Maximum capacity
Cartridge	Mainframes	14 in.	30 megabytes
Disk pack	Mainframes	(5 or more)	1000 megabytes
Diskette	Micros	8 in.	600 kilobytes
Diskette	Micros	5.25 in.	300 kilobytes
Diskette	Micros	3.5 in.	100 kilobytes
Hard disk	Micros	8 in.	500 megabytes

Industrial standard tape for reel-to-reel recording of digital data is 0.5 in. wide in lengths of 1200 or 2400 ft.

Tapes for audio recording are 1/4 in. wide, and may be of any length for reel-to-reel recording. Cassettes use narrower tape, usually 0.15 in. Cartridges use 1/4 in. tape.

Videotape cassette recorders (VCRs) use a tape 1/2 in. wide, in which the video information is recorded in slanting tracks on the tape by a revolving head. In broadcasting, a 1-in. tape is used.

The data in each type is recorded on the magnetic material by means of a magnetic head. This is a magnet consisting of soft iron-pole pieces wound with a wire coil. The pole pieces are separated by a small gap which allows the flux induced in the core to spread out so that it penetrates the tape, which is contact with it, or extremely close. As the tape or disk travels past the gap, variations in the magnetic flux due to the information in the signal produce corresponding variations in the magnetization of the magnetic particles.

Diskettes revolve at 3600 rpm; cartridges at 2400 or 3600 rpm. Audio tapes travel at 15, 7.5, 3.75, and 1.875 in. per second. The most usual speed is 7.5 ips. In domestic video systems, the speed is 1.0 ips (but the actual speed of the video recording is much higher).

As mentioned above, video cassette recorders record the video information in slanting tracks on the tape. In this way, a revolving head can achieve the high head-to-tape speed required for video while the tape itself travels at normal speed.

The present generation of machines is of the *helical* type. In the type used for broadcasting, a one-inch-wide tape moves from a supply reel to a take-up reel at 9.6 inches per second (ips). For recording the video, it is wrapped spirally once around a rotating drum. Inside the drum an inner drum, called a scanner, concentric with the outer one, carries one or two heads that make contact with the tape through a slot in the outer drum. Because of the spiral path taken by the tape, the head records on a succession of tracks that slant across the tape. The combined rates of rotation of the scanner and the outer drum give a head-to-tape speed of 999.06 ips.

Domestic systems are condensed versions of the broadcasting system, but use half-inch tape. Both VHS and Beta use two revolving heads. Because of their slower speed, resolution is not so good, but is satisfactory for most purposes.

Magnetism Magnetic phenomena are associated with moving charges. Electrons, when visualized as particles, are said to have an axial spin, and this results in a minute magnetic field, which is called a *Bohr magneton*.

In an iron atom, the *K*, *L*, and *N* shells have equal numbers of electrons with opposite spin directions that cancel. But the *M* shell contains nine electrons spinning in one direction and five in the other, so there are four magnetons in the iron atom. Cobalt has three, and nickel two.

An iron crystal is divided into a large number of *domains* in which the various magnetic directions of the atoms form closed paths. If a crystal is exposed to an external magnetic field, those domains having axes in the favorable direction grow at the expense of the others. This is called domain-wall displacement.

If wall movement makes a domain acquire more internal energy, then the movement will relax again when the external field is removed. But if it results in loss of energy, the movement is irreversible, and only external force can reverse it. This accounts for *hysteresis* and *remanence*. The movement of the domains also deforms the crystal slightly, giving rise to *magnetostriction*.

Magneton *See* Constants.

Magnetron *See* Vacuum Tubes.

Mantissa *See* Mathematical Data.

MATHEMATICAL DATA

With the widespread use of pocket calculators and microcomputers, continued use for mathematical tables would seem minimal. However, many engineers and technicians have complained when such tables have been omitted, so a few of the most important are retained in this section, together with a computer program that can be used instead.

Common Logarithms (Figure M-4)

A common logarithm is the power to which the base 10 must be raised to equal the number. By taking the logarithms of two numbers, they may be added instead of multiplying the numbers together. The four-figure groups in the table are all understood to have a decimal point in front of them. The number in the column headed *N* is the number of which you want the logarithm. If it has only one figure to the left of the decimal point, then the decimal point is assumed to be located between the two figures in that column. If the decimal part of the number has one figure, read the logarithm from the column headed 0; if there is a second figure, read the logarithm from the column headed with that figure on the same line. For example, to find the logarithm of 4.75, find 47 in the *N* column, and move horizontally to the 5 column, which gives you .6767.

Figure M-4 Table of Common Logarithms

N	0	1	2	3	4	5	6	7	8	9	N
10	0000	0043	0086	0128	0170	0212	0253	0294	0334	0374	10
11	0414	0453	0492	0531	0569	0607	0645	0682	0719	0755	11
12	0792	0828	0864	0899	0934	0969	1004	1038	1072	1106	12
13	1139	1173	1206	1239	1271	1303	1335	1367	1399	1430	13
14	1461	1492	1523	1553	1584	1614	1644	1673	1703	1732	14
15	1761	1790	1818	1847	1875	1903	1931	1959	1987	2014	15
16	2041	2068	2095	2122	2148	2175	2201	2227	2253	2279	16
17	2304	2330	2355	2380	2405	2430	2455	2480	2504	2529	17
18	2553	2577	2601	2625	2648	2672	2695	2718	2742	2765	18
19	2788	2810	2833	2856	2878	2900	2923	2945	2967	2989	19
20	3010	3032	3054	3075	3096	3118	3139	3160	3181	3201	20
21	3222	3243	3263	3284	3304	3324	3345	3365	3385	3404	21
22	3424	3444	3464	3483	3502	3522	3541	3560	3579	3598	22
23	3617	3636	3655	3674	3692	3711	3729	3747	3766	3784	23
24	3802	3820	3838	3856	3874	3892	3909	3927	3945	3962	24
25	3979	3997	4014	4031	4048	4065	4082	4099	4116	4133	25
26	4150	4166	4183	4200	4216	4232	4249	4265	4281	4298	26
27	4314	4330	4346	4362	4378	4393	4409	4425	4440	4456	27
28	4472	4487	4502	4518	4533	4548	4564	4579	4594	4609	28
29	4624	4639	4654	4669	4683	4698	4713	4728	4742	4757	29
30	4771	4786	4800	4814	4829	4843	4857	4871	4886	4900	30
31	4914	4928	4942	4955	4969	4983	4997	5011	5024	5038	31
32	5051	5065	5079	5092	5105	5119	5132	5145	5159	5172	32
33	5185	5198	5211	5224	5237	5250	5263	5276	5289	5302	33
34	5315	5328	5340	5353	5366	5378	5391	5403	5416	5428	34
35	5441	5453	5465	5478	5490	5502	5514	5527	5539	5551	35
36	5563	5575	5587	5599	5611	5623	5635	5647	5658	5670	36
37	5682	5694	5705	5717	5729	5740	5752	5763	5775	5786	37
38	5798	5809	5821	5832	5843	5855	5866	5877	5888	5899	38
39	5911	5922	5933	5944	5955	5966	5977	5988	5999	6010	39
40	6021	6031	6042	6053	6064	6075	6085	6096	6107	6117	40
41	6128	6138	6149	6160	6170	6180	6191	6201	6212	6222	41
42	6232	6243	6253	6263	6274	6284	6294	6304	6314	6325	42
43	6335	6345	6355	6365	6375	6385	6395	6405	6415	6425	43
44	6435	6444	6454	6464	6474	6484	6493	6503	6513	6522	44
45	6532	6542	6551	6561	6571	6580	6590	6599	6609	6618	45
46	6628	6637	6646	6656	6665	6675	6684	6693	6702	6712	46
47	6721	6730	6739	6749	6758	6767	6776	6785	6794	6803	47
48	6812	6821	6830	6839	6848	6857	6866	6875	6884	6893	48
49	6902	6911	6920	6928	6937	6946	6955	6964	6972	6981	49
50	6990	6998	7007	7016	7024	7033	7042	7050	7059	7067	50
51	7076	7084	7093	7101	7110	7118	7127	7135	7143	7152	51
52	7160	7168	7177	7185	7193	7202	7210	7218	7226	7235	52
53	7243	7251	7259	7267	7275	7284	7292	7300	7308	7316	53
54	7324	7332	7340	7348	7356	7364	7372	7380	7388	7396	54
N	0	1	2	3	4	5	6	7	8	9	N

Figure M-4 Table of Common Logarithms
(continued)

N	0	1	2	3	4	5	6	7	8	9	N
55	7404	7412	7419	7427	7435	7443	7451	7459	7466	7474	55
56	7482	7490	7497	7505	7513	7520	7528	7536	7543	7551	56
57	7559	7566	7574	7582	7589	7597	7604	7612	7619	7627	57
58	7634	7642	7649	7657	7664	7672	7679	7686	7694	7701	58
59	7709	7716	7723	7731	7738	7745	7752	7760	7767	7774	59
60	7782	7789	7796	7803	7810	7818	7825	7832	7839	7846	60
61	7853	7860	7868	7875	7882	7889	7896	7903	7910	7917	61
62	7924	7931	7938	7945	7952	7959	7966	7973	7980	7987	62
63	7993	8000	8007	8014	8021	8028	8035	8041	8048	8055	63
64	8062	8069	8075	8082	8089	8096	8102	8109	8116	8122	64
65	8129	8136	8142	8149	8156	8162	8169	8176	8182	8189	65
66	8195	8202	8209	8215	8222	8228	8235	8241	8248	8254	66
67	8261	8267	8274	8280	8287	8293	8299	8306	8312	8319	67
68	8325	8331	8338	8344	8351	8357	8363	8370	8376	8382	68
69	8389	8395	8401	8407	8414	8420	8426	8432	8439	8445	69
70	8451	8457	8463	8470	8476	8482	8488	8494	8500	8506	70
71	8513	8519	8525	8531	8537	8543	8549	8555	8561	8567	71
72	8573	8579	8585	8591	8597	8603	8609	8615	8621	8627	72
73	8633	8639	8645	8651	8657	8663	8669	8675	8681	8686	73
74	8692	8698	8704	8710	8716	8722	8727	8733	8739	8745	74
75	8751	8756	8762	8768	8774	8779	8785	8791	8797	8802	75
76	8808	8814	8820	8825	8831	8837	8842	8848	8854	8859	76
77	8865	8871	8876	8882	8887	8893	8899	8904	8910	8915	77
78	8921	8927	8932	8938	8943	8949	8954	8960	8965	8971	78
79	8976	8982	8987	8993	8998	9004	9009	9015	9020	9025	79
80	9031	9036	9042	9047	9053	9058	9063	9069	9074	9080	80
81	9085	9090	9096	9101	9106	9112	9117	9122	9128	9133	81
82	9138	9143	9149	9154	9159	9165	9170	9175	9180	9186	82
83	9191	9196	9201	9206	9212	9217	9222	9227	9232	9238	83
84	9243	9248	9253	9258	9263	9269	9274	9279	9284	9289	84
85	9294	9299	9304	9310	9315	9320	9325	9330	9335	9340	85
86	9345	9350	9355	9360	9365	9370	9375	9380	9385	9390	86
87	9395	9400	9405	9410	9415	9420	9425	9430	9435	9440	87
88	9445	9450	9455	9460	9465	9469	9474	9479	9484	9489	88
89	9494	9499	9504	9509	9513	9518	9523	9528	9533	9538	89
90	9542	9547	9552	9557	9562	9567	9571	9576	9581	9586	90
91	9590	9595	9600	9605	9610	9614	9619	9624	9628	9633	91
92	9638	9643	9647	9652	9657	9661	9666	9671	9676	9680	92
93	9685	9690	9694	9699	9704	9708	9713	9717	9722	9727	93
94	9731	9736	9741	9745	9750	9754	9759	9764	9768	9773	94
95	9777	9782	9786	9791	9796	9800	9805	9809	9814	9818	95
96	9823	9827	9832	9836	9841	9845	9850	9854	9859	9863	96
97	9868	9872	9877	9881	9886	9890	9895	9899	9903	9908	97
98	9912	9917	9921	9926	9930	9934	9939	9943	9948	9952	98
99	9956	9961	9965	9970	9974	9978	9983	9987	9991	9996	99
N	0	1	2	3	4	5	6	7	8	9	N

If the number is higher than 9.99, for example 47.5, you find 47 in the N column, and move horizontally to the 5 column to get .6767 as before. However, you now place a 1 in front of the number from the table, giving 1.6767, because the number in scientific notation is 4.75×10^1. Similarly, if the number is 475, you place a 2 in front of the number from the table, giving 2.6767, because the number in scientific notation is 4.75 $\times 10^2$.

The part of the logarithm to the right of the decimal point (.6767) is called the *mantissa*. The part to the left of the decimal point is called the *characteristic*.

If the number is all decimal, as in 0.475, you find the mantissa from the table as before, but the characteristic is now -1, since the number in scientific notation would be 4.75×10^{-1}. Similarly, if the number is 0.00475, its characteristic would be -3, since the number in scientific notation is 4.75×10^{-3}. Negative characteristics are written with a bar above instead of a minus sign in front, so that no one will think the whole logarithm is negative. For instance, $\log 4.75 \times 10^{-3} = \overline{3}.6767$.

The antilogarithm is the number of which it is the logarithm. The antilog of .6767 is therefore 4.75. To get it, you just work the table backwards: look for the closest logarithm, and read the figure in the N column opposite, and the figure at the head of the column. For example, if you had the logarithm 2.8774, you would first find .8774, which is in the 4 column opposite 75. This would give you 7.54. The characteristic is 2; therefore the antiogarithm is 7.54×10^2, or 754.

The abbreviation log is used for common logarithms.

Natural Logarithms (Figure M-5)

Natural, or Napierian, logarithms are powers to the base ε. This is a constant (Euler's number), and with the approximate value of 2.71828. The tables are used in the same way as those for common logarithms, except that the whole logarithm (characteristic and mantissa) is given.

Figure M-5 Table of Natural Logarithms

N	0	1	2	3	4	5	6	7	8	9
0	$-\infty$	-6.9078	-6.2146	-5.8091	-5.5215	-5.2983	-5.1160	-4.9618	-4.8283	-4.7105
.01	-4.6052	-4.5099	-4.4228	-4.3428	-4.2687	-4.1997	-4.1352	-4.0745	-4.0174	-3.9633
.02	-3.9120	-3.8632	-3.8167	-3.7723	-3.7297	-3.6889	-3.6497	-3.6119	-3.5756	-3.5405
.03	-3.5066	-3.4738	-3.4420	-3.4112	-3.3814	-3.3524	-3.3242	-3.2968	-3.2702	-3.2442
.04	-3.2189	-3.1942	-3.1701	-3.1466	-3.1236	-3.1011	-3.0791	-3.0576	-3.0366	-3.0159
.05	-2.9957	-2.9759	-2.9565	-2.9375	-2.9188	-2.9004	-2.8824	-2.8647	-2.8473	-2.8302
.06	-2.8134	-2.7969	-2.7806	-2.7646	-2.7489	-2.7334	-2.7181	-2.7031	-2.6882	-2.6736
.07	-2.6593	-2.6451	-2.6311	-2.6173	-2.6037	-2.5903	-2.5770	-2.5640	-2.5510	-2.5383
.08	-2.5257	-2.5133	-2.5010	-2.4889	-2.4769	-2.4651	-2.4534	-2.4418	-2.4304	-2.4191
.09	-2.4079	-2.3969	-2.3860	-2.3752	-2.3645	-2.3539	-2.3434	-2.3330	-2.3228	-2.3126
.1	-2.3026	-2.2926	-2.2828	-2.2730	-2.2634	-2.2538	-2.2443	-2.2349	-2.2256	-2.2164
.11	-2.2073	-2.1982	-2.1893	-2.1804	-2.1716	-2.1628	-2.1542	-2.1456	-2.1371	-2.1286
.12	-2.1203	-2.1120	-2.1037	-2.0956	-2.0875	-2.0794	-2.0715	-2.0636	-2.0557	-2.0479
.13	-2.0402	-2.0326	-2.0250	-2.0174	-2.0099	-2.0025	-1.9951	-1.9878	-1.9805	-1.9733
.14	-1.9661	-1.9590	-1.9519	-1.9449	-1.9379	-1.9310	-1.9241	-1.9173	-1.9105	-1.9038
.15	-1.8971	-1.8905	-1.8839	-1.8773	-1.8708	-1.8643	-1.8579	-1.8515	-1.8452	-1.8389
.16	-1.8326	-1.8264	-1.8202	-1.8140	-1.8079	-1.8018	-1.7958	-1.7898	-1.7838	-1.7779
.17	-1.7720	-1.7661	-1.7603	-1.7545	-1.7487	-1.7430	-1.7373	-1.7316	-1.7260	-1.7204
.18	-1.7148	-1.7093	-1.7037	-1.6983	-1.6928	-1.6874	-1.6820	-1.6766	-1.6713	-1.6660
.19	-1.6607	-1.6555	-1.6503	-1.6451	-1.6399	-1.6348	-1.6296	-1.6246	-1.6195	-1.6144
.2	-1.6094	-1.6044	-1.5995	-1.5945	-1.5896	-1.5847	-1.5799	-1.5750	-1.5702	-1.5654
.21	-1.5606	-1.5559	-1.5512	-1.5465	-1.5418	-1.5371	-1.5325	-1.5279	-1.5233	-1.5187
.22	-1.5141	-1.5096	-1.5051	-1.5006	-1.4961	-1.4917	-1.4872	-1.4828	-1.4784	-1.4740
.23	-1.4697	-1.4653	-1.4610	-1.4567	-1.4524	-1.4482	-1.4439	-1.4397	-1.4355	-1.4313
.24	-1.4271	-1.4230	-1.4188	-1.4147	-1.4106	-1.4065	-1.4024	-1.3984	-1.3943	-1.3903
.25	-1.3863	-1.3823	-1.3783	-1.3744	-1.3704	-1.3665	-1.3626	-1.3587	-1.3548	-1.3509
.26	-1.3471	-1.3432	-1.3394	-1.3356	-1.3318	-1.3280	-1.3243	-1.3205	-1.3168	-1.3130
.27	-1.3093	-1.3056	-1.3020	-1.2983	-1.2946	-1.2910	-1.2874	-1.2837	-1.2801	-1.2765
.28	-1.2730	-1.2694	-1.2658	-1.2623	-1.2588	-1.2553	-1.2518	-1.2483	-1.2448	-1.2413
.29	-1.2379	-1.2344	-1.2310	-1.2276	-1.2242	-1.2208	-1.2174	-1.2140	-1.2107	-1.2073
.3	-1.2040	-1.2006	-1.1973	-1.1940	-1.1907	-1.1874	-1.1842	-1.1809	-1.1777	-1.1744
.31	-1.1712	-1.1680	-1.1648	-1.1616	-1.1584	-1.1552	-1.1520	-1.1489	-1.1457	-1.1426
.32	-1.1394	-1.1363	-1.1332	-1.1301	-1.1270	-1.1239	-1.1209	-1.1178	-1.1147	-1.1117
.33	-1.1087	-1.1056	-1.1026	-1.0996	-1.0966	-1.0936	-1.0906	-1.0877	-1.0847	-1.0818
.34	-1.0788	-1.0759	-1.0729	-1.0700	-1.0671	-1.0642	-1.0613	-1.0584	-1.0556	-1.0527
.35	-1.0498	-1.0470	-1.0441	-1.0413	-1.0385	-1.0356	-1.0328	-1.0300	-1.0272	-1.0244
.36	-1.0217	-1.0189	-1.0161	-1.0134	-1.0106	-1.0079	-1.0051	-1.0024	-0.9997	-0.9970
.37	-0.9943	-0.9916	-0.9889	-0.9862	-0.9835	-0.9808	-0.9782	-0.9755	-0.9729	-0.9702
.38	-0.9676	-0.9650	-0.9623	-0.9597	-0.9571	-0.9545	-0.9519	-0.9493	-0.9468	-0.9442
.39	-0.9416	-0.9391	-0.9365	-0.9339	-0.9314	-0.9289	-0.9263	-0.9238	-0.9213	-0.9188
.4	-0.9163	-0.9138	-0.9113	-0.9088	-0.9063	-0.9039	-0.9014	-0.8989	-0.8965	-0.8940
.41	-0.8916	-0.8892	-0.8867	-0.8843	-0.8819	-0.8795	-0.8771	-0.8747	-0.8723	-0.8699
.42	-0.8675	-0.8651	-0.8628	-0.8604	-0.8580	-0.8557	-0.8533	-0.8510	-0.8486	-0.8463
.43	-0.8440	-0.8417	-0.8393	-0.8370	-0.8347	-0.8324	-0.8301	-0.8278	-0.8255	-0.8233
.44	-0.8210	-0.8187	-0.8165	-0.8142	-0.8119	-0.8097	-0.8074	-0.8052	-0.8030	-0.8007
.45	-0.7985	-0.7963	-0.7941	-0.7919	-0.7897	-0.7875	-0.7853	-0.7831	-0.7809	-0.7787
.46	-0.7765	-0.7744	-0.7722	-0.7700	-0.7679	-0.7657	-0.7636	-0.7614	-0.7593	-0.7572
.47	-0.7550	-0.7529	-0.7508	-0.7487	-0.7466	-0.7444	-0.7423	-0.7402	-0.7382	-0.7361
.48	-0.7340	-0.7319	-0.7298	-0.7277	-0.7257	-0.7236	-0.7216	-0.7195	-0.7174	-0.7154
.49	-0.7134	-0.7113	-0.7093	-0.7073	-0.7052	-0.7032	-0.7012	-0.6992	-0.6972	-0.6952
N	0	1	2	3	4	5	6	7	8	9

Figure M-5 Table of Natural Logarithms
(continued)

N	0	1	2	3	4	5	6	7	8	9
.5	-0.6931	-0.6911	-0.6892	-0.6872	-0.6852	-0.6832	-0.6812	-0.6792	-0.6773	-0.6753
.51	-0.6733	-0.6714	-0.6694	-0.6675	-0.6655	-0.6636	-0.6616	-0.6597	-0.6578	-0.6559
.52	-0.6539	-0.6520	-0.6501	-0.6482	-0.6463	-0.6444	-0.6425	-0.6406	-0.6387	-0.6368
.53	-0.6349	-0.6330	-0.6311	-0.6292	-0.6274	-0.6255	-0.6236	-0.6218	-0.6199	-0.6180
.54	-0.6162	-0.6143	-0.6125	-0.6106	-0.6088	-0.6070	-0.6051	-0.6033	-0.6015	-0.5997
.55	-0.5978	-0.5960	-0.5942	-0.5924	-0.5906	-0.5888	-0.5870	-0.5852	-0.5834	-0.5816
.56	-0.5798	-0.5780	-0.5763	-0.5745	-0.5727	-0.5709	-0.5692	-0.5674	-0.5656	-0.5639
.57	-0.5621	-0.5604	-0.5586	-0.5569	-0.5551	-0.5534	-0.5516	-0.5499	-0.5482	-0.5465
.58	-0.5447	-0.5430	-0.5413	-0.5396	-0.5379	-0.5361	-0.5344	-0.5327	-0.5310	-0.5293
.59	-0.5276	-0.5259	-0.5243	-0.5226	-0.5209	-0.5192	-0.5175	-0.5158	-0.5142	-0.5125
.6	-0.5108	-0.5092	-0.5075	-0.5058	-0.5042	-0.5025	-0.5009	-0.4992	-0.4976	-0.4959
.61	-0.4943	-0.4927	-0.4910	-0.4894	-0.4878	-0.4861	-0.4845	-0.4829	-0.4813	-0.4797
.62	-0.4780	-0.4764	-0.4748	-0.4732	-0.4716	-0.4700	-0.4684	-0.4668	-0.4652	-0.4636
.63	-0.4620	-0.4605	-0.4589	-0.4573	-0.4557	-0.4541	-0.4526	-0.4510	-0.4494	-0.4479
.64	-0.4463	-0.4447	-0.4432	-0.4416	-0.4401	-0.4385	-0.4370	-0.4354	-0.4339	-0.4323
.65	-0.4308	-0.4292	-0.4277	-0.4262	-0.4247	-0.4231	-0.4216	-0.4201	-0.4186	-0.4170
.66	-0.4155	-0.4140	-0.4125	-0.4110	-0.4095	-0.4080	-0.4065	-0.4050	-0.4035	-0.4020
.67	-0.4005	-0.3990	-0.3975	-0.3960	-0.3945	-0.3930	-0.3916	-0.3901	-0.3886	-0.3871
.68	-0.3857	-0.3842	-0.3827	-0.3813	-0.3798	-0.3783	-0.3769	-0.3754	-0.3740	-0.3725
.69	-0.3711	-0.3696	-0.3682	-0.3667	-0.3653	-0.3638	-0.3624	-0.3610	-0.3595	-0.3581
.7	-0.3567	-0.3553	-0.3538	-0.3524	-0.3510	-0.3496	-0.3481	-0.3467	-0.3453	-0.3439
.71	-0.3425	-0.3411	-0.3397	-0.3383	-0.3369	-0.3355	-0.3341	-0.3327	-0.3313	-0.3299
.72	-0.3285	-0.3271	-0.3257	-0.3244	-0.3230	-0.3216	-0.3202	-0.3188	-0.3175	-0.3161
.73	-0.3147	-0.3133	-0.3120	-0.3106	-0.3093	-0.3079	-0.3065	-0.3052	-0.3038	-0.3025
.74	-0.3011	-0.2998	-0.2984	-0.2971	-0.2957	-0.2944	-0.2930	-0.2917	-0.2904	-0.2890
.75	-0.2877	-0.2864	-0.2850	-0.2837	-0.2824	-0.2810	-0.2797	-0.2784	-0.2771	-0.2758
.76	-0.2744	-0.2731	-0.2718	-0.2705	-0.2692	-0.2679	-0.2666	-0.2653	-0.2640	-0.2627
.77	-0.2614	-0.2601	-0.2588	-0.2575	-0.2562	-0.2549	-0.2536	-0.2523	-0.2510	-0.2497
.78	-0.2485	-0.2472	-0.2459	-0.2446	-0.2434	-0.2421	-0.2408	-0.2395	-0.2383	-0.2370
.79	-0.2357	-0.2345	-0.2332	-0.2319	-0.2307	-0.2294	-0.2282	-0.2269	-0.2257	-0.2244
.8	-0.2231	-0.2219	-0.2207	-0.2194	-0.2182	-0.2169	-0.2157	-0.2144	-0.2132	-0.2120
.81	-0.2107	-0.2095	-0.2083	-0.2070	-0.2058	-0.2046	-0.2033	-0.2021	-0.2009	-0.1997
.82	-0.1985	-0.1972	-0.1960	-0.1948	-0.1936	-0.1924	-0.1912	-0.1900	-0.1887	-0.1875
.83	-0.1863	-0.1851	-0.1839	-0.1827	-0.1815	-0.1803	-0.1791	-0.1779	-0.1767	-0.1755
.84	-0.1744	-0.1732	-0.1720	-0.1708	-0.1696	-0.1684	-0.1672	-0.1661	-0.1649	-0.1637
.85	-0.1625	-0.1613	-0.1602	-0.1590	-0.1578	-0.1567	-0.1555	-0.1543	-0.1532	-0.1520
.86	-0.1508	-0.1497	-0.1485	-0.1473	-0.1462	-0.1450	-0.1439	-0.1427	-0.1416	-0.1404
.87	-0.1393	-0.1381	-0.1370	-0.1358	-0.1347	-0.1335	-0.1324	-0.1313	-0.1301	-0.1290
.88	-0.1278	-0.1267	-0.1256	-0.1244	-0.1233	-0.1222	-0.1210	-0.1199	-0.1188	-0.1177
.89	-0.1165	-0.1154	-0.1143	-0.1132	-0.1121	-0.1109	-0.1098	-0.1087	-0.1076	-0.1065
.9	-0.1054	-0.1043	-0.1031	-0.1020	-0.1009	-0.0998	-0.0987	-0.0976	-0.0965	-0.0954
.91	-0.0943	-0.0932	-0.0921	-0.0910	-0.0899	-0.0888	-0.0877	-0.0867	-0.0856	-0.0845
.92	-0.0834	-0.0823	-0.0812	-0.0801	-0.0790	-0.0780	-0.0769	-0.0758	-0.0747	-0.0737
.93	-0.0726	-0.0715	-0.0704	-0.0694	-0.0683	-0.0672	-0.0661	-0.0651	-0.0640	-0.0629
.94	-0.0619	-0.0608	-0.0598	-0.0587	-0.0576	-0.0566	-0.0555	-0.0545	-0.0534	-0.0524
.95	-0.0513	-0.0502	-0.0492	-0.0481	-0.0471	-0.0461	-0.0450	-0.0440	-0.0429	-0.0419
.96	-0.0408	-0.0398	-0.0387	-0.0377	-0.0367	-0.0356	-0.0346	-0.0336	-0.0325	-0.0315
.97	-0.0305	-0.0294	-0.0284	-0.0274	-0.0264	-0.0253	-0.0243	-0.0233	-0.0223	-0.0212
.98	-0.0202	-0.0192	-0.0182	-0.0172	-0.0161	-0.0151	-0.0141	-0.0131	-0.0121	-0.0111
.99	-0.0101	-0.0090	-0.0080	-0.0070	-0.0060	-0.0050	-0.0040	-0.0030	-0.0020	-0.0010
N	0	1	2	3	4	5	6	7	8	9

Figure M-5 Table of Natural Logarithms
(continued)

N	0	1	2	3	4	5	6	7	8	9
1	0.0000	0.0100	0.0198	0.0296	0.0392	0.0488	0.0583	0.0677	0.0770	0.0862
1.1	0.0953	0.1044	0.1133	0.1222	0.1310	0.1398	0.1484	0.1570	0.1655	0.1740
1.2	0.1823	0.1906	0.1989	0.2070	0.2151	0.2231	0.2311	0.2390	0.2469	0.2546
1.3	0.2624	0.2700	0.2776	0.2852	0.2927	0.3001	0.3075	0.3148	0.3221	0.3293
1.4	0.3365	0.3436	0.3507	0.3577	0.3646	0.3716	0.3784	0.3853	0.3920	0.3988
1.5	0.4055	0.4121	0.4187	0.4253	0.4318	0.4383	0.4447	0.4511	0.4574	0.4637
1.6	0.4700	0.4762	0.4824	0.4886	0.4947	0.5008	0.5068	0.5128	0.5188	0.5247
1.7	0.5306	0.5365	0.5423	0.5481	0.5539	0.5596	0.5653	0.5710	0.5766	0.5822
1.8	0.5878	0.5933	0.5988	0.6043	0.6098	0.6152	0.6206	0.6259	0.6313	0.6366
1.9	0.6419	0.6471	0.6523	0.6575	0.6627	0.6678	0.6729	0.6780	0.6831	0.6881
2	0.6931	0.6981	0.7031	0.7080	0.7129	0.7178	0.7227	0.7275	0.7324	0.7372
2.1	0.7419	0.7467	0.7514	0.7561	0.7608	0.7655	0.7701	0.7747	0.7793	0.7839
2.2	0.7885	0.7930	0.7975	0.8020	0.8065	0.8109	0.8154	0.8198	0.8242	0.8286
2.3	0.8329	0.8372	0.8416	0.8459	0.8502	0.8544	0.8587	0.8629	0.8671	0.8713
2.4	0.8755	0.8796	0.8838	0.8879	0.8920	0.8961	0.9002	0.9042	0.9083	0.9123
2.5	0.9163	0.9203	0.9243	0.9282	0.9322	0.9361	0.9400	0.9439	0.9478	0.9517
2.6	0.9555	0.9593	0.9632	0.9670	0.9708	0.9746	0.9783	0.9821	0.9858	0.9895
2.7	0.9933	0.9969	1.0006	1.0043	1.0080	1.0116	1.0152	1.0188	1.0225	1.0260
2.8	1.0296	1.0332	1.0367	1.0403	1.0438	1.0473	1.0508	1.0543	1.0578	1.0613
2.9	1.0647	1.0682	1.0716	1.0750	1.0784	1.0818	1.0852	1.0886	1.0919	1.0953
3	1.0986	1.1019	1.1053	1.1086	1.1119	1.1151	1.1184	1.1217	1.1249	1.1282
3.1	1.1314	1.1346	1.1378	1.1410	1.1442	1.1474	1.1506	1.1537	1.1569	1.1600
3.2	1.1632	1.1663	1.1694	1.1725	1.1756	1.1787	1.1817	1.1848	1.1878	1.1909
3.3	1.1939	1.1969	1.2000	1.2030	1.2060	1.2090	1.2119	1.2149	1.2179	1.2208
3.4	1.2238	1.2267	1.2296	1.2326	1.2355	1.2384	1.2413	1.2442	1.2470	1.2499
3.5	1.2528	1.2556	1.2585	1.2613	1.2641	1.2669	1.2698	1.2726	1.2754	1.2782
3.6	1.2809	1.2837	1.2865	1.2892	1.2920	1.2947	1.2975	1.3002	1.3029	1.3056
3.7	1.3083	1.3110	1.3137	1.3164	1.3191	1.3218	1.3244	1.3271	1.3297	1.3324
3.8	1.3350	1.3376	1.3402	1.3429	1.3455	1.3481	1.3507	1.3533	1.3558	1.3584
3.9	1.3610	1.3635	1.3661	1.3686	1.3712	1.3737	1.3762	1.3788	1.3813	1.3838
4	1.3863	1.3888	1.3913	1.3938	1.3962	1.3987	1.4012	1.4036	1.4061	1.4085
4.1	1.4110	1.4134	1.4159	1.4183	1.4207	1.4231	1.4255	1.4279	1.4303	1.4327
4.2	1.4351	1.4375	1.4398	1.4422	1.4446	1.4469	1.4493	1.4516	1.4540	1.4563
4.3	1.4586	1.4609	1.4633	1.4656	1.4679	1.4702	1.4725	1.4748	1.4771	1.4793
4.4	1.4816	1.4839	1.4861	1.4884	1.4907	1.4929	1.4952	1.4974	1.4996	1.5019
4.5	1.5041	1.5063	1.5085	1.5107	1.5129	1.5151	1.5173	1.5195	1.5217	1.5239
4.6	1.5261	1.5282	1.5304	1.5326	1.5347	1.5369	1.5390	1.5412	1.5433	1.5454
4.7	1.5476	1.5497	1.5518	1.5539	1.5560	1.5581	1.5603	1.5623	1.5644	1.5665
4.8	1.5686	1.5707	1.5728	1.5748	1.5769	1.5790	1.5810	1.5831	1.5851	1.5872
4.9	1.5892	1.5913	1.5933	1.5953	1.5974	1.5994	1.6014	1.6034	1.6054	1.6074
N	0	1	2	3	4	5	6	7	8	9

Figure M-5 Table of Natural Logarithms
(continued)

N	0	1	2	3	4	5	6	7	8	9
5	1.6094	1.6114	1.6134	1.6154	1.6174	1.6194	1.6214	1.6233	1.6253	1.6273
5.1	1.6292	1.6312	1.6332	1.6351	1.6371	1.6390	1.6409	1.6429	1.6448	1.6467
5.2	1.6487	1.6506	1.6525	1.6544	1.6563	1.6582	1.6601	1.6620	1.6639	1.6658
5.3	1.6677	1.6696	1.6715	1.6734	1.6752	1.6771	1.6790	1.6808	1.6827	1.6845
5.4	1.6864	1.6883	1.6901	1.6919	1.6938	1.6956	1.6975	1.6993	1.7011	1.7029
5.5	1.7048	1.7066	1.7084	1.7102	1.7120	1.7138	1.7156	1.7174	1.7192	1.7210
5.6	1.7228	1.7246	1.7263	1.7281	1.7299	1.7317	1.7334	1.7352	1.7370	1.7387
5.7	1.7405	1.7422	1.7440	1.7457	1.7475	1.7492	1.7509	1.7527	1.7544	1.7561
5.8	1.7579	1.7596	1.7613	1.7630	1.7647	1.7664	1.7682	1.7699	1.7716	1.7733
5.9	1.7750	1.7766	1.7783	1.7800	1.7817	1.7834	1.7851	1.7868	1.7884	1.7901
6	1.7918	1.7934	1.7951	1.7968	1.7984	1.8001	1.8017	1.8034	1.8050	1.8067
6.1	1.8083	1.8099	1.8116	1.8132	1.8148	1.8165	1.8181	1.8197	1.8213	1.8229
6.2	1.8246	1.8262	1.8278	1.8294	1.8310	1.8326	1.8342	1.8358	1.8374	1.8390
6.3	1.8406	1.8421	1.8437	1.8453	1.8469	1.8485	1.8500	1.8516	1.8532	1.8547
6.4	1.8563	1.8579	1.8594	1.8610	1.8625	1.8641	1.8656	1.8672	1.8687	1.8703
6.5	1.8718	1.8733	1.8749	1.8764	1.8779	1.8795	1.8810	1.8825	1.8840	1.8856
6.6	1.8871	1.8886	1.8901	1.8916	1.8931	1.8946	1.8961	1.8976	1.8991	1.9006
6.7	1.9021	1.9036	1.9051	1.9066	1.9081	1.9095	1.9110	1.9125	1.9140	1.9155
6.8	1.9169	1.9184	1.9199	1.9213	1.9228	1.9243	1.9257	1.9272	1.9286	1.9301
6.9	1.9315	1.9330	1.9344	1.9359	1.9373	1.9387	1.9402	1.9416	1.9431	1.9445
7	1.9459	1.9473	1.9488	1.9502	1.9516	1.9530	1.9545	1.9559	1.9573	1.9587
7.1	1.9601	1.9615	1.9629	1.9643	1.9657	1.9671	1.9685	1.9699	1.9713	1.9727
7.2	1.9741	1.9755	1.9769	1.9782	1.9796	1.9810	1.9824	1.9838	1.9851	1.9865
7.3	1.9879	1.9893	1.9906	1.9920	1.9933	1.9947	1.9961	1.9974	1.9988	2.0001
7.4	2.0015	2.0028	2.0042	2.0055	2.0069	2.0082	2.0096	2.0109	2.0122	2.0136
7.5	2.0149	2.0162	2.0176	2.0189	2.0202	2.0216	2.0229	2.0242	2.0255	2.0268
7.6	2.0282	2.0295	2.0308	2.0321	2.0334	2.0347	2.0360	2.0373	2.0386	2.0399
7.7	2.0412	2.0425	2.0438	2.0451	2.0464	2.0477	2.0490	2.0503	2.0516	2.0528
7.8	2.0541	2.0554	2.0567	2.0580	2.0592	2.0605	2.0618	2.0631	2.0643	2.0656
7.9	2.0669	2.0681	2.0694	2.0707	2.0719	2.0732	2.0744	2.0757	2.0769	2.0782
8	2.0795	2.0807	2.0819	2.0832	2.0844	2.0857	2.0869	2.0882	2.0894	2.0906
8.1	2.0919	2.0931	2.0943	2.0956	2.0968	2.0980	2.0993	2.1005	2.1017	2.1029
8.2	2.1041	2.1054	2.1066	2.1078	2.1090	2.1102	2.1114	2.1126	2.1139	2.1151
8.3	2.1163	2.1175	2.1187	2.1199	2.1211	2.1223	2.1235	2.1247	2.1259	2.1270
8.4	2.1282	2.1294	2.1306	2.1318	2.1330	2.1342	2.1354	2.1365	2.1377	2.1389
8.5	2.1401	2.1413	2.1424	2.1436	2.1448	2.1459	2.1471	2.1483	2.1494	2.1506
8.6	2.1518	2.1529	2.1541	2.1553	2.1564	2.1576	2.1587	2.1599	2.1610	2.1622
8.7	2.1633	2.1645	2.1656	2.1668	2.1679	2.1691	2.1702	2.1713	2.1725	2.1736
8.8	2.1748	2.1759	2.1770	2.1782	2.1793	2.1804	2.1816	2.1827	2.1838	2.1849
8.9	2.1861	2.1872	2.1883	2.1894	2.1905	2.1917	2.1928	2.1939	2.1950	2.1961
9	2.1972	2.1983	2.1995	2.2006	2.2017	2.2028	2.2039	2.2050	2.2061	2.2072
9.1	2.2083	2.2094	2.2105	2.2116	2.2127	2.2138	2.2149	2.2159	2.2170	2.2181
9.2	2.2192	2.2203	2.2214	2.2225	2.2236	2.2246	2.2257	2.2268	2.2279	2.2289
9.3	2.2300	2.2311	2.2322	2.2332	2.2343	2.2354	2.2365	2.2375	2.2386	2.2397
9.4	2.2407	2.2418	2.2428	2.2439	2.2450	2.2460	2.2471	2.2481	2.2492	2.2502
9.5	2.2513	2.2524	2.2534	2.2545	2.2555	2.2566	2.2576	2.2586	2.2597	2.2607
9.6	2.2618	2.2628	2.2639	2.2649	2.2659	2.2670	2.2680	2.2690	2.2701	2.2711
9.7	2.2721	2.2732	2.2742	2.2752	2.2763	2.2773	2.2783	2.2793	2.2804	2.2814
9.8	2.2824	2.2834	2.2844	2.2855	2.2865	2.2875	2.2885	2.2895	2.2905	2.2915
9.9	2.2925	2.2936	2.2946	2.2956	2.2966	2.2976	2.2986	2.2996	2.3006	2.3016
N	0	1	2	3	4	5	6	7	8	9

Figure M-5 Table of Natural Logarithms
(continued)

N	0	1	2	3	4	5	6	7	8	9
10	2.3026	2.3125	2.3224	2.3321	2.3418	2.3514	2.3609	2.3702	2.3795	2.3888
11	2.3979	2.4069	2.4159	2.4248	2.4336	2.4423	2.4510	2.4596	2.4681	2.4765
12	2.4849	2.4932	2.5014	2.5096	2.5177	2.5257	2.5337	2.5416	2.5494	2.5572
13	2.5650	2.5726	2.5802	2.5878	2.5953	2.6027	2.6101	2.6174	2.6247	2.6319
14	2.6391	2.6462	2.6532	2.6603	2.6672	2.6742	2.6810	2.6878	2.6946	2.7014
15	2.7081	2.7147	2.7213	2.7279	2.7344	2.7408	2.7473	2.7537	2.7600	2.7663
16	2.7726	2.7788	2.7850	2.7912	2.7973	2.8034	2.8094	2.8154	2.8214	2.8273
17	2.8332	2.8391	2.8449	2.8507	2.8565	2.8622	2.8679	2.8736	2.8792	2.8848
18	2.8904	2.8959	2.9014	2.9069	2.9124	2.9178	2.9232	2.9285	2.9339	2.9392
19	2.9444	2.9497	2.9549	2.9601	2.9653	2.9704	2.9755	2.9806	2.9857	2.9907
20	2.9957	3.0007	3.0057	3.0106	3.0155	3.0204	3.0253	3.0301	3.0350	3.0398
21	3.0445	3.0493	3.0540	3.0587	3.0634	3.0681	3.0727	3.0773	3.0819	3.0865
22	3.0910	3.0956	3.1001	3.1046	3.1091	3.1135	3.1180	3.1224	3.1268	3.1311
23	3.1355	3.1398	3.1442	3.1485	3.1527	3.1570	3.1612	3.1655	3.1697	3.1739
24	3.1781	3.1822	3.1864	3.1905	3.1946	3.1987	3.2027	3.2068	3.2108	3.2149
25	3.2189	3.2229	3.2268	3.2308	3.2348	3.2387	3.2426	3.2465	3.2504	3.2542
26	3.2581	3.2619	3.2658	3.2696	3.2734	3.2771	3.2809	3.2847	3.2884	3.2921
27	3.2958	3.2995	3.3032	3.3069	3.3105	3.3142	3.3178	3.3214	3.3250	3.3286
28	3.3322	3.3358	3.3393	3.3429	3.3464	3.3499	3.3534	3.3569	3.3604	3.3638
29	3.3673	3.3707	3.3742	3.3776	3.3810	3.3844	3.3878	3.3911	3.3945	3.3979
30	3.4012	3.4045	3.4078	3.4112	3.4144	3.4177	3.4210	3.4243	3.4275	3.4308
31	3.4340	3.4372	3.4404	3.4436	3.4468	3.4500	3.4532	3.4563	3.4595	3.4626
32	3.4657	3.4689	3.4720	3.4751	3.4782	3.4812	3.4843	3.4874	3.4904	3.4935
33	3.4965	3.4995	3.5026	3.5056	3.5086	3.5115	3.5145	3.5175	3.5205	3.5234
34	3.5264	3.5293	3.5322	3.5351	3.5381	3.5410	3.5439	3.5467	3.5496	3.5525
35	3.5553	3.5582	3.5610	3.5639	3.5667	3.5695	3.5723	3.5752	3.5779	3.5807
36	3.5835	3.5863	3.5891	3.5918	3.5946	3.5973	3.6000	3.6028	3.6055	3.6082
37	3.6109	3.6136	3.6163	3.6190	3.6217	3.6243	3.6270	3.6297	3.6323	3.6350
38	3.6376	3.6402	3.6428	3.6455	3.6481	3.6507	3.6533	3.6558	3.6584	3.6610
39	3.6636	3.6661	3.6687	3.6712	3.6738	3.6763	3.6788	3.6814	3.6839	3.6864
40	3.6889	3.6914	3.6939	3.6964	3.6988	3.7013	3.7038	3.7062	3.7087	3.7111
41	3.7136	3.7160	3.7184	3.7209	3.7233	3.7257	3.7281	3.7305	3.7329	3.7353
42	3.7377	3.7400	3.7424	3.7448	3.7471	3.7495	3.7519	3.7542	3.7565	3.7589
43	3.7612	3.7635	3.7658	3.7682	3.7705	3.7728	3.7751	3.7773	3.7796	3.7819
44	3.7842	3.7865	3.7887	3.7910	3.7932	3.7955	3.7977	3.8000	3.8022	3.8044
45	3.8067	3.8089	3.8111	3.8133	3.8155	3.8177	3.8199	3.8221	3.8243	3.8265
46	3.8286	3.8308	3.8330	3.8351	3.8373	3.8394	3.8416	3.8437	3.8459	3.8480
47	3.8501	3.8523	3.8544	3.8565	3.8586	3.8607	3.8628	3.8649	3.8670	3.8691
48	3.8712	3.8733	3.8754	3.8774	3.8795	3.8816	3.8836	3.8857	3.8877	3.8898
49	3.8918	3.8939	3.8959	3.8979	3.8999	3.9020	3.9040	3.9060	3.9080	3.9100
N	0	1	2	3	4	5	6	7	8	9

Figure M-5 Table of Natural Logarithms
(continued)

N	0	1	2	3	4	5	6	7	8	9
50	3.9120	3.9140	3.9160	3.9180	3.9200	3.9220	3.9240	3.9259	3.9279	3.9299
51	3.9318	3.9338	3.9357	3.9377	3.9396	3.9416	3.9435	3.9455	3.9474	3.9493
52	3.9512	3.9532	3.9551	3.9570	3.9589	3.9608	3.9627	3.9646	3.9665	3.9684
53	3.9703	3.9722	3.9741	3.9759	3.9778	3.9797	3.9815	3.9834	3.9853	3.9871
54	3.9890	3.9908	3.9927	3.9945	3.9964	3.9982	4.0000	4.0019	4.0037	4.0055
55	4.0073	4.0091	4.0110	4.0128	4.0146	4.0164	4.0182	4.0200	4.0218	4.0236
56	4.0254	4.0271	4.0289	4.0307	4.0325	4.0342	4.0360	4.0378	4.0395	4.0413
57	4.0430	4.0448	4.0466	4.0483	4.0500	4.0518	4.0535	4.0553	4.0570	4.0587
58	4.0604	4.0622	4.0639	4.0656	4.0673	4.0690	4.0707	4.0724	4.0741	4.0758
59	4.0775	4.0792	4.0809	4.0826	4.0843	4.0860	4.0877	4.0893	4.0910	4.0927
60	4.0943	4.0960	4.0977	4.0993	4.1010	4.1026	4.1043	4.1059	4.1076	4.1092
61	4.1109	4.1125	4.1141	4.1158	4.1174	4.1190	4.1207	4.1223	4.1239	4.1255
62	4.1271	4.1287	4.1304	4.1320	4.1336	4.1352	4.1368	4.1384	4.1400	4.1415
63	4.1431	4.1447	4.1463	4.1479	4.1495	4.1510	4.1526	4.1542	4.1558	4.1573
64	4.1589	4.1604	4.1620	4.1636	4.1651	4.1667	4.1682	4.1698	4.1713	4.1728
65	4.1744	4.1759	4.1775	4.1790	4.1805	4.1820	4.1836	4.1851	4.1866	4.1881
66	4.1897	4.1912	4.1927	4.1942	4.1957	4.1972	4.1987	4.2002	4.2017	4.2032
67	4.2047	4.2062	4.2077	4.2092	4.2106	4.2121	4.2136	4.2151	4.2166	4.2180
68	4.2195	4.2210	4.2224	4.2239	4.2254	4.2268	4.2283	4.2297	4.2312	4.2327
69	4.2341	4.2356	4.2370	4.2384	4.2399	4.2413	4.2428	4.2442	4.2456	4.2471
70	4.2485	4.2499	4.2513	4.2528	4.2542	4.2556	4.2570	4.2584	4.2599	4.2613
71	4.2627	4.2641	4.2655	4.2669	4.2683	4.2697	4.2711	4.2725	4.2739	4.2753
72	4.2767	4.2781	4.2794	4.2808	4.2822	4.2836	4.2850	4.2863	4.2877	4.2891
73	4.2905	4.2918	4.2932	4.2946	4.2959	4.2973	4.2986	4.3000	4.3014	4.3027
74	4.3041	4.3054	4.3068	4.3081	4.3095	4.3108	4.3121	4.3135	4.3148	4.3161
75	4.3175	4.3188	4.3201	4.3215	4.3228	4.3241	4.3255	4.3268	4.3281	4.3294
76	4.3307	4.3320	4.3334	4.3347	4.3360	4.3373	4.3386	4.3399	4.3412	4.3425
77	4.3438	4.3451	4.3464	4.3477	4.3490	4.3503	4.3516	4.3529	4.3541	4.3554
78	4.3567	4.3580	4.3593	4.3605	4.3618	4.3631	4.3644	4.3656	4.3669	4.3682
79	4.3694	4.3707	4.3720	4.3732	4.3745	4.3758	4.3770	4.3783	4.3795	4.3808
80	4.3820	4.3833	4.3845	4.3858	4.3870	4.3883	4.3895	4.3907	4.3920	4.3932
81	4.3944	4.3957	4.3969	4.3981	4.3994	4.4006	4.4018	4.4030	4.4043	4.4055
82	4.4067	4.4079	4.4091	4.4104	4.4116	4.4128	4.4140	4.4152	4.4164	4.4176
83	4.4188	4.4200	4.4212	4.4224	4.4236	4.4248	4.4260	4.4272	4.4284	4.4296
84	4.4308	4.4320	4.4332	4.4344	4.4356	4.4367	4.4379	4.4391	4.4403	4.4415
85	4.4426	4.4438	4.4450	4.4462	4.4473	4.4485	4.4497	4.4508	4.4520	4.4532
86	4.4543	4.4555	4.4567	4.4578	4.4590	4.4601	4.4613	4.4624	4.4636	4.4648
87	4.4659	4.4671	4.4682	4.4693	4.4705	4.4716	4.4728	4.4739	4.4751	4.4762
88	4.4773	4.4785	4.4796	4.4807	4.4819	4.4830	4.4841	4.4853	4.4864	4.4875
89	4.4886	4.4898	4.4909	4.4920	4.4931	4.4942	4.4953	4.4965	4.4976	4.4987
90	4.4998	4.5009	4.5020	4.5031	4.5042	4.5053	4.5064	4.5076	4.5087	4.5098
91	4.5109	4.5120	4.5130	4.5141	4.5152	4.5163	4.5174	4.5185	4.5196	4.5207
92	4.5218	4.5229	4.5240	4.5250	4.5261	4.5272	4.5283	4.5294	4.5304	4.5315
93	4.5326	4.5337	4.5347	4.5358	4.5369	4.5380	4.5390	4.5401	4.5412	4.5422
94	4.5433	4.5444	4.5454	4.5465	4.5475	4.5486	4.5497	4.5507	4.5518	4.5528
95	4.5539	4.5549	4.5560	4.5570	4.5581	4.5591	4.5602	4.5612	4.5623	4.5633
96	4.5643	4.5654	4.5664	4.5675	4.5685	4.5695	4.5706	4.5716	4.5726	4.5737
97	4.5747	4.5757	4.5768	4.5778	4.5788	4.5798	4.5809	4.5819	4.5829	4.5839
98	4.5850	4.5860	4.5870	4.5880	4.5890	4.5900	4.5911	4.5921	4.5931	4.5941
99	4.5951	4.5961	4.5971	4.5981	4.5991	4.6002	4.6012	4.6022	4.6032	4.6042
N	0	1	2	3	4	5	6	7	8	9

Figure M-5 Table of Natural Logarithms
(continued)

N	0	1	2	3	4	5	6	7	8	9
100	4.6052	4.6151	4.6250	4.6347	4.6444	4.6540	4.6634	4.6728	4.6821	4.6913
110	4.7005	4.7095	4.7185	4.7274	4.7362	4.7449	4.7536	4.7622	4.7707	4.7791
120	4.7875	4.7958	4.8040	4.8122	4.8203	4.8283	4.8363	4.8442	4.8520	4.8598
130	4.8675	4.8752	4.8828	4.8903	4.8978	4.9053	4.9127	4.9200	4.9273	4.9345
140	4.9416	4.9488	4.9558	4.9628	4.9698	4.9767	4.9836	4.9904	4.9972	5.0039
150	5.0106	5.0173	5.0239	5.0304	5.0370	5.0434	5.0499	5.0562	5.0626	5.0689
160	5.0752	5.0814	5.0876	5.0938	5.0999	5.1059	5.1120	5.1180	5.1240	5.1299
170	5.1358	5.1417	5.1475	5.1533	5.1591	5.1648	5.1705	5.1762	5.1818	5.1874
180	5.1930	5.1985	5.2040	5.2095	5.2149	5.2204	5.2257	5.2311	5.2364	5.2417
190	5.2470	5.2523	5.2575	5.2627	5.2679	5.2730	5.2781	5.2832	5.2883	5.2933
200	5.2983	5.3033	5.3083	5.3132	5.3181	5.3230	5.3279	5.3327	5.3375	5.3423
210	5.3471	5.3519	5.3566	5.3613	5.3660	5.3706	5.3753	5.3799	5.3845	5.3891
220	5.3936	5.3982	5.4027	5.4072	5.4116	5.4161	5.4205	5.4250	5.4293	5.4337
230	5.4381	5.4424	5.4467	5.4510	5.4553	5.4596	5.4638	5.4681	5.4723	5.4765
240	5.4806	5.4848	5.4889	5.4931	5.4972	5.5013	5.5053	5.5094	5.5134	5.5175
250	5.5215	5.5255	5.5294	5.5334	5.5373	5.5413	5.5452	5.5491	5.5530	5.5568
260	5.5607	5.5645	5.5683	5.5722	5.5759	5.5797	5.5835	5.5872	5.5910	5.5947
270	5.5984	5.6021	5.6058	5.6095	5.6131	5.6168	5.6204	5.6240	5.6276	5.6312
280	5.6348	5.6384	5.6419	5.6454	5.6490	5.6525	5.6560	5.6595	5.6630	5.6664
290	5.6699	5.6733	5.6768	5.6802	5.6836	5.6870	5.6904	5.6937	5.6971	5.7004
300	5.7038	5.7071	5.7104	5.7137	5.7170	5.7203	5.7236	5.7268	5.7301	5.7333
310	5.7366	5.7398	5.7430	5.7462	5.7494	5.7526	5.7557	5.7589	5.7621	5.7652
320	5.7683	5.7714	5.7746	5.7777	5.7807	5.7838	5.7869	5.7900	5.7930	5.7961
330	5.7991	5.8021	5.8051	5.8081	5.8111	5.8141	5.8171	5.8201	5.8230	5.8260
340	5.8289	5.8319	5.8348	5.8377	5.8406	5.8435	5.8464	5.8493	5.8522	5.8551
350	5.8579	5.8608	5.8636	5.8665	5.8693	5.8721	5.8749	5.8777	5.8805	5.8833
360	5.8861	5.8889	5.8916	5.8944	5.8972	5.8999	5.9026	5.9054	5.9081	5.9108
370	5.9135	5.9162	5.9189	5.9216	5.9243	5.9269	5.9296	5.9322	5.9349	5.9375
380	5.9402	5.9428	5.9454	5.9480	5.9506	5.9532	5.9558	5.9584	5.9610	5.9636
390	5.9661	5.9687	5.9713	5.9738	5.9764	5.9789	5.9814	5.9839	5.9865	5.9890
400	5.9915	5.9940	5.9965	5.9989	6.0014	6.0039	6.0064	6.0088	6.0113	6.0137
410	6.0162	6.0186	6.0210	6.0234	6.0259	6.0283	6.0307	6.0331	6.0355	6.0379
420	6.0403	6.0426	6.0450	6.0474	6.0497	6.0521	6.0544	6.0568	6.0591	6.0615
430	6.0638	6.0661	6.0684	6.0707	6.0730	6.0753	6.0776	6.0799	6.0822	6.0845
440	6.0868	6.0890	6.0913	6.0936	6.0958	6.0981	6.1003	6.1026	6.1048	6.1070
450	6.1092	6.1115	6.1137	6.1159	6.1181	6.1203	6.1225	6.1247	6.1269	6.1291
460	6.1312	6.1334	6.1356	6.1377	6.1399	6.1420	6.1442	6.1463	6.1485	6.1506
470	6.1527	6.1549	6.1570	6.1591	6.1612	6.1633	6.1654	6.1675	6.1696	6.1717
480	6.1738	6.1759	6.1779	6.1800	6.1821	6.1841	6.1862	6.1883	6.1903	6.1924
490	6.1944	6.1964	6.1985	6.2005	6.2025	6.2046	6.2066	6.2086	6.2106	6.2126
N	0	1	2	3	4	5	6	7	8	9

Figure M-5 Table of Natural Logarithms
(continued)

N	0	1	2	3	4	5	6	7	8	9
500	6.2146	6.2166	6.2186	6.2206	6.2226	6.2246	6.2265	6.2285	6.2305	6.2324
510	6.2344	6.2364	6.2383	6.2403	6.2422	6.2442	6.2461	6.2480	6.2500	6.2519
520	6.2538	6.2558	6.2577	6.2596	6.2615	6.2634	6.2653	6.2672	6.2691	6.2710
530	6.2729	6.2748	6.2766	6.2785	6.2804	6.2823	6.2841	6.2860	6.2879	6.2897
540	6.2916	6.2934	6.2953	6.2971	6.2989	6.3008	6.3026	6.3044	6.3063	6.3081
550	6.3099	6.3117	6.3135	6.3154	6.3172	6.3190	6.3208	6.3226	6.3244	6.3261
560	6.3279	6.3297	6.3315	6.3333	6.3351	6.3368	6.3386	6.3404	6.3421	6.3439
570	6.3456	6.3474	6.3491	6.3509	6.3526	6.3544	6.3561	6.3578	6.3596	6.3613
580	6.3630	6.3648	6.3665	6.3682	6.3699	6.3716	6.3733	6.3750	6.3767	6.3784
590	6.3801	6.3818	6.3835	6.3852	6.3869	6.3886	6.3902	6.3919	6.3936	6.3953
600	6.3969	6.3986	6.4003	6.4019	6.4036	6.4052	6.4069	6.4085	6.4102	6.4118
610	6.4135	6.4151	6.4167	6.4184	6.4200	6.4216	6.4232	6.4249	6.4265	6.4281
620	6.4297	6.4313	6.4329	6.4345	6.4362	6.4378	6.4394	6.4409	6.4425	6.4441
630	6.4457	6.4473	6.4489	6.4505	6.4521	6.4536	6.4552	6.4568	6.4583	6.4599
640	6.4615	6.4630	6.4646	6.4661	6.4677	6.4693	6.4708	6.4723	6.4739	6.4754
650	6.4770	6.4785	6.4800	6.4816	6.4831	6.4846	6.4862	6.4877	6.4892	6.4907
660	6.4922	6.4938	6.4953	6.4968	6.4983	6.4998	6.5013	6.5028	6.5043	6.5058
670	6.5073	6.5088	6.5103	6.5117	6.5132	6.5147	6.5162	6.5177	6.5191	6.5206
680	6.5221	6.5236	6.5250	6.5265	6.5280	6.5294	6.5309	6.5323	6.5338	6.5352
690	6.5367	6.5381	6.5396	6.5410	6.5425	6.5439	6.5453	6.5468	6.5482	6.5497
700	6.5511	6.5525	6.5539	6.5554	6.5568	6.5582	6.5596	6.5610	6.5624	6.5639
710	6.5653	6.5667	6.5681	6.5695	6.5709	6.5723	6.5737	6.5751	6.5765	6.5779
720	6.5793	6.5806	6.5820	6.5834	6.5848	6.5862	6.5876	6.5889	6.5903	6.5917
730	6.5930	6.5944	6.5958	6.5971	6.5985	6.5999	6.6012	6.6026	6.6039	6.6053
740	6.6067	6.6080	6.6094	6.6107	6.6120	6.6134	6.6147	6.6161	6.6174	6.6187
750	6.6201	6.6214	6.6227	6.6241	6.6254	6.6267	6.6280	6.6294	6.6307	6.6320
760	6.6333	6.6346	6.6359	6.6373	6.6386	6.6399	6.6412	6.6425	6.6438	6.6451
770	6.6464	6.6477	6.6490	6.6503	6.6516	6.6529	6.6542	6.6554	6.6567	6.6580
780	6.6593	6.6606	6.6619	6.6631	6.6644	6.6657	6.6670	6.6682	6.6695	6.6708
790	6.6720	6.6733	6.6746	6.6758	6.6771	6.6783	6.6796	6.6809	6.6821	6.6834
800	6.6846	6.6859	6.6871	6.6884	6.6896	6.6908	6.6921	6.6933	6.6946	6.6958
810	6.6970	6.6983	6.6995	6.7007	6.7020	6.7032	6.7044	6.7056	6.7069	6.7081
820	6.7093	6.7105	6.7117	6.7130	6.7142	6.7154	6.7166	6.7178	6.7190	6.7202
830	6.7214	6.7226	6.7238	6.7250	6.7262	6.7274	6.7286	6.7298	6.7310	6.7322
840	6.7334	6.7346	6.7358	6.7370	6.7382	6.7393	6.7405	6.7417	6.7429	6.7441
850	6.7452	6.7464	6.7476	6.7488	6.7499	6.7511	6.7523	6.7534	6.7546	6.7558
860	6.7569	6.7581	6.7593	6.7604	6.7616	6.7627	6.7639	6.7650	6.7662	6.7673
870	6.7685	6.7696	6.7708	6.7719	6.7731	6.7742	6.7754	6.7765	6.7776	6.7788
880	6.7799	6.7811	6.7822	6.7833	6.7845	6.7856	6.7867	6.7878	6.7890	6.7901
890	6.7912	6.7923	6.7935	6.7946	6.7957	6.7968	6.7979	6.7991	6.8002	6.8013
900	6.8024	6.8035	6.8046	6.8057	6.8068	6.8079	6.8090	6.8101	6.8112	6.8123
910	6.8134	6.8145	6.8156	6.8167	6.8178	6.8189	6.8200	6.8211	6.8222	6.8233
920	6.8244	6.8255	6.8265	6.8276	6.8287	6.8298	6.8309	6.8320	6.8330	6.8341
930	6.8352	6.8363	6.8373	6.8384	6.8395	6.8405	6.8416	6.8427	6.8438	6.8448
940	6.8459	6.8469	6.8480	6.8491	6.8501	6.8512	6.8522	6.8533	6.8544	6.8554
950	6.8565	6.8575	6.8586	6.8596	6.8607	6.8617	6.8628	6.8638	6.8648	6.8659
960	6.8669	6.8680	6.8690	6.8701	6.8711	6.8721	6.8732	6.8742	6.8752	6.8763
970	6.8773	6.8783	6.8794	6.8804	6.8814	6.8824	6.8835	6.8845	6.8855	6.8865
980	6.8876	6.8886	6.8896	6.8906	6.8916	6.8926	6.8937	6.8947	6.8957	6.8967
990	6.8977	6.8987	6.8997	6.9007	6.9017	6.9027	6.9037	6.9048	6.9058	6.9068
N	0	1	2	3	4	5	6	7	8	9

These tables run from 0 to 999. To find the natural logarithm of a number which is 10, 100, 1000, etc., times a number whose logarithm is given, add to the given logarithm $\log_\varepsilon 10$, $2 \log_\varepsilon 10$, $3 \log_\varepsilon 10$, etc. For example:

$$\log_\varepsilon 10 = 2.30259$$

$$2 \log_\varepsilon 10 = 4.60517$$

$$3 \log_\varepsilon 10 = 6.90776, \text{ and so on.}$$

To find the natural logarithm of a number which is 1/10, 1/100, 1/1000, etc., of a number whose logarithm is given, subtract from the given logarithm $\log_\varepsilon 10$, $2 \log_\varepsilon 10$, $3 \log_\varepsilon 10$, etc.

The abbreviation ln is used for natural logarithms.

Natural Trigonometric Functions (Figure M-6)

The values of the trigonometric functions are given for each 6 minutes of arc from 0 to 90 degrees. They are also given for degrees and decimals, and for radians. Angles from 0 to 45 degrees are listed at the left of each page; use the column headings at the top of the page for them. Angles from 45 to 90 degrees are listed at the right of each page; use the column indications at the bottom.

Signs and Limits of Value Assumed by the Functions

Function	Quadrant I		Quadrant II		Quadrant III		Quadrant IV	
	Sign	Value	Sign	Value	Sign	Value	Sign	Value
sin	+	0 to 1	+	1 to 0	−	0 to 1	−	1 to 0
cos	+	1 to 0	−	0 to 1	−	1 to 0	+	0 to 1
tan	+	0 to ∞	−	∞ to 0	+	0 to ∞	−	∞ to 0
cot	+	∞ to 0	−	0 to ∞	+	∞ to 0	−	0 to ∞

Figure M-6 Table of Natural Trigonometrical Functions

Angle				Function				Angle			
Deg	Min	Deg.	Rad	Sin	Tan	Cot	Cos	Rad	Deg.	Deg	Min
0	0	0.0	0.00000	0.00000	0.00000	∞	1.00000	1.57080	90.0	90	0
0	6	0.1	0.00175	0.00175	0.00175	572.957	1.00000	1.56905	89.9	89	54
0	12	0.2	0.00349	0.00349	0.00349	286.478	0.99999	1.56731	89.8	89	48
0	18	0.3	0.00524	0.00524	0.00524	190.984	0.99999	1.56556	89.7	89	42
0	24	0.4	0.00698	0.00698	0.00698	143.237	0.99998	1.56381	89.6	89	36
0	30	0.5	0.00873	0.00873	0.00873	114.589	0.99996	1.56207	89.5	89	30
0	36	0.6	0.01047	0.01047	0.01047	95.4895	0.99995	1.56032	89.4	89	24
0	42	0.7	0.01222	0.01222	0.01222	81.8471	0.99993	1.55858	89.3	89	18
0	48	0.8	0.01396	0.01396	0.01396	71.6151	0.99990	1.55683	89.2	89	12
0	54	0.9	0.01571	0.01571	0.01571	63.6568	0.99988	1.55509	89.1	89	6
1	0	1.0	0.01745	0.01745	0.01746	57.2900	0.99985	1.55334	89.0	89	0
1	6	1.1	0.01920	0.01920	0.01920	52.0807	0.99982	1.55160	88.9	88	54
1	12	1.2	0.02094	0.02094	0.02095	47.7395	0.99978	1.54985	88.8	88	48
1	18	1.3	0.02269	0.02269	0.02269	44.0661	0.99974	1.54811	88.7	88	42
1	24	1.4	0.02443	0.02443	0.02444	40.9174	0.99970	1.54636	88.6	88	36
1	30	1.5	0.02618	0.02618	0.02619	38.1885	0.99966	1.54462	88.5	88	30
1	36	1.6	0.02793	0.02792	0.02793	35.8006	0.99961	1.54287	88.4	88	24
1	42	1.7	0.02967	0.02967	0.02968	33.6935	0.99956	1.54113	88.3	88	18
1	48	1.8	0.03142	0.03141	0.03143	31.8205	0.99951	1.53938	88.2	88	12
1	54	1.9	0.03316	0.03316	0.03317	30.1446	0.99945	1.53764	88.1	88	6
2	0	2.0	0.03491	0.03490	0.03492	28.6363	0.99939	1.53589	88.0	88	0
2	6	2.1	0.03665	0.03664	0.03667	27.2715	0.99933	1.53414	87.9	87	54
2	12	2.2	0.03840	0.03839	0.03842	26.0308	0.99926	1.53240	87.8	87	48
2	18	2.3	0.04014	0.04013	0.04016	24.8978	0.99919	1.53065	87.7	87	42
2	24	2.4	0.04189	0.04188	0.04191	23.8593	0.99912	1.52891	87.6	87	36
2	30	2.5	0.04363	0.04362	0.04366	22.9038	0.99905	1.52716	87.5	87	30
2	36	2.6	0.04538	0.04536	0.04541	22.0217	0.99897	1.52542	87.4	87	24
2	42	2.7	0.04712	0.04711	0.04716	21.2050	0.99889	1.52367	87.3	87	18
2	48	2.8	0.04887	0.04885	0.04891	20.4465	0.99881	1.52193	87.2	87	12
2	54	2.9	0.05061	0.05059	0.05066	19.7403	0.99872	1.52018	87.1	87	6
3	0	3.0	0.05236	0.05234	0.05241	19.0811	0.99863	1.51844	87.0	87	0
3	6	3.1	0.05411	0.05408	0.05416	18.4645	0.99854	1.51669	86.9	86	54
3	12	3.2	0.05585	0.05582	0.05591	17.8863	0.99844	1.51495	86.8	86	48
3	18	3.3	0.05760	0.05756	0.05766	17.3432	0.99834	1.51320	86.7	86	42
3	24	3.4	0.05934	0.05931	0.05941	16.8319	0.99824	1.51146	86.6	86	36
3	30	3.5	0.06109	0.06105	0.06116	16.3499	0.99814	1.50971	86.5	86	30
3	36	3.6	0.06283	0.06279	0.06291	15.8946	0.99803	1.50797	86.4	86	24
3	42	3.7	0.06458	0.06453	0.06467	15.4638	0.99792	1.50622	86.3	86	18
3	48	3.8	0.06632	0.06627	0.06642	15.0557	0.99780	1.50447	86.2	86	12
3	54	3.9	0.06807	0.06802	0.06817	14.6685	0.99768	1.50273	86.1	86	6
4	0	4.0	0.06981	0.06976	0.06993	14.3007	0.99756	1.50098	86.0	86	0
4	6	4.1	0.07156	0.07150	0.07168	13.9507	0.99744	1.49924	85.9	85	54
4	12	4.2	0.07330	0.07324	0.07344	13.6174	0.99731	1.49749	85.8	85	48
4	18	4.3	0.07505	0.07498	0.07519	13.2996	0.99719	1.49575	85.7	85	42
4	24	4.4	0.07679	0.07672	0.07695	12.9962	0.99705	1.49400	85.6	85	36
4	30	4.5	0.07854	0.07846	0.07870	12.7062	0.99692	1.49226	85.5	85	30
4	36	4.6	0.08029	0.08020	0.08046	12.4288	0.99678	1.49051	85.4	85	24
4	42	4.7	0.08203	0.08194	0.08221	12.1632	0.99664	1.48877	85.3	85	18
4	48	4.8	0.08378	0.08368	0.08397	11.9087	0.99649	1.48702	85.2	85	12
4	54	4.9	0.08552	0.08542	0.08573	11.6645	0.99635	1.48528	85.1	85	6
5	0	5.0	0.08727	0.08716	0.08749	11.4301	0.99619	1.48353	85.0	85	0
Deg	Min	Deg.	Rad	Cos	Cot	Tan	Sin	Rad	Deg.	Deg	Min

Figure M-6 Table of Natural Trigonometrical Functions (continued)

Deg	Min	Deg.	Rad	Sin	Tan	Cot	Cos	Rad	Deg.	Deg	Min
5	0	5.0	0.08727	0.08716	0.08749	11.4301	0.99619	1.48353	85.0	85	0
5	6	5.1	0.08901	0.08889	0.08925	11.2048	0.99604	1.48178	84.9	84	54
5	12	5.2	0.09076	0.09063	0.09101	10.9882	0.99588	1.48004	84.8	84	48
5	18	5.3	0.09250	0.09237	0.09277	10.7797	0.99572	1.47829	84.7	84	42
5	24	5.4	0.09425	0.09411	0.09453	10.5789	0.99556	1.47655	84.6	84	36
5	30	5.5	0.09599	0.09585	0.09629	10.3854	0.99540	1.47480	84.5	84	30
5	36	5.6	0.09774	0.09758	0.09805	10.1988	0.99523	1.47306	84.4	84	24
5	42	5.7	0.09948	0.09932	0.09981	10.0187	0.99506	1.47131	84.3	84	18
5	48	5.8	0.10123	0.10106	0.10158	9.84482	0.99488	1.46957	84.2	84	12
5	54	5.9	0.10297	0.10279	0.10334	9.67681	0.99470	1.46782	84.1	84	6
6	0	6.0	0.10472	0.10453	0.10510	9.51437	0.99452	1.46608	84.0	84	0
6	6	6.1	0.10647	0.10626	0.10687	9.35724	0.99434	1.46433	83.9	83	54
6	12	6.2	0.10821	0.10800	0.10863	9.20516	0.99415	1.46259	83.8	83	48
6	18	6.3	0.10996	0.10973	0.11040	9.05789	0.99396	1.46084	83.7	83	42
6	24	6.4	0.11170	0.11147	0.11217	8.91521	0.99377	1.45910	83.6	83	36
6	30	6.5	0.11345	0.11320	0.11394	8.77689	0.99357	1.45735	83.5	83	30
6	36	6.6	0.11519	0.11494	0.11570	8.64275	0.99337	1.45560	83.4	83	24
6	42	6.7	0.11694	0.11667	0.11747	8.51260	0.99317	1.45386	83.3	83	18
6	48	6.8	0.11868	0.11840	0.11924	8.38626	0.99297	1.45211	83.2	83	12
6	54	6.9	0.12043	0.12014	0.12101	8.26356	0.99276	1.45037	83.1	83	6
7	0	7.0	0.12217	0.12187	0.12278	8.14435	0.99255	1.44862	83.0	83	0
7	6	7.1	0.12392	0.12360	0.12456	8.02848	0.99233	1.44688	82.9	82	54
7	12	7.2	0.12566	0.12533	0.12633	7.91582	0.99211	1.44513	82.8	82	48
7	18	7.3	0.12741	0.12706	0.12810	7.80623	0.99189	1.44339	82.7	82	42
7	24	7.4	0.12915	0.12880	0.12988	7.69958	0.99167	1.44164	82.6	82	36
7	30	7.5	0.13090	0.13053	0.13165	7.59576	0.99144	1.43990	82.5	82	30
7	36	7.6	0.13264	0.13226	0.13343	7.49466	0.99122	1.43815	82.4	82	24
7	42	7.7	0.13439	0.13399	0.13521	7.39617	0.99098	1.43641	82.3	82	18
7	48	7.8	0.13614	0.13572	0.13698	7.30018	0.99075	1.43466	82.2	82	12
7	54	7.9	0.13788	0.13744	0.13876	7.20662	0.99051	1.43292	82.1	82	6
8	0	8.0	0.13963	0.13917	0.14054	7.11538	0.99027	1.43117	82.0	82	0
8	6	8.1	0.14137	0.14090	0.14232	7.02637	0.99002	1.42943	81.9	81	54
8	12	8.2	0.14312	0.14263	0.14410	6.93952	0.98978	1.42768	81.8	81	48
8	18	8.3	0.14486	0.14436	0.14588	6.85476	0.98953	1.42593	81.7	81	42
8	24	8.4	0.14661	0.14608	0.14767	6.77199	0.98927	1.42419	81.6	81	36
8	30	8.5	0.14835	0.14781	0.14945	6.69116	0.98902	1.42244	81.5	81	30
8	36	8.6	0.15010	0.14954	0.15124	6.61220	0.98876	1.42070	81.4	81	24
8	42	8.7	0.15184	0.15126	0.15302	6.53503	0.98849	1.41895	81.3	81	18
8	48	8.8	0.15359	0.15299	0.15481	6.45961	0.98823	1.41721	81.2	81	12
8	54	8.9	0.15533	0.15471	0.15660	6.38587	0.98796	1.41546	81.1	81	6
9	0	9.0	0.15708	0.15643	0.15838	6.31375	0.98769	1.41372	81.0	81	0
9	6	9.1	0.15882	0.15816	0.16017	6.24321	0.98741	1.41197	80.9	80	54
9	12	9.2	0.16057	0.15988	0.16196	6.17419	0.98714	1.41023	80.8	80	48
9	18	9.3	0.16232	0.16160	0.16376	6.10664	0.98686	1.40848	80.7	80	42
9	24	9.4	0.16406	0.16333	0.16555	6.04051	0.98657	1.40674	80.6	80	36
9	30	9.5	0.16581	0.16505	0.16734	5.97577	0.98629	1.40499	80.5	80	30
9	36	9.6	0.16755	0.16677	0.16914	5.91236	0.98600	1.40325	80.4	80	24
9	42	9.7	0.16930	0.16849	0.17093	5.85024	0.98570	1.40150	80.3	80	18
9	48	9.8	0.17104	0.17021	0.17273	5.78938	0.98541	1.39976	80.2	80	12
9	54	9.9	0.17279	0.17193	0.17453	5.72974	0.98511	1.39801	80.1	80	6
10	0	10.0	0.17453	0.17365	0.17633	5.67128	0.98481	1.39626	80.0	80	0
Deg	Min	Deg.	Rad	Cos	Cot	Tan	Sin	Rad	Deg.	Deg	Min

Figure M-6 Table of Natural Trigonometrical Functions (continued

Deg	Min	Deg.	Rad	Sin	Tan	Cot	Cos	Rad	Deg.	Deg	Min
		Angle			Function				Angle		
10	0	10.0	0.17453	0.17365	0.17633	5.67128	0.98481	1.39626	80.0	80	0
10	6	10.1	0.17628	0.17537	0.17813	5.61397	0.98450	1.39452	79.9	79	54
10	12	10.2	0.17802	0.17708	0.17993	5.55777	0.98420	1.39277	79.8	79	48
10	18	10.3	0.17977	0.17880	0.18173	5.50265	0.98389	1.39103	79.7	79	42
10	24	10.4	0.18151	0.18052	0.18353	5.44857	0.98357	1.38928	79.6	79	36
10	30	10.5	0.18326	0.18224	0.18534	5.39552	0.98326	1.38754	79.5	79	30
10	36	10.6	0.18500	0.18395	0.18714	5.34345	0.98294	1.38579	79.4	79	24
10	42	10.7	0.18675	0.18567	0.18895	5.29235	0.98261	1.38405	79.3	79	18
10	48	10.8	0.18850	0.18738	0.19076	5.24218	0.98229	1.38230	79.2	79	12
10	54	10.9	0.19024	0.18910	0.19257	5.19293	0.98196	1.38056	79.1	79	6
11	0	11.0	0.19199	0.19081	0.19438	5.14455	0.98163	1.37881	79.0	79	0
11	6	11.1	0.19373	0.19252	0.19619	5.09704	0.98129	1.37706	78.9	78	54
11	12	11.2	0.19548	0.19423	0.19801	5.05037	0.98096	1.37532	78.8	78	48
11	18	11.3	0.19722	0.19595	0.19982	5.00451	0.98061	1.37357	78.7	78	42
11	24	11.4	0.19897	0.19766	0.20164	4.95945	0.98027	1.37183	78.6	78	36
11	30	11.5	0.20071	0.19937	0.20345	4.91516	0.97992	1.37008	78.5	78	30
11	36	11.6	0.20246	0.20108	0.20527	4.87162	0.97958	1.36834	78.4	78	24
11	42	11.7	0.20420	0.20279	0.20709	4.82882	0.97922	1.36659	78.3	78	18
11	48	11.8	0.20595	0.20450	0.20891	4.78673	0.97887	1.36485	78.2	78	12
11	54	11.9	0.20769	0.20620	0.21073	4.74534	0.97851	1.36310	78.1	78	6
12	0	12.0	0.20944	0.20791	0.21256	4.70463	0.97815	1.36136	78.0	78	0
12	6	12.1	0.21118	0.20962	0.21438	4.66458	0.97778	1.35961	77.9	77	54
12	12	12.2	0.21293	0.21132	0.21621	4.62518	0.97742	1.35787	77.8	77	48
12	18	12.3	0.21468	0.21303	0.21804	4.58641	0.97705	1.35612	77.7	77	42
12	24	12.4	0.21642	0.21474	0.21986	4.54826	0.97667	1.35438	77.6	77	36
12	30	12.5	0.21817	0.21644	0.22169	4.51071	0.97630	1.35263	77.5	77	30
12	36	12.6	0.21991	0.21814	0.22353	4.47374	0.97592	1.35089	77.4	77	24
12	42	12.7	0.22166	0.21985	0.22536	4.43735	0.97553	1.34914	77.3	77	18
12	48	12.8	0.22340	0.22155	0.22719	4.40152	0.97515	1.34739	77.2	77	12
12	54	12.9	0.22515	0.22325	0.22903	4.36623	0.97476	1.34565	77.1	77	6
13	0	13.0	0.22689	0.22495	0.23087	4.33147	0.97437	1.34390	77.0	77	0
13	6	13.1	0.22864	0.22665	0.23271	4.29724	0.97398	1.34216	76.9	76	54
13	12	13.2	0.23038	0.22835	0.23455	4.26352	0.97358	1.34041	76.8	76	48
13	18	13.3	0.23213	0.23005	0.23639	4.23030	0.97318	1.33867	76.7	76	42
13	24	13.4	0.23387	0.23175	0.23823	4.19756	0.97278	1.33692	76.6	76	36
13	30	13.5	0.23562	0.23345	0.24008	4.16530	0.97237	1.33518	76.5	76	30
13	36	13.6	0.23736	0.23514	0.24193	4.13350	0.97196	1.33343	76.4	76	24
13	42	13.7	0.23911	0.23684	0.24377	4.10216	0.97155	1.33169	76.3	76	18
13	48	13.8	0.24086	0.23853	0.24562	4.07127	0.97113	1.32994	76.2	76	12
13	54	13.9	0.24260	0.24023	0.24748	4.04081	0.97072	1.32820	76.1	76	6
14	0	14.0	0.24435	0.24192	0.24933	4.01078	0.97030	1.32645	76.0	76	0
14	6	14.1	0.24609	0.24362	0.25118	3.98116	0.96987	1.32471	75.9	75	54
14	12	14.2	0.24784	0.24531	0.25304	3.95196	0.96945	1.32296	75.8	75	48
14	18	14.3	0.24958	0.24700	0.25490	3.92315	0.96902	1.32122	75.7	75	42
14	24	14.4	0.25133	0.24869	0.25676	3.89474	0.96858	1.31947	75.6	75	36
14	30	14.5	0.25307	0.25038	0.25862	3.86671	0.96815	1.31772	75.5	75	30
14	36	14.6	0.25482	0.25207	0.26048	3.83906	0.96771	1.31598	75.4	75	24
14	42	14.7	0.25656	0.25376	0.26235	3.81177	0.96727	1.31423	75.3	75	18
14	48	14.8	0.25831	0.25545	0.26421	3.78485	0.96682	1.31249	75.2	75	12
14	54	14.9	0.26005	0.25713	0.26608	3.75827	0.96638	1.31074	75.1	75	6
15	0	15.0	0.26180	0.25882	0.26795	3.73205	0.96593	1.30900	75.0	75	0
Deg	Min	Deg.	Rad	Cos	Cot	Tan	Sin	Rad	Deg.	Deg	Min

Figure M-6 Table of Natural Trigonometrical Functions (continued)

Deg	Min	Angle Deg.	Rad	Sin	Function Tan	Cot	Cos	Angle Rad	Deg.	Deg	Min
15	0	15.0	0.26180	0.25882	0.26795	3.73205	0.96593	1.30900	75.0	75	0
15	6	15.1	0.26354	0.26050	0.26982	3.70617	0.96547	1.30725	74.9	74	54
15	12	15.2	0.26529	0.26219	0.27169	3.68061	0.96502	1.30551	74.8	74	48
15	18	15.3	0.26704	0.26387	0.27357	3.65539	0.96456	1.30376	74.7	74	42
15	24	15.4	0.26878	0.26556	0.27545	3.63048	0.96410	1.30202	74.6	74	36
15	30	15.5	0.27053	0.26724	0.27732	3.60588	0.96363	1.30027	74.5	74	30
15	36	15.6	0.27227	0.26892	0.27920	3.58160	0.96316	1.29852	74.4	74	24
15	42	15.7	0.27402	0.27060	0.28109	3.55761	0.96269	1.29678	74.3	74	18
15	48	15.8	0.27576	0.27228	0.28297	3.53393	0.96222	1.29503	74.2	74	12
15	54	15.9	0.27751	0.27396	0.28486	3.51053	0.96174	1.29329	74.1	74	6
16	0	16.0	0.27925	0.27564	0.28675	3.48741	0.96126	1.29154	74.0	74	0
16	6	16.1	0.28100	0.27731	0.28864	3.46458	0.96078	1.28980	73.9	73	54
16	12	16.2	0.28274	0.27899	0.29053	3.44202	0.96029	1.28805	73.8	73	48
16	18	16.3	0.28449	0.28067	0.29242	3.41973	0.95981	1.28631	73.7	73	42
16	24	16.4	0.28623	0.28234	0.29432	3.39771	0.95931	1.28456	73.6	73	36
16	30	16.5	0.28798	0.28402	0.29621	3.37594	0.95882	1.28282	73.5	73	30
16	36	16.6	0.28972	0.28569	0.29811	3.35443	0.95832	1.28107	73.4	73	24
16	42	16.7	0.29147	0.28736	0.30001	3.33317	0.95782	1.27933	73.3	73	18
16	48	16.8	0.29322	0.28903	0.30192	3.31216	0.95732	1.27758	73.2	73	12
16	54	16.9	0.29496	0.29070	0.30382	3.29139	0.95681	1.27584	73.1	73	6
17	0	17.0	0.29671	0.29237	0.30573	3.27085	0.95630	1.27409	73.0	73	0
17	6	17.1	0.29845	0.29404	0.30764	3.25055	0.95579	1.27235	72.9	72	54
17	12	17.2	0.30020	0.29571	0.30955	3.23048	0.95528	1.27060	72.8	72	48
17	18	17.3	0.30194	0.29737	0.31147	3.21063	0.95476	1.26885	72.7	72	42
17	24	17.4	0.30369	0.29904	0.31338	3.19100	0.95424	1.26711	72.6	72	36
17	30	17.5	0.30543	0.30071	0.31530	3.17159	0.95372	1.26536	72.5	72	30
17	36	17.6	0.30718	0.30237	0.31722	3.15240	0.95319	1.26362	72.4	72	24
17	42	17.7	0.30892	0.30403	0.31914	3.13341	0.95266	1.26187	72.3	72	18
17	48	17.8	0.31067	0.30570	0.32106	3.11464	0.95213	1.26013	72.2	72	12
17	54	17.9	0.31241	0.30736	0.32299	3.09606	0.95159	1.25838	72.1	72	6
18	0	18.0	0.31416	0.30902	0.32492	3.07768	0.95106	1.25664	72.0	72	0
18	6	18.1	0.31590	0.31068	0.32685	3.05950	0.95052	1.25489	71.9	71	54
18	12	18.2	0.31765	0.31233	0.32878	3.04152	0.94997	1.25315	71.8	71	48
18	18	18.3	0.31940	0.31399	0.33072	3.02372	0.94943	1.25140	71.7	71	42
18	24	18.4	0.32114	0.31565	0.33266	3.00611	0.94888	1.24966	71.6	71	36
18	30	18.5	0.32289	0.31730	0.33460	2.98868	0.94832	1.24791	71.5	71	30
18	36	18.6	0.32463	0.31896	0.33654	2.97144	0.94777	1.24617	71.4	71	24
18	42	18.7	0.32638	0.32061	0.33848	2.95437	0.94721	1.24442	71.3	71	18
18	48	18.8	0.32812	0.32227	0.34043	2.93748	0.94665	1.24268	71.2	71	12
18	54	18.9	0.32987	0.32392	0.34238	2.92076	0.94609	1.24093	71.1	71	6
19	0	19.0	0.33161	0.32557	0.34433	2.90421	0.94552	1.23918	71.0	71	0
19	6	19.1	0.33336	0.32722	0.34628	2.88783	0.94495	1.23744	70.9	70	54
19	12	19.2	0.33510	0.32887	0.34824	2.87161	0.94438	1.23569	70.8	70	48
19	18	19.3	0.33685	0.33051	0.35020	2.85555	0.94380	1.23395	70.7	70	42
19	24	19.4	0.33859	0.33216	0.35216	2.83965	0.94322	1.23220	70.6	70	36
19	30	19.5	0.34034	0.33381	0.35412	2.82391	0.94264	1.23046	70.5	70	30
19	36	19.6	0.34208	0.33545	0.35608	2.80833	0.94206	1.22871	70.4	70	24
19	42	19.7	0.34383	0.33710	0.35805	2.79289	0.94147	1.22697	70.3	70	18
19	48	19.8	0.34558	0.33874	0.36002	2.77761	0.94088	1.22522	70.2	70	12
19	54	19.9	0.34732	0.34038	0.36200	2.76247	0.94029	1.22348	70.1	70	6
20	0	20.0	0.34907	0.34202	0.36397	2.74748	0.93969	1.22173	70.0	70	0
Deg	Min	Deg.	Rad	Cos	Cot	Tan	Sin	Rad	Deg.	Deg	Min

Figure M-6 Table of Natural Trigonometrical Functions (continued)

Angle				Function				Angle			
Deg	Min	Deg.	Rad	Sin	Tan	Cot	Cos	Rad	Deg.	Deg	Min
20	0	20.0	0.34907	0.34202	0.36397	2.74748	0.93969	1.22173	70.0	70	0
20	6	20.1	0.35081	0.34366	0.36595	2.73263	0.93909	1.21998	69.9	69	54
20	12	20.2	0.35256	0.34530	0.36793	2.71792	0.93849	1.21824	69.8	69	48
20	18	20.3	0.35430	0.34694	0.36991	2.70335	0.93789	1.21649	69.7	69	42
20	24	20.4	0.35605	0.34857	0.37190	2.68892	0.93728	1.21475	69.6	69	36
20	30	20.5	0.35779	0.35021	0.37388	2.67462	0.93667	1.21300	69.5	69	30
20	36	20.6	0.35954	0.35184	0.37588	2.66046	0.93606	1.21126	69.4	69	24
20	42	20.7	0.36128	0.35347	0.37787	2.64642	0.93544	1.20951	69.3	69	18
20	48	20.8	0.36303	0.35511	0.37986	2.63252	0.93483	1.20777	69.2	69	12
20	54	20.9	0.36477	0.35674	0.38186	2.61874	0.93420	1.20602	69.1	69	6
21	0	21.0	0.36652	0.35837	0.38386	2.60509	0.93358	1.20428	69.0	69	0
21	6	21.1	0.36826	0.36000	0.38587	2.59156	0.93295	1.20253	68.9	68	54
21	12	21.2	0.37001	0.36162	0.38787	2.57815	0.93232	1.20079	68.8	68	48
21	18	21.3	0.37176	0.36325	0.38988	2.56487	0.93169	1.19904	68.7	68	42
21	24	21.4	0.37350	0.36488	0.39190	2.55170	0.93106	1.19730	68.6	68	36
21	30	21.5	0.37525	0.36650	0.39391	2.53865	0.93042	1.19555	68.5	68	30
21	36	21.6	0.37699	0.36812	0.39593	2.52571	0.92978	1.19381	68.4	68	24
21	42	21.7	0.37874	0.36975	0.39795	2.51289	0.92913	1.19206	68.3	68	18
21	48	21.8	0.38048	0.37137	0.39997	2.50018	0.92849	1.19031	68.2	68	12
21	54	21.9	0.38223	0.37299	0.40200	2.48758	0.92784	1.18857	68.1	68	6
22	0	22.0	0.38397	0.37461	0.40403	2.47509	0.92718	1.18682	68.0	68	0
22	6	22.1	0.38572	0.37622	0.40606	2.46270	0.92653	1.18508	67.9	67	54
22	12	22.2	0.38746	0.37784	0.40809	2.45043	0.92587	1.18333	67.8	67	48
22	18	22.3	0.38921	0.37946	0.41013	2.43825	0.92521	1.18159	67.7	67	42
22	24	22.4	0.39095	0.38107	0.41217	2.42618	0.92455	1.17984	67.6	67	36
22	30	22.5	0.39270	0.38268	0.41421	2.41421	0.92388	1.17810	67.5	67	30
22	36	22.6	0.39444	0.38430	0.41626	2.40235	0.92321	1.17635	67.4	67	24
22	42	22.7	0.39619	0.38591	0.41831	2.39058	0.92254	1.17461	67.3	67	18
22	48	22.8	0.39794	0.38752	0.42036	2.37891	0.92186	1.17286	67.2	67	12
22	54	22.9	0.39968	0.38912	0.42242	2.36733	0.92119	1.17112	67.1	67	6
23	0	23.0	0.40143	0.39073	0.42447	2.35585	0.92050	1.16937	67.0	67	0
23	6	23.1	0.40317	0.39234	0.42654	2.34447	0.91982	1.16763	66.9	66	54
23	12	23.2	0.40492	0.39394	0.42860	2.33317	0.91914	1.16588	66.8	66	48
23	18	23.3	0.40666	0.39555	0.43067	2.32197	0.91845	1.16414	66.7	66	42
23	24	23.4	0.40841	0.39715	0.43274	2.31086	0.91775	1.16239	66.6	66	36
23	30	23.5	0.41015	0.39875	0.43481	2.29984	0.91706	1.16064	66.5	66	30
23	36	23.6	0.41190	0.40035	0.43689	2.28891	0.91636	1.15890	66.4	66	24
23	42	23.7	0.41364	0.40195	0.43897	2.27806	0.91566	1.15715	66.3	66	18
23	48	23.8	0.41539	0.40355	0.44105	2.26730	0.91496	1.15541	66.2	66	12
23	54	23.9	0.41713	0.40514	0.44314	2.25663	0.91425	1.15366	66.1	66	6
24	0	24.0	0.41888	0.40674	0.44523	2.24604	0.91355	1.15192	66.0	66	0
24	6	24.1	0.42062	0.40833	0.44732	2.23553	0.91283	1.15017	65.9	65	54
24	12	24.2	0.42237	0.40992	0.44942	2.22510	0.91212	1.14843	65.8	65	48
24	18	24.3	0.42412	0.41151	0.45152	2.21475	0.91140	1.14668	65.7	65	42
24	24	24.4	0.42586	0.41310	0.45362	2.20449	0.91068	1.14494	65.6	65	36
24	30	24.5	0.42761	0.41469	0.45573	2.19430	0.90996	1.14319	65.5	65	30
24	36	24.6	0.42935	0.41628	0.45784	2.18419	0.90924	1.14145	65.4	65	24
24	42	24.7	0.43110	0.41787	0.45995	2.17416	0.90851	1.13970	65.3	65	18
24	48	24.8	0.43284	0.41945	0.46207	2.16420	0.90778	1.13796	65.2	65	12
24	54	24.9	0.43459	0.42104	0.46418	2.15432	0.90704	1.13621	65.1	65	6
25	0	25.0	0.43633	0.42262	0.46631	2.14451	0.90631	1.13447	65.0	65	0
Deg	Min	Deg.	Rad	Cos	Cot	Tan	Sin	Rad	Deg.	Deg	Min

Figure M-6 Table of Natural Trigonometrical Functions (continued

Deg	Min	Deg.	Rad	Sin	Tan	Cot	Cos	Rad	Deg.	Deg	Min
		Angle			Function				Angle		
25	0	25.0	0.43633	0.42262	0.46631	2.14451	0.90631	1.13446	65.0	65	0
25	6	25.1	0.43808	0.42420	0.46843	2.13477	0.90557	1.13272	64.9	64	54
25	12	25.2	0.43982	0.42578	0.47056	2.12511	0.90483	1.13097	64.8	64	48
25	18	25.3	0.44157	0.42736	0.47270	2.11552	0.90408	1.12923	64.7	64	42
25	24	25.4	0.44331	0.42894	0.47483	2.10600	0.90334	1.12748	64.6	64	36
25	30	25.5	0.44506	0.43051	0.47698	2.09654	0.90259	1.12574	64.5	64	30
25	36	25.6	0.44680	0.43209	0.47912	2.08716	0.90183	1.12399	64.4	64	24
25	42	25.7	0.44855	0.43366	0.48127	2.07785	0.90108	1.12225	64.3	64	18
25	48	25.8	0.45029	0.43523	0.48342	2.06860	0.90032	1.12050	64.2	64	12
25	54	25.9	0.45204	0.43680	0.48557	2.05942	0.89956	1.11876	64.1	64	6
26	0	26.0	0.45379	0.43837	0.48773	2.05030	0.89879	1.11701	64.0	64	0
26	6	26.1	0.45553	0.43994	0.48989	2.04125	0.89803	1.11527	63.9	63	54
26	12	26.2	0.45728	0.44151	0.49206	2.03227	0.89726	1.11352	63.8	63	48
26	18	26.3	0.45902	0.44307	0.49423	2.02335	0.89649	1.11177	63.7	63	42
26	24	26.4	0.46077	0.44464	0.49640	2.01449	0.89571	1.11003	63.6	63	36
26	30	26.5	0.46251	0.44620	0.49858	2.00569	0.89493	1.10828	63.5	63	30
26	36	26.6	0.46426	0.44776	0.50076	1.99695	0.89415	1.10654	63.4	63	24
26	42	26.7	0.46600	0.44932	0.50295	1.98828	0.89337	1.10479	63.3	63	18
26	48	26.8	0.46775	0.45088	0.50514	1.97966	0.89259	1.10305	63.2	63	12
26	54	26.9	0.46949	0.45243	0.50733	1.97111	0.89180	1.10130	63.1	63	6
27	0	27.0	0.47124	0.45399	0.50953	1.96261	0.89101	1.09956	63.0	63	0
27	6	27.1	0.47298	0.45554	0.51173	1.95417	0.89021	1.09781	62.9	62	54
27	12	27.2	0.47473	0.45710	0.51393	1.94579	0.88942	1.09607	62.8	62	48
27	18	27.3	0.47647	0.45865	0.51614	1.93746	0.88862	1.09432	62.7	62	42
27	24	27.4	0.47822	0.46020	0.51835	1.92920	0.88782	1.09258	62.6	62	36
27	30	27.5	0.47997	0.46175	0.52057	1.92098	0.88701	1.09083	62.5	62	30
27	36	27.6	0.48171	0.46330	0.52279	1.91282	0.88620	1.08909	62.4	62	24
27	42	27.7	0.48346	0.46484	0.52501	1.90472	0.88539	1.08734	62.3	62	18
27	48	27.8	0.48520	0.46639	0.52724	1.89667	0.88458	1.08560	62.2	62	12
27	54	27.9	0.48695	0.46793	0.52947	1.88867	0.88377	1.08385	62.1	62	6
28	0	28.0	0.48869	0.46947	0.53171	1.88073	0.88295	1.08210	62.0	62	0
28	6	28.1	0.49044	0.47101	0.53395	1.87283	0.88213	1.08036	61.9	61	54
28	12	28.2	0.49218	0.47255	0.53620	1.86499	0.88130	1.07861	61.8	61	48
28	18	28.3	0.49393	0.47409	0.53844	1.85720	0.88048	1.07687	61.7	61	42
28	24	28.4	0.49567	0.47562	0.54070	1.84946	0.87965	1.07512	61.6	61	36
28	30	28.5	0.49742	0.47716	0.54296	1.84177	0.87882	1.07338	61.5	61	30
28	36	28.6	0.49916	0.47869	0.54522	1.83413	0.87798	1.07163	61.4	61	24
28	42	28.7	0.50091	0.48022	0.54748	1.82654	0.87715	1.06989	61.3	61	18
28	48	28.8	0.50266	0.48175	0.54975	1.81899	0.87631	1.06814	61.2	61	12
28	54	28.9	0.50440	0.48328	0.55203	1.81150	0.87546	1.06640	61.1	61	6
29	0	29.0	0.50615	0.48481	0.55431	1.80405	0.87462	1.06465	61.0	61	0
29	6	29.1	0.50789	0.48634	0.55659	1.79664	0.87377	1.06291	60.9	60	54
29	12	29.2	0.50964	0.48786	0.55888	1.78929	0.87292	1.06116	60.8	60	48
29	18	29.3	0.51138	0.48938	0.56117	1.78198	0.87207	1.05942	60.7	60	42
29	24	29.4	0.51313	0.49090	0.56347	1.77471	0.87121	1.05767	60.6	60	36
29	30	29.5	0.51487	0.49242	0.56577	1.76749	0.87036	1.05593	60.5	60	30
29	36	29.6	0.51662	0.49394	0.56808	1.76032	0.86949	1.05418	60.4	60	24
29	42	29.7	0.51836	0.49546	0.57039	1.75319	0.86863	1.05243	60.3	60	18
29	48	29.8	0.52011	0.49697	0.57271	1.74610	0.86777	1.05069	60.2	60	12
29	54	29.9	0.52185	0.49849	0.57503	1.73905	0.86690	1.04894	60.1	60	6
30	0	30.0	0.52360	0.50000	0.57735	1.73205	0.86603	1.04720	60.0	60	0
Deg	Min	Deg.	Rad	Cos	Cot	Tan	Sin	Rad	Deg.	Deg	Min

Figure M-6 Table of Natural Trigonometrical Functions (continued)

Deg	Min	Deg.	Rad	Sin	Tan	Cot	Cos	Rad	Deg.	Deg	Min
		Angle		Function				Angle			
30	0	30.0	0.52360	0.50000	0.57735	1.73205	0.86603	1.04720	60.0	60	0
30	6	30.1	0.52534	0.50151	0.57968	1.72509	0.86515	1.04545	59.9	59	54
30	12	30.2	0.52709	0.50302	0.58201	1.71817	0.86427	1.04371	59.8	59	48
30	18	30.3	0.52883	0.50453	0.58435	1.71130	0.86340	1.04196	59.7	59	42
30	24	30.4	0.53058	0.50603	0.58670	1.70446	0.86251	1.04022	59.6	59	36
30	30	30.5	0.53233	0.50754	0.58904	1.69766	0.86163	1.03847	59.5	59	30
30	36	30.6	0.53407	0.50904	0.59140	1.69091	0.86074	1.03673	59.4	59	24
30	42	30.7	0.53582	0.51054	0.59376	1.68419	0.85985	1.03498	59.3	59	18
30	48	30.8	0.53756	0.51204	0.59612	1.67752	0.85896	1.03323	59.2	59	12
30	54	30.9	0.53931	0.51354	0.59849	1.67088	0.85806	1.03149	59.1	59	6
31	0	31.0	0.54105	0.51504	0.60086	1.66428	0.85717	1.02974	59.0	59	0
31	6	31.1	0.54280	0.51653	0.60324	1.65772	0.85627	1.02800	58.9	58	54
31	12	31.2	0.54454	0.51803	0.60562	1.65120	0.85536	1.02625	58.8	58	48
31	18	31.3	0.54629	0.51952	0.60801	1.64471	0.85446	1.02451	58.7	58	42
31	24	31.4	0.54803	0.52101	0.61040	1.63826	0.85355	1.02276	58.6	58	36
31	30	31.5	0.54978	0.52250	0.61280	1.63185	0.85264	1.02102	58.5	58	30
31	36	31.6	0.55152	0.52399	0.61520	1.62548	0.85173	1.01927	58.4	58	24
31	42	31.7	0.55327	0.52547	0.61761	1.61914	0.85081	1.01753	58.3	58	18
31	48	31.8	0.55501	0.52696	0.62003	1.61284	0.84989	1.01578	58.2	58	12
31	54	31.9	0.55676	0.52844	0.62245	1.60657	0.84897	1.01404	58.1	58	6
32	0	32.0	0.55851	0.52992	0.62487	1.60033	0.84805	1.01229	58.0	58	0
32	6	32.1	0.56025	0.53140	0.62730	1.59414	0.84712	1.01055	57.9	57	54
32	12	32.2	0.56200	0.53288	0.62973	1.58797	0.84619	1.00880	57.8	57	48
32	18	32.3	0.56374	0.53435	0.63217	1.58184	0.84526	1.00706	57.7	57	42
32	24	32.4	0.56549	0.53583	0.63462	1.57575	0.84433	1.00531	57.6	57	36
32	30	32.5	0.56723	0.53730	0.63707	1.56969	0.84339	1.00356	57.5	57	30
32	36	32.6	0.56898	0.53877	0.63953	1.56366	0.84245	1.00182	57.4	57	24
32	42	32.7	0.57072	0.54024	0.64199	1.55766	0.84151	1.00007	57.3	57	18
32	48	32.8	0.57247	0.54171	0.64446	1.55170	0.84057	0.99833	57.2	57	12
32	54	32.9	0.57421	0.54317	0.64693	1.54577	0.83962	0.99658	57.1	57	6
33	0	33.0	0.57596	0.54464	0.64941	1.53987	0.83867	0.99484	57.0	57	0
33	6	33.1	0.57770	0.54610	0.65189	1.53400	0.83772	0.99309	56.9	56	54
33	12	33.2	0.57945	0.54756	0.65438	1.52816	0.83676	0.99135	56.8	56	48
33	18	33.3	0.58119	0.54902	0.65688	1.52236	0.83581	0.98960	56.7	56	42
33	24	33.4	0.58294	0.55048	0.65938	1.51658	0.83485	0.98786	56.6	56	36
33	30	33.5	0.58468	0.55194	0.66188	1.51084	0.83389	0.98611	56.5	56	30
33	36	33.6	0.58643	0.55339	0.66440	1.50512	0.83292	0.98437	56.4	56	24
33	42	33.7	0.58818	0.55484	0.66692	1.49944	0.83195	0.98262	56.3	56	18
33	48	33.8	0.58992	0.55630	0.66944	1.49378	0.83098	0.98088	56.2	56	12
33	54	33.9	0.59167	0.55774	0.67197	1.48816	0.83001	0.97913	56.1	56	6
34	0	34.0	0.59341	0.55919	0.67451	1.48256	0.82904	0.97739	56.0	56	0
34	6	34.1	0.59516	0.56064	0.67705	1.47700	0.82806	0.97564	55.9	55	54
34	12	34.2	0.59690	0.56208	0.67960	1.47146	0.82708	0.97389	55.8	55	48
34	18	34.3	0.59865	0.56353	0.68215	1.46595	0.82610	0.97215	55.7	55	42
34	24	34.4	0.60039	0.56497	0.68471	1.46047	0.82511	0.97040	55.6	55	36
34	30	34.5	0.60214	0.56641	0.68728	1.45501	0.82413	0.96866	55.5	55	30
34	36	34.6	0.60388	0.56784	0.68985	1.44959	0.82314	0.96691	55.4	55	24
34	42	34.7	0.60563	0.56928	0.69243	1.44419	0.82214	0.96517	55.3	55	18
34	48	34.8	0.60737	0.57071	0.69502	1.43881	0.82115	0.96342	55.2	55	12
34	54	34.9	0.60912	0.57215	0.69761	1.43347	0.82015	0.96168	55.1	55	6
35	0	35.0	0.61086	0.57358	0.70021	1.42815	0.81915	0.95993	55.0	55	0
Deg	Min	Deg.	Rad	Cos	Cot	Tan	Sin	Rad	Deg.	Deg	Min

Figure M-6 Table of Natural Trigonometrical Functions (continued)

Deg	Min	Deg.	Rad	Sin	Tan	Cot	Cos	Rad	Deg.	Deg	Min
		Angle			Function				Angle		
35	0	35.0	0.61087	0.57358	0.70021	1.42815	0.81915	0.95993	55.0	55	0
35	6	35.1	0.61261	0.57501	0.70281	1.42286	0.81815	0.95819	54.9	54	54
35	12	35.2	0.61436	0.57643	0.70542	1.41759	0.81715	0.95644	54.8	54	48
35	18	35.3	0.61610	0.57786	0.70804	1.41235	0.81614	0.95469	54.7	54	42
35	24	35.4	0.61785	0.57928	0.71066	1.40714	0.81513	0.95295	54.6	54	36
35	30	35.5	0.61959	0.58070	0.71329	1.40195	0.81412	0.95120	54.5	54	30
35	36	35.6	0.62134	0.58212	0.71593	1.39679	0.81310	0.94946	54.4	54	24
35	42	35.7	0.62308	0.58354	0.71857	1.39165	0.81208	0.94771	54.3	54	18
35	48	35.8	0.62483	0.58496	0.72122	1.38654	0.81106	0.94597	54.2	54	12
35	54	35.9	0.62657	0.58637	0.72388	1.38145	0.81004	0.94422	54.1	54	6
36	0	36.0	0.62832	0.58778	0.72654	1.37638	0.80902	0.94248	54.0	54	0
36	6	36.1	0.63006	0.58920	0.72921	1.37134	0.80799	0.94073	53.9	53	54
36	12	36.2	0.63181	0.59061	0.73189	1.36633	0.80696	0.93899	53.8	53	48
36	18	36.3	0.63355	0.59201	0.73457	1.36134	0.80593	0.93724	53.7	53	42
36	24	36.4	0.63530	0.59342	0.73726	1.35637	0.80489	0.93550	53.6	53	36
36	30	36.5	0.63704	0.59482	0.73996	1.35142	0.80386	0.93375	53.5	53	30
36	36	36.6	0.63879	0.59622	0.74266	1.34650	0.80282	0.93201	53.4	53	24
36	42	36.7	0.64054	0.59762	0.74538	1.34161	0.80178	0.93026	53.3	53	18
36	48	36.8	0.64228	0.59902	0.74809	1.33673	0.80073	0.92852	53.2	53	12
36	54	36.9	0.64403	0.60042	0.75082	1.33188	0.79969	0.92677	53.1	53	6
37	0	37.0	0.64577	0.60181	0.75355	1.32705	0.79864	0.92502	53.0	53	0
37	6	37.1	0.64752	0.60321	0.75629	1.32224	0.79758	0.92328	52.9	52	54
37	12	37.2	0.64926	0.60460	0.75904	1.31745	0.79653	0.92153	52.8	52	48
37	18	37.3	0.65101	0.60599	0.76179	1.31269	0.79547	0.91979	52.7	52	42
37	24	37.4	0.65275	0.60738	0.76456	1.30795	0.79442	0.91804	52.6	52	36
37	30	37.5	0.65450	0.60876	0.76733	1.30323	0.79335	0.91630	52.5	52	30
37	36	37.6	0.65624	0.61014	0.77010	1.29853	0.79229	0.91455	52.4	52	24
37	42	37.7	0.65799	0.61153	0.77289	1.29385	0.79122	0.91281	52.3	52	18
37	48	37.8	0.65973	0.61291	0.77568	1.28919	0.79016	0.91106	52.2	52	12
37	54	37.9	0.66148	0.61428	0.77848	1.28456	0.78908	0.90932	52.1	52	6
38	0	38.0	0.66322	0.61566	0.78128	1.27994	0.78801	0.90757	52.0	52	0
38	6	38.1	0.66497	0.61704	0.78410	1.27535	0.78694	0.90583	51.9	51	54
38	12	38.2	0.66671	0.61841	0.78692	1.27078	0.78586	0.90408	51.8	51	48
38	18	38.3	0.66846	0.61978	0.78975	1.26622	0.78478	0.90234	51.7	51	42
38	24	38.4	0.67021	0.62115	0.79259	1.26169	0.78369	0.90059	51.6	51	36
38	30	38.5	0.67195	0.62251	0.79543	1.25718	0.78261	0.89885	51.5	51	30
38	36	38.6	0.67370	0.62388	0.79829	1.25268	0.78152	0.89710	51.4	51	24
38	42	38.7	0.67544	0.62524	0.80115	1.24821	0.78043	0.89535	51.3	51	18
38	48	38.8	0.67719	0.62660	0.80402	1.24375	0.77934	0.89361	51.2	51	12
38	54	38.9	0.67893	0.62796	0.80690	1.23932	0.77824	0.89186	51.1	51	6
39	0	39.0	0.68068	0.62932	0.80978	1.23490	0.77715	0.89012	51.0	51	0
39	6	39.1	0.68242	0.63067	0.81268	1.23050	0.77605	0.88837	50.9	50	54
39	12	39.2	0.68417	0.63203	0.81558	1.22612	0.77495	0.88663	50.8	50	48
39	18	39.3	0.68591	0.63338	0.81849	1.22176	0.77384	0.88488	50.7	50	42
39	24	39.4	0.68766	0.63473	0.82141	1.21742	0.77273	0.88314	50.6	50	36
39	30	39.5	0.68940	0.63608	0.82433	1.21310	0.77163	0.88139	50.5	50	30
39	36	39.6	0.69115	0.63742	0.82727	1.20880	0.77051	0.87965	50.4	50	24
39	42	39.7	0.69289	0.63877	0.83021	1.20451	0.76940	0.87790	50.3	50	18
39	48	39.8	0.69464	0.64011	0.83317	1.20024	0.76828	0.87616	50.2	50	12
39	54	39.9	0.69638	0.64145	0.83613	1.19599	0.76717	0.87441	50.1	50	6
40	0	40.0	0.69813	0.64279	0.83910	1.19176	0.76605	0.87267	50.0	50	0
Deg	Min	Deg.	Rad	Cos	Cot	Tan	Sin	Rad	Deg.	Deg	Min

Figure M-6 Table of Natural Trigonometrical Functions (continued)

		Angle		Sin	Function Tan	Cot	Cos	Angle Rad	Deg.	Deg	Min
Deg	Min	Deg.	Rad	Sin	Tan	Cot	Cos	Rad	Deg.	Deg	Min
40	0	40.0	0.69813	0.64279	0.83910	1.19175	0.76604	0.87266	50.0	50	0
40	6	40.1	0.69988	0.64412	0.84208	1.18754	0.76492	0.87092	49.9	49	54
40	12	40.2	0.70162	0.64546	0.84507	1.18334	0.76380	0.86917	49.8	49	48
40	18	40.3	0.70337	0.64679	0.84806	1.17916	0.76267	0.86743	49.7	49	42
40	24	40.4	0.70511	0.64812	0.85107	1.17500	0.76154	0.86568	49.6	49	36
40	30	40.5	0.70686	0.64945	0.85408	1.17085	0.76041	0.86394	49.5	49	30
40	36	40.6	0.70860	0.65077	0.85710	1.16672	0.75927	0.86219	49.4	49	24
40	42	40.7	0.71035	0.65210	0.86013	1.16261	0.75813	0.86045	49.3	49	18
40	48	40.8	0.71209	0.65342	0.86318	1.15851	0.75700	0.85870	49.2	49	12
40	54	40.9	0.71384	0.65474	0.86623	1.15443	0.75585	0.85696	49.1	49	6
41	0	41.0	0.71558	0.65606	0.86929	1.15037	0.75471	0.85521	49.0	49	0
41	6	41.1	0.71733	0.65737	0.87235	1.14632	0.75356	0.85347	48.9	48	54
41	12	41.2	0.71908	0.65869	0.87543	1.14229	0.75242	0.85172	48.8	48	48
41	18	41.3	0.72082	0.66000	0.87852	1.13828	0.75126	0.84998	48.7	48	42
41	24	41.4	0.72257	0.66131	0.88162	1.13428	0.75011	0.84823	48.6	48	36
41	30	41.5	0.72431	0.66262	0.88472	1.13030	0.74896	0.84648	48.5	48	30
41	36	41.6	0.72606	0.66393	0.88784	1.12633	0.74780	0.84474	48.4	48	24
41	42	41.7	0.72780	0.66523	0.89097	1.12238	0.74664	0.84299	48.3	48	18
41	48	41.8	0.72955	0.66653	0.89410	1.11844	0.74548	0.84125	48.2	48	12
41	54	41.9	0.73129	0.66783	0.89725	1.11452	0.74431	0.83950	48.1	48	6
42	0	42.0	0.73304	0.66913	0.90040	1.11061	0.74315	0.83776	48.0	48	0
42	6	42.1	0.73478	0.67043	0.90357	1.10672	0.74198	0.83601	47.9	47	54
42	12	42.2	0.73653	0.67172	0.90674	1.10285	0.74081	0.83427	47.8	47	48
42	18	42.3	0.73827	0.67301	0.90993	1.09899	0.73963	0.83252	47.7	47	42
42	24	42.4	0.74002	0.67430	0.91312	1.09514	0.73846	0.83078	47.6	47	36
42	30	42.5	0.74176	0.67559	0.91633	1.09131	0.73728	0.82903	47.5	47	30
42	36	42.6	0.74351	0.67688	0.91955	1.08749	0.73610	0.82729	47.4	47	24
42	42	42.7	0.74525	0.67816	0.92277	1.08369	0.73492	0.82554	47.3	47	18
42	48	42.8	0.74700	0.67944	0.92601	1.07990	0.73373	0.82380	47.2	47	12
42	54	42.9	0.74875	0.68072	0.92926	1.07613	0.73254	0.82205	47.1	47	6
43	0	43.0	0.75049	0.68200	0.93251	1.07237	0.73135	0.82031	47.0	47	0
43	6	43.1	0.75224	0.68327	0.93578	1.06863	0.73016	0.81856	46.9	46	54
43	12	43.2	0.75398	0.68455	0.93906	1.06489	0.72897	0.81681	46.8	46	48
43	18	43.3	0.75573	0.68582	0.94235	1.06118	0.72777	0.81507	46.7	46	42
43	24	43.4	0.75747	0.68709	0.94565	1.05747	0.72658	0.81332	46.6	46	36
43	30	43.5	0.75922	0.68835	0.94896	1.05378	0.72538	0.81158	46.5	46	30
43	36	43.6	0.76096	0.68962	0.95228	1.05011	0.72417	0.80983	46.4	46	24
43	42	43.7	0.76271	0.69088	0.95562	1.04644	0.72297	0.80809	46.3	46	18
43	48	43.8	0.76445	0.69214	0.95896	1.04279	0.72176	0.80634	46.2	46	12
43	54	43.9	0.76620	0.69340	0.96232	1.03916	0.72055	0.80460	46.1	46	6
44	0	44.0	0.76794	0.69466	0.96569	1.03553	0.71934	0.80285	46.0	46	0
44	6	44.1	0.76969	0.69591	0.96906	1.03192	0.71813	0.80111	45.9	45	54
44	12	44.2	0.77143	0.69716	0.97245	1.02833	0.71691	0.79936	45.8	45	48
44	18	44.3	0.77318	0.69841	0.97586	1.02474	0.71569	0.79762	45.7	45	42
44	24	44.4	0.77492	0.69966	0.97927	1.02117	0.71447	0.79587	45.6	45	36
44	30	44.5	0.77667	0.70091	0.98269	1.01761	0.71325	0.79413	45.5	45	30
44	36	44.6	0.77842	0.70215	0.98613	1.01406	0.71203	0.79238	45.4	45	24
44	42	44.7	0.78016	0.70339	0.98958	1.01053	0.71080	0.79064	45.3	45	18
44	48	44.8	0.78191	0.70463	0.99304	1.00701	0.70957	0.78889	45.2	45	12
44	54	44.9	0.78365	0.70587	0.99651	1.00350	0.70834	0.78714	45.1	45	6
45	0	45.0	0.78540	0.70711	1.00000	1.00000	0.70711	0.78540	45.0	45	0
Deg	Min	Deg.	Rad	Cos	Cot	Tan	Sin	Rad	Deg.	Deg	Min

Tables of Squares, Cubes, and Roots of Numbers (Figure M-7)

This table is self-explanatory.

Figure M-7 Table of Number Functions

NUMBER	SQUARE	CUBE	SQUARE ROOT	CUBE ROOT
1	1	1	1.00000	1.00000
2	4	8	1.41421	1.25992
3	9	27	1.73205	1.44225
4	16	64	2.00000	1.58740
5	25	125	2.23607	1.70998
6	36	216	2.44949	1.81712
7	49	343	2.64575	1.91293
8	64	512	2.82843	2.00000
9	81	729	3.00000	2.08008
10	100	1000	3.16228	2.15443
11	121	1331	3.31662	2.22398
12	144	1728	3.46410	2.28943
13	169	2197	3.60555	2.35133
14	196	2744	3.74166	2.41014
15	225	3375	3.87298	2.46621
16	256	4096	4.00000	2.51984
17	289	4913	4.12311	2.57128
18	324	5832	4.24264	2.62074
19	361	6859	4.35890	2.66840
20	400	8000	4.47214	2.71442
21	441	9261	4.58258	2.75892
22	484	10648	4.69042	2.80204
23	529	12167	4.79583	2.84387
24	576	13824	4.89898	2.88450
25	625	15625	5.00000	2.92402
26	676	17576	5.09902	2.96250
27	729	19683	5.19615	3.00000
28	784	21952	5.29150	3.03659
29	841	24389	5.38517	3.07232
30	900	27000	5.47723	3.10723
31	961	29791	5.56777	3.14138
32	1024	32768	5.65686	3.17480
33	1089	35937	5.74456	3.20753
34	1156	39304	5.83095	3.23961
35	1225	42875	5.91608	3.27107
36	1296	46656	6.00000	3.30193
37	1369	50653	6.08276	3.33222
38	1444	54872	6.16441	3.36198
39	1521	59319	6.24500	3.39121
40	1600	64000	6.32456	3.41995
41	1681	68921	6.40312	3.44822
42	1764	74088	6.48074	3.47603
43	1849	79507	6.55744	3.50340
44	1936	85184	6.63325	3.53035
45	2025	91125	6.70821	3.55689
46	2116	97336	6.78233	3.58305
47	2209	103823	6.85566	3.60883
48	2304	110592	6.92820	3.63424
49	2401	117649	7.00000	3.65931
50	2500	125000	7.07107	3.68403

Figure M-7 Table of Number Functions
(continued)

NUMBER	SQUARE	CUBE	SQUARE ROOT	CUBE ROOT
51	2601	132651	7.14143	3.70843
52	2704	140608	7.21110	3.73251
53	2809	148877	7.28011	3.75629
54	2916	157464	7.34847	3.77976
55	3025	166375	7.41620	3.80295
56	3136	175616	7.48331	3.82586
57	3249	185193	7.54983	3.84850
58	3364	195112	7.61578	3.87088
59	3481	205379	7.68115	3.89300
60	3600	216000	7.74597	3.91487
61	3721	226981	7.81025	3.93650
62	3844	238328	7.87401	3.95789
63	3969	250047	7.93726	3.97906
64	4096	262144	8.00000	4.00000
65	4225	274625	8.06226	4.02073
66	4356	287496	8.12404	4.04124
67	4489	300763	8.18536	4.06155
68	4624	314432	8.24621	4.08166
69	4761	328509	8.30662	4.10157
70	4900	343000	8.36660	4.12128
71	5041	357911	8.42615	4.14082
72	5184	373248	8.48528	4.16017
73	5329	389017	8.54400	4.17934
74	5476	405224	8.60233	4.19834
75	5625	421875	8.66026	4.21716
76	5776	438976	8.71780	4.23582
77	5929	456533	8.77496	4.25432
78	6084	474553	8.83176	4.27266
79	6241	493039	8.88819	4.29084
80	6400	512000	8.94427	4.30887
81	6561	531441	9.00000	4.32675
82	6724	551368	9.05539	4.34448
83	6889	571788	9.11043	4.36207
84	7056	592703	9.16515	4.37952
85	7225	614126	9.21954	4.39683
86	7396	636056	9.27362	4.41401
87	7569	658503	9.32738	4.43105
88	7744	681472	9.38083	4.44796
89	7921	704969	9.43398	4.46474
90	8100	729000	9.48683	4.48140
91	8281	753571	9.53939	4.49794
92	8464	778688	9.59166	4.51436
93	8649	804357	9.64365	4.53066
94	8836	830584	9.69536	4.54684
95	9025	857375	9.74680	4.56290
96	9216	884736	9.79796	4.57886
97	9409	912673	9.84886	4.59470
98	9604	941192	9.89950	4.61044
99	9801	970300	9.94988	4.62607
100	10000	1000000	10.00000	4.64159

Figure M-7 Table of Number Functions
(continued)

NUMBER	SQUARE	CUBE	SQUARE ROOT	CUBE ROOT
101	10201	1030300	10.0499	4.65701
102	10404	1061210	10.0995	4.67233
103	10609	1092730	10.1489	4.68755
104	10816	1124860	10.1980	4.70267
105	11025	1157620	10.2470	4.71769
106	11236	1191020	10.2956	4.73262
107	11449	1225040	10.3441	4.74746
108	11664	1259710	10.3923	4.76220
109	11881	1295030	10.4403	4.77686
110	12100	1331000	10.4881	4.79142
111	12321	1367630	10.5357	4.80590
112	12544	1404930	10.5830	4.82028
113	12769	1442900	10.6301	4.83459
114	12996	1481540	10.6771	4.84881
115	13225	1520880	10.7238	4.86295
116	13456	1560900	10.7703	4.87700
117	13689	1601610	10.8167	4.89097
118	13924	1643030	10.8628	4.90487
119	14161	1685160	10.9087	4.91869
120	14400	1728000	10.9545	4.93242
121	14641	1771560	11.0000	4.94609
122	14884	1815850	11.0454	4.95968
123	15129	1860870	11.0905	4.97319
124	15376	1906620	11.1355	4.98663
125	15625	1953120	11.1803	5.00000
126	15876	2000380	11.2250	5.01330
127	16129	2048380	11.2694	5.02653
128	16384	2097150	11.3137	5.03968
129	16641	2146690	11.3578	5.05277
130	16900	2197000	11.4018	5.06580
131	17161	2248090	11.4455	5.07875
132	17424	2299970	11.4891	5.09164
133	17689	2352640	11.5326	5.10447
134	17956	2406110	11.5758	5.11723
135	18225	2460380	11.6190	5.12993
136	18496	2515460	11.6619	5.14256
137	18769	2571350	11.7047	5.15514
138	19044	2628070	11.7473	5.16765
139	19321	2685620	11.7898	5.18010
140	19600	2744000	11.8322	5.19249
141	19881	2803220	11.8743	5.20483
142	20164	2863280	11.9164	5.21710
143	20449	2924210	11.9583	5.22932
144	20736	2985980	12.0000	5.24148
145	21025	3048630	12.0416	5.25359
146	21316	3112140	12.0830	5.26564
147	21609	3176530	12.1244	5.27763
148	21904	3241790	12.1655	5.28957
149	22201	3307950	12.2066	5.30146
150	22500	3375000	12.2475	5.31329

Figure M-7 Table of Number Functions
(continued)

NUMBER	SQUARE	CUBE	SQUARE ROOT	CUBE ROOT
151	22801	3442950	12.2882	5.32507
152	23104	3511810	12.3288	5.33680
153	23409	3581580	12.3693	5.34848
154	23716	3652260	12.4097	5.36011
155	24025	3723870	12.4499	5.37169
156	24336	3796420	12.4900	5.38321
157	24649	3869890	12.5300	5.39469
158	24964	3944310	12.5698	5.40612
159	25281	4019680	12.6095	5.41750
160	25600	4096000	12.6491	5.42884
161	25921	4173280	12.6886	5.44012
162	26244	4251530	12.7279	5.45136
163	26569	4330740	12.7671	5.46256
164	26896	4410950	12.8062	5.47370
165	27225	4492130	12.8452	5.48481
166	27556	4574300	12.8841	5.49587
167	27889	4657470	12.9229	5.50688
168	28224	4741630	12.9615	5.51785
169	28561	4826810	13.0000	5.52877
170	28900	4913000	13.0384	5.53966
171	29241	5000210	13.0767	5.55050
172	29584	5088450	13.1149	5.56130
173	29929	5177720	13.1529	5.57206
174	30276	5268030	13.1909	5.58277
175	30625	5359380	13.2288	5.59345
176	30976	5451780	13.2665	5.60408
177	31329	5545230	13.3041	5.61467
178	31684	5639750	13.3417	5.62523
179	32041	5735340	13.3791	5.63574
180	32400	5832000	13.4164	5.64622
181	32761	5929740	13.4536	5.65665
182	33124	6028570	13.4907	5.66705
183	33489	6128480	13.5277	5.67741
184	33856	6229510	13.5647	5.68773
185	34225	6331630	13.6015	5.69802
186	34596	6434860	13.6382	5.70827
187	34969	6539210	13.6748	5.71848
188	35344	6644670	13.7113	5.72866
189	35721	6751260	13.7477	5.73879
190	36100	6859010	13.7841	5.74890
191	36481	6967870	13.8203	5.75897
192	36864	7077890	13.8564	5.76900
193	37249	7189060	13.8924	5.77900
194	37636	7301380	13.9284	5.78896
195	38025	7414880	13.9642	5.79889
196	38416	7529540	14.0000	5.80879
197	38809	7645370	14.0357	5.81865
198	39204	7762390	14.0713	5.82848
199	39601	7880600	14.1067	5.83827
200	40000	8000000	14.1421	5.84804

Figure M-7 Table of Number Functions
(continued)

NUMBER	SQUARE	CUBE	SQUARE ROOT	CUBE ROOT
201	40401	8120590	14.1774	5.85777
202	40804	8242420	14.2127	5.86747
203	41209	8365440	14.2478	5.87713
204	41616	8489660	14.2829	5.88677
205	42025	8615130	14.3178	5.89637
206	42436	8741820	14.3527	5.90594
207	42849	8869750	14.3875	5.91548
208	43264	8998920	14.4222	5.92499
209	43681	9129320	14.4568	5.93447
210	44100	9261000	14.4914	5.94392
211	44521	9393930	14.5258	5.95334
212	44944	9528130	14.5602	5.96273
213	45369	9663610	14.5945	5.97209
214	45796	9800340	14.6287	5.98142
215	46225	9938370	14.6629	5.99073
216	46656	10077700	14.6969	6.00000
217	47089	10218300	14.7309	6.00925
218	47524	10360200	14.7648	6.01846
219	47961	10503500	14.7986	6.02765
220	48400	10648000	14.8324	6.03681
221	48841	10793800	14.8661	6.04594
222	49284	10941000	14.8997	6.05505
223	49729	11089600	14.9332	6.06413
224	50176	11239400	14.9666	6.07318
225	50625	11390600	15.0000	6.08220
226	51076	11543200	15.0333	6.09120
227	51529	11697100	15.0665	6.10017
228	51984	11852300	15.0997	6.10912
229	52441	12009000	15.1327	6.11803
230	52900	12167000	15.1658	6.12693
231	53361	12326400	15.1987	6.13579
232	53824	12487200	15.2316	6.14464
233	54289	12649300	15.2643	6.15345
234	54756	12812900	15.2971	6.16224
235	55225	12977900	15.3297	6.17101
236	55696	13144300	15.3623	6.17975
237	56169	13312100	15.3948	6.18846
238	56644	13481300	15.4273	6.19716
239	57121	13651900	15.4596	6.20582
240	57600	13824000	15.4919	6.21447
241	58081	13997500	15.5242	6.22309
242	58564	14172500	15.5563	6.23168
243	59049	14348900	15.5885	6.24025
244	59536	14526800	15.6205	6.24880
245	60025	14706100	15.6525	6.25732
246	60516	14886900	15.6844	6.26583
247	61009	15069200	15.7162	6.27431
248	61504	15253000	15.7480	6.28276
249	62001	15438200	15.7797	6.29119
250	62500	15625000	15.8114	6.29961

Figure M-7 Table of Number Functions
(continued)

NUMBER	SQUARE	CUBE	SQUARE ROOT	CUBE ROOT
251	63001	15813300	15.8430	6.30799
252	63504	16003000	15.8745	6.31636
253	64009	16194300	15.9060	6.32470
254	64516	16387100	15.9374	6.33303
255	65025	16581400	15.9687	6.34133
256	65536	16777200	16.0000	6.34961
257	66049	16974600	16.0312	6.35786
258	66564	17173500	16.0624	6.36610
259	67081	17374000	16.0935	6.37431
260	67600	17576000	16.1245	6.38250
261	68121	17779600	16.1555	6.39068
262	68644	17984700	16.1864	6.39883
263	69169	18191400	16.2173	6.40696
264	69696	18399700	16.2481	6.41507
265	70225	18609700	16.2788	6.42316
266	70756	18821100	16.3095	6.43123
267	71289	19034200	16.3401	6.43928
268	71824	19248800	16.3707	6.44731
269	72361	19465100	16.4012	6.45532
270	72900	19683000	16.4317	6.46331
271	73441	19902500	16.4621	6.47127
272	73984	20123600	16.4924	6.47922
273	74529	20346400	16.5227	6.48715
274	75076	20570800	16.5529	6.49507
275	75625	20796900	16.5831	6.50296
276	76176	21024600	16.6132	6.51083
277	76729	21253900	16.6433	6.51868
278	77284	21484900	16.6733	6.52652
279	77841	21717700	16.7033	6.53434
280	78400	21952000	16.7332	6.54213
281	78961	22188000	16.7631	6.54991
282	79524	22425700	16.7929	6.55767
283	80089	22665200	16.8226	6.56541
284	80656	22906300	16.8523	6.57314
285	81225	23149200	16.8819	6.58085
286	81796	23393700	16.9115	6.58853
287	82369	23639900	16.9411	6.59620
288	82944	23887900	16.9706	6.60386
289	83521	24137600	17.0000	6.61149
290	84100	24389000	17.0294	6.61911
291	84681	24642200	17.0587	6.62671
292	85264	24897000	17.0880	6.63429
293	85849	25153800	17.1172	6.64185
294	86436	25412200	17.1464	6.64940
295	87025	25672300	17.1756	6.65693
296	87616	25934300	17.2047	6.66444
297	88209	26198100	17.2337	6.67194
298	88804	26463600	17.2627	6.67942
299	89401	26730900	17.2916	6.68688
300	90000	27000000	17.3205	6.69433

Figure M-7 Table of Number Functions
(continued)

NUMBER	SQUARE	CUBE	SQUARE ROOT	CUBE ROOT
301	90601	27270900	17.3494	6.70176
302	91204	27543600	17.3781	6.70917
303	91809	27818100	17.4069	6.71657
304	92416	28094500	17.4356	6.72395
305	93025	28372600	17.4643	6.73132
306	93636	28652600	17.4929	6.73867
307	94249	28934500	17.5214	6.74600
308	94864	29218100	17.5499	6.75331
309	95481	29503700	17.5784	6.76062
310	96100	29791000	17.6068	6.76790
311	96721	30080300	17.6352	6.77517
312	97344	30371300	17.6635	6.78242
313	97969	30664300	17.6918	6.78966
314	98596	30959100	17.7200	6.79688
315	99225	31255900	17.7482	6.80409
316	99856	31554500	17.7764	6.81128
317	100489	31855000	17.8045	6.81846
318	101124	32157500	17.8326	6.82563
319	101761	32461800	17.8606	6.83277
320	102400	32768000	17.8885	6.83991
321	103041	33076200	17.9165	6.84702
322	103684	33386200	17.9444	6.85413
323	104329	33698200	17.9722	6.86121
324	104976	34012300	18.0000	6.86829
325	105625	34328100	18.0278	6.87534
326	106276	34645900	18.0555	6.88239
327	106929	34965800	18.0831	6.88942
328	107584	35287500	18.1108	6.89643
329	108241	35611300	18.1384	6.90344
330	108900	35937000	18.1659	6.91042
331	109561	36264700	18.1934	6.91740
332	110224	36594400	18.2209	6.92436
333	110889	36926100	18.2483	6.93130
334	111556	37259700	18.2757	6.93823
335	112225	37595400	18.3030	6.94515
336	112896	37933100	18.3303	6.95206
337	113569	38272700	18.3576	6.95894
338	114244	38614400	18.3848	6.96582
339	114921	38958200	18.4120	6.97268
340	115600	39303900	18.4391	6.97953
341	116281	39651800	18.4662	6.98637
342	116964	40001700	18.4932	6.99319
343	117649	40353600	18.5203	7.00000
344	118336	40707600	18.5472	7.00680
345	119025	41063700	18.5742	7.01358
346	119716	41421700	18.6011	7.02035
347	120409	41782000	18.6279	7.02711
348	121104	42144200	18.6548	7.03385
349	121801	42508500	18.6815	7.04058
350	122500	42875000	18.7083	7.04730

Figure M-7 Table of Number Functions
(continued)

NUMBER	SQUARE	CUBE	SQUARE ROOT	CUBE ROOT
351	123201	43243500	18.7350	7.05400
352	123904	43614200	18.7617	7.06070
353	124609	43986900	18.7883	7.06738
354	125316	44361900	18.8149	7.07405
355	126025	44738800	18.8414	7.08070
356	126736	45118000	18.8680	7.08734
357	127449	45499300	18.8944	7.09397
358	128164	45882800	18.9209	7.10059
359	128881	46268300	18.9473	7.10719
360	129600	46656000	18.9737	7.11379
361	130321	47046000	19.0000	7.12037
362	131044	47437900	19.0263	7.12694
363	131769	47832100	19.0526	7.13349
364	132496	48228600	19.0788	7.14004
365	133225	48627200	19.1050	7.14657
366	133956	49027900	19.1311	7.15309
367	134689	49430900	19.1572	7.15960
368	135424	49835900	19.1833	7.16609
369	136161	50243400	19.2094	7.17258
370	136900	50653000	19.2354	7.17906
371	137641	51064800	19.2614	7.18552
372	138384	51478800	19.2873	7.19197
373	139129	51895200	19.3132	7.19841
374	139876	52313500	19.3391	7.20483
375	140625	52734400	19.3649	7.21125
376	141376	53157500	19.3907	7.21765
377	142129	53582700	19.4165	7.22405
378	142884	54010100	19.4422	7.23043
379	143641	54439900	19.4679	7.23680
380	144400	54872100	19.4936	7.24316
381	145161	55306400	19.5192	7.24951
382	145924	55743000	19.5448	7.25584
383	146689	56182000	19.5704	7.26217
384	147456	56623100	19.5959	7.26848
385	148225	57066600	19.6214	7.27479
386	148996	57512400	19.6469	7.28108
387	149769	57960700	19.6723	7.28736
388	150544	58411100	19.6977	7.29363
389	151321	58863900	19.7231	7.29989
390	152100	59319100	19.7484	7.30614
391	152881	59776400	19.7737	7.31238
392	153664	60236300	19.7990	7.31861
393	154449	60698400	19.8242	7.32483
394	155236	61163100	19.8494	7.33104
395	156025	61629800	19.8746	7.33723
396	156816	62099100	19.8997	7.34342
397	157609	62570900	19.9249	7.34960
398	158404	63044700	19.9499	7.35576
399	159201	63521200	19.9750	7.36192
400	160000	64000000	20.0000	7.36806

Figure M-7 Table of Number Functions
(continued)

NUMBER	SQUARE	CUBE	SQUARE ROOT	CUBE ROOT
401	160801	64481200	20.0250	7.37420
402	161604	64964700	20.0499	7.38032
403	162409	65450900	20.0749	7.38644
404	163216	65939300	20.0998	7.39254
405	164025	66430100	20.1246	7.39864
406	164836	66923300	20.1494	7.40472
407	165649	67419100	20.1742	7.41080
408	166464	67917300	20.1990	7.41686
409	167281	68417900	20.2237	7.42292
410	168100	68921100	20.2485	7.42896
411	168921	69426600	20.2731	7.43499
412	169744	69934500	20.2978	7.44102
413	170569	70445000	20.3224	7.44703
414	171396	70958000	20.3470	7.45304
415	172225	71473400	20.3715	7.45904
416	173056	71991200	20.3961	7.46502
417	173889	72511700	20.4206	7.47100
418	174724	73034700	20.4451	7.47697
419	175561	73560200	20.4695	7.48293
420	176400	74088100	20.4939	7.48887
421	177241	74618300	20.5183	7.49481
422	178084	75151400	20.5426	7.50074
423	178929	75687000	20.5670	7.50666
424	179776	76225000	20.5913	7.51257
425	180625	76765700	20.6155	7.51848
426	181476	77308900	20.6398	7.52437
427	182329	77854500	20.6640	7.53025
428	183184	78402800	20.6882	7.53612
429	184041	78953700	20.7123	7.54199
430	184900	79506900	20.7364	7.54784
431	185761	80062900	20.7605	7.55369
432	186624	80621500	20.7846	7.55953
433	187489	81182700	20.8087	7.56536
434	188356	81746500	20.8327	7.57117
435	189225	82312900	20.8567	7.57698
436	190096	82881900	20.8806	7.58279
437	190969	83453500	20.9045	7.58858
438	191844	84027600	20.9285	7.59436
439	192721	84604500	20.9523	7.60014
440	193600	85184100	20.9762	7.60591
441	194481	85766000	21.0000	7.61166
442	195364	86350800	21.0238	7.61741
443	196249	86938200	21.0476	7.62315
444	197136	87528400	21.0713	7.62888
445	198025	88121200	21.0950	7.63461
446	198916	88716500	21.1187	7.64032
447	199809	89314800	21.1424	7.64603
448	200704	89915300	21.1660	7.65172
449	201601	90518700	21.1896	7.65742
450	202500	91125000	21.2132	7.66309

Figure M-7 Table of Number Functions
(continued)

NUMBER	SQUARE	CUBE	SQUARE ROOT	CUBE ROOT
451	203401	91733700	21.2368	7.66877
452	204304	92345400	21.2603	7.67443
453	205209	92959600	21.2838	7.68009
454	206116	93576600	21.3073	7.68573
455	207025	94196500	21.3307	7.69137
456	207936	94818900	21.3542	7.69700
457	208849	95443900	21.3776	7.70263
458	209764	96071900	21.4009	7.70824
459	210681	96702500	21.4243	7.71384
460	211600	97336200	21.4476	7.71945
461	212521	97972100	21.4709	7.72503
462	213444	98611200	21.4942	7.73062
463	214369	99252900	21.5174	7.73619
464	215296	99897300	21.5407	7.74175
465	216225	100545000	21.5639	7.74731
466	217156	101195000	21.5870	7.75286
467	218089	101848000	21.6102	7.75840
468	219024	102503000	21.6333	7.76394
469	219961	103162000	21.6564	7.76946
470	220900	103823000	21.6795	7.77498
471	221841	104487000	21.7025	7.78049
472	222784	105154000	21.7256	7.78599
473	223729	105824000	21.7486	7.79149
474	224676	106497000	21.7715	7.79698
475	225625	107172000	21.7945	7.80245
476	226576	107850000	21.8174	7.80793
477	227529	108531000	21.8403	7.81339
478	228484	109215000	21.8632	7.81885
479	229441	109902000	21.8861	7.82429
480	230400	110592000	21.9089	7.82974
481	231361	111284000	21.9317	7.83517
482	232324	111980000	21.9545	7.84059
483	233289	112679000	21.9773	7.84601
484	234256	113380000	22.0000	7.85142
485	235225	114084000	22.0227	7.85683
486	236196	114791000	22.0454	7.86223
487	237169	115501000	22.0681	7.86761
488	238144	116214000	22.0907	7.87300
489	239121	116930000	22.1134	7.87837
490	240100	117649000	22.1359	7.88374
491	241081	118371000	22.1585	7.88910
492	242064	119095000	22.1811	7.89445
493	243049	119823000	22.2036	7.89979
494	244036	120554000	22.2261	7.90513
495	245025	121287000	22.2486	7.91046
496	246016	122024000	22.2711	7.91578
497	247009	122764000	22.2935	7.92110
498	248004	123506000	22.3159	7.92641
499	249001	124252000	22.3383	7.93171
500	250000	125000000	22.3607	7.93701

Figure M-7 Table of Number Functions
(continued)

NUMBER	SQUARE	CUBE	SQUARE ROOT	CUBE ROOT
501	251001	125751000	22.3830	7.94229
502	252004	126506000	22.4054	7.94757
503	253009	127263000	22.4277	7.95285
504	254016	128024000	22.4499	7.95812
505	255025	128788000	22.4722	7.96337
506	256036	129554000	22.4945	7.96863
507	257049	130324000	22.5167	7.97387
508	258064	131096000	22.5389	7.97911
509	259081	131872000	22.5610	7.98435
510	260100	132651000	22.5832	7.98957
511	261121	133433000	22.6053	7.99479
512	262144	134218000	22.6274	8.00000
513	263169	135006000	22.6495	8.00521
514	264196	135797000	22.6716	8.01040
515	265225	136591000	22.6936	8.01559
516	266256	137388000	22.7156	8.02078
517	267289	138188000	22.7376	8.02596
518	268324	138992000	22.7596	8.03113
519	269361	139798000	22.7816	8.03629
520	270400	140608000	22.8035	8.04145
521	271441	141421000	22.8254	8.04660
522	272484	142237000	22.8473	8.05175
523	273529	143056000	22.8692	8.05689
524	274576	143878000	22.8911	8.06202
525	275625	144703000	22.9129	8.06715
526	276676	145531000	22.9347	8.07226
527	277729	146363000	22.9565	8.07737
528	278784	147198000	22.9782	8.08248
529	279841	148036000	23.0000	8.08758
530	280900	148877000	23.0217	8.09267
531	281961	149721000	23.0434	8.09776
532	283024	150569000	23.0651	8.10284
533	284089	151420000	23.0868	8.10791
534	285156	152273000	23.1084	8.11298
535	286225	153130000	23.1301	8.11804
536	287296	153997000	23.1517	8.12310
537	288369	154854000	23.1733	8.12814
538	289444	155721000	23.1948	8.13319
539	290521	156591000	23.2164	8.13822
540	291600	157464000	23.2379	8.14325
541	292681	158340000	23.2594	8.14828
542	293764	159220000	23.2809	8.15329
543	294849	160103000	23.3024	8.15831
544	295936	160989000	23.3238	8.16331
545	297025	161879000	23.3452	8.16831
546	298116	162771000	23.3666	8.17330
547	299209	163667000	23.3880	8.17829
548	300304	164567000	23.4094	8.18327
549	301401	165469000	23.4307	8.18824
550	302500	166375000	23.4521	8.19321

Figure M-7 Table of Number Functions
(continued)

NUMBER	SQUARE	CUBE	SQUARE ROOT	CUBE ROOT
551	303601	167284000	23.4734	8.19818
552	304704	168197000	23.4947	8.20313
553	305809	169112000	23.5160	8.20808
554	306916	170031000	23.5372	8.21303
555	308025	170954000	23.5584	8.21796
556	309136	171880000	23.5797	8.22290
557	310249	172809000	23.6008	8.22783
558	311364	173741000	23.6220	8.23275
559	312481	174677000	23.6432	8.23766
560	313600	175616000	23.6643	8.24257
561	314721	176558000	23.6854	8.24747
562	315844	177505000	23.7065	8.25237
563	316969	178453000	23.7276	8.25726
564	318096	179406000	23.7487	8.26215
565	319225	180362000	23.7697	8.26703
566	320356	181321000	23.7908	8.27191
567	321489	182285000	23.8118	8.27677
568	322624	183250000	23.8328	8.28164
569	323761	184220000	23.8537	8.28649
570	324900	185193000	23.8747	8.29135
571	326041	186169000	23.8956	8.29619
572	327184	187149000	23.9165	8.30103
573	328329	188133000	23.9374	8.30587
574	329476	189119000	23.9583	8.31069
575	330625	190109000	23.9792	8.31552
576	331776	191103000	24.0000	8.32034
577	332929	192100000	24.0208	8.32515
578	334084	193100000	24.0416	8.32996
579	335241	194105000	24.0624	8.33476
580	336400	195112000	24.0832	8.33955
581	337561	196123000	24.1039	8.34434
582	338724	197137000	24.1247	8.34913
583	339889	198155000	24.1454	8.35391
584	341056	199177000	24.1661	8.35868
585	342225	200202000	24.1868	8.36345
586	343396	201230000	24.2074	8.36821
587	344569	202262000	24.2281	8.37297
588	345744	203298000	24.2487	8.37772
589	346921	204336000	24.2693	8.38247
590	348100	205379000	24.2899	8.38721
591	349281	206425000	24.3105	8.39194
592	350464	207475000	24.3311	8.39667
593	351649	208528000	24.3516	8.40140
594	352836	209585000	24.3721	8.40612
595	354025	210645000	24.3926	8.41083
596	355216	211709000	24.4131	8.41554
597	356409	212776000	24.4336	8.42025
598	357604	213847000	24.4540	8.42495
599	358801	214921000	24.4745	8.42964
600	360000	216000000	24.4949	8.43433

Figure M-7 Table of Number Functions
(continued)

NUMBER	SQUARE	CUBE	SQUARE ROOT	CUBE ROOT
601	361201	217082000	24.5153	8.43901
602	362404	218167000	24.5357	8.44369
603	363609	219256000	24.5561	8.44836
604	364816	220349000	24.5764	8.45303
605	366025	221445000	24.5967	8.45769
606	367236	222545000	24.6171	8.46235
607	368449	223648000	24.6374	8.46700
608	369664	224756000	24.6577	8.47165
609	370881	225867000	24.6779	8.47629
610	372100	226981000	24.6982	8.48093
611	373321	228099000	24.7184	8.48556
612	374544	229221000	24.7386	8.49018
613	375769	230347000	24.7588	8.49481
614	376996	231475000	24.7790	8.49942
615	378225	232609000	24.7992	8.50404
616	379456	233745000	24.8193	8.50864
617	380689	234885000	24.8395	8.51324
618	381924	236029000	24.8596	8.51784
619	383161	237177000	24.8797	8.52243
620	384400	238328000	24.8998	8.52702
621	385641	239483000	24.9199	8.53160
622	386884	240642000	24.9399	8.53618
623	388129	241805000	24.9600	8.54075
624	389376	242971000	24.9800	8.54532
625	390625	244140000	25.0000	8.54988
626	391876	245315000	25.0200	8.55444
627	393129	246492000	25.0400	8.55899
628	394384	247673000	25.0599	8.56354
629	395641	248858000	25.0799	8.56808
630	396900	250047000	25.0998	8.57262
631	398161	251240000	25.1197	8.57715
632	399424	252436000	25.1396	8.58168
633	400689	253636000	25.1595	8.58621
634	401956	254840000	25.1794	8.59073
635	403225	256048000	25.1992	8.59524
636	404496	257260000	25.2190	8.59975
637	405769	258474000	25.2389	8.60425
638	407044	259694000	25.2587	8.60875
639	408321	260918000	25.2785	8.61325
640	409600	262144000	25.2982	8.61774
641	410881	263374000	25.3180	8.62223
642	412164	264609000	25.3377	8.62671
643	413449	265848000	25.3575	8.63118
644	414736	267090000	25.3772	8.63566
645	416025	268336000	25.3969	8.64012
646	417316	269586000	25.4165	8.64459
647	418609	270840000	25.4362	8.64904
648	419904	272098000	25.4559	8.65350
649	421201	273359000	25.4755	8.65795
650	422500	274625000	25.4951	8.66239

Figure M-7 Table of Number Functions
(continued)

NUMBER	SQUARE	CUBE	SQUARE ROOT	CUBE ROOT
651	423801	275894000	25.5147	8.66683
652	425104	277168000	25.5343	8.67127
653	426409	278445000	25.5539	8.67570
654	427716	279726000	25.5734	8.68012
655	429025	281012000	25.5930	8.68455
656	430336	282300000	25.6125	8.68896
657	431649	283593000	25.6320	8.69338
658	432964	284891000	25.6515	8.69779
659	434281	286191000	25.6710	8.70219
660	435600	287496000	25.6905	8.70659
661	436921	288805000	25.7099	8.71098
662	438244	290117000	25.7294	8.71537
663	439569	291434000	25.7488	8.71976
664	440896	292755000	25.7682	8.72414
665	442225	294080000	25.7876	8.72852
666	443556	295408000	25.8070	8.73289
667	444889	296741000	25.8263	8.73726
668	446224	298078000	25.8457	8.74162
669	447561	299419000	25.8650	8.74598
670	448900	300763000	25.8844	8.75034
671	450241	302112000	25.9037	8.75469
672	451584	303465000	25.9230	8.75904
673	452929	304821000	25.9422	8.76338
674	454276	306182000	25.9615	8.76772
675	455625	307547000	25.9808	8.77206
676	456976	308915000	26.0000	8.77638
677	458329	310289000	26.0192	8.78071
678	459684	311666000	26.0384	8.78503
679	461041	313047000	26.0576	8.78935
680	462400	314431000	26.0768	8.79366
681	463761	315821000	26.0960	8.79797
682	465124	317214000	26.1151	8.80227
683	466489	318612000	26.1343	8.80657
684	467856	320013000	26.1534	8.81087
685	469225	321419000	26.1725	8.81516
686	470596	322829000	26.1916	8.81945
687	471969	324243000	26.2107	8.82373
688	473344	325660000	26.2298	8.82801
689	474721	327083000	26.2488	8.83228
690	476100	328509000	26.2679	8.83656
691	477481	329940000	26.2869	8.84082
692	478864	331374000	26.3059	8.84509
693	480249	332813000	26.3249	8.84934
694	481636	334255000	26.3439	8.85360
695	483025	335703000	26.3629	8.85785
696	484416	337154000	26.3818	8.86210
697	485809	338609000	26.4008	8.86634
698	487204	340068000	26.4197	8.87058
699	488601	341532000	26.4386	8.87481
700	490000	343000000	26.4575	8.87904

Figure M-7 Table of Number Functions
(continued)

NUMBER	SQUARE	CUBE	SQUARE ROOT	CUBE ROOT
701	491401	344472000	26.4764	8.88327
702	492804	345949000	26.4953	8.88749
703	494209	347429000	26.5142	8.89171
704	495616	348914000	26.5330	8.89592
705	497025	350402000	26.5518	8.90013
706	498436	351896000	26.5707	8.90434
707	499849	353393000	26.5895	8.90854
708	501264	354895000	26.6083	8.91274
709	502681	356401000	26.6271	8.91693
710	504100	357911000	26.6458	8.92112
711	505521	359426000	26.6646	8.92531
712	506944	360945000	26.6833	8.92949
713	508369	362467000	26.7021	8.93367
714	509796	363994000	26.7208	8.93784
715	511225	365525000	26.7395	8.94201
716	512656	367062000	26.7582	8.94618
717	514089	368603000	26.7769	8.95034
718	515524	370146000	26.7955	8.95450
719	516961	371695000	26.8142	8.95866
720	518400	373247000	26.8328	8.96281
721	519841	374806000	26.8514	8.96696
722	521284	376367000	26.8701	8.97110
723	522729	377933000	26.8887	8.97524
724	524176	379503000	26.9072	8.97938
725	525625	381078000	26.9258	8.98351
726	527076	382658000	26.9444	8.98764
727	528529	384241000	26.9629	8.99176
728	529984	385828000	26.9815	8.99588
729	531441	387421000	27.0000	9.00000
730	532900	389017000	27.0185	9.00412
731	534361	390618000	27.0370	9.00822
732	535824	392223000	27.0555	9.01233
733	537289	393834000	27.0740	9.01643
734	538756	395447000	27.0924	9.02053
735	540225	397066000	27.1109	9.02462
736	541696	398688000	27.1293	9.02871
737	543169	400316000	27.1477	9.03280
738	544644	401947000	27.1662	9.03689
739	546121	403584000	27.1846	9.04097
740	547600	405225000	27.2029	9.04504
741	549081	406870000	27.2213	9.04912
742	550564	408519000	27.2397	9.05318
743	552049	410173000	27.2580	9.05725
744	553536	411831000	27.2764	9.06131
745	555025	413493000	27.2947	9.06537
746	556516	415161000	27.3130	9.06942
747	558009	416833000	27.3313	9.07347
748	559504	418508000	27.3496	9.07752
749	561001	420190000	27.3679	9.08156
750	562500	421875000	27.3861	9.08560

Figure M-7 Table of Number Functions
(continued)

NUMBER	SQUARE	CUBE	SQUARE ROOT	CUBE ROOT
751	564001	423565000	27.4044	9.08964
752	565504	425259000	27.4226	9.09367
753	567009	426958000	27.4408	9.09770
754	568516	428662000	27.4591	9.10173
755	570025	430369000	27.4773	9.10575
756	571536	432081000	27.4955	9.10977
757	573049	433798000	27.5136	9.11378
758	574564	435520000	27.5318	9.11779
759	576081	437246000	27.5500	9.12180
760	577600	438976000	27.5681	9.12581
761	579121	440711000	27.5862	9.12981
762	580644	442451000	27.6044	9.13380
763	582169	444194000	27.6225	9.13780
764	583696	445944000	27.6406	9.14179
765	585225	447697000	27.6586	9.14577
766	586756	449455000	27.6767	9.14976
767	588289	451218000	27.6948	9.15374
768	589824	452985000	27.7128	9.15771
769	591361	454757000	27.7308	9.16169
770	592900	456532000	27.7489	9.16566
771	594441	458313000	27.7669	9.16962
772	595984	460099000	27.7849	9.17359
773	597529	461890000	27.8029	9.17755
774	599076	463685000	27.8209	9.18150
775	600625	465486000	27.8388	9.18545
776	602176	467288000	27.8568	9.18940
777	603729	469098000	27.8747	9.19335
778	605284	470910000	27.8927	9.19729
779	606841	472729000	27.9106	9.20123
780	608400	474552000	27.9285	9.20517
781	609961	476379000	27.9464	9.20909
782	611524	478212000	27.9643	9.21302
783	613089	480049000	27.9821	9.21695
784	614656	481890000	28.0000	9.22087
785	616225	483736000	28.0179	9.22479
786	617796	485588000	28.0357	9.22871
787	619369	487444000	28.0535	9.23262
788	620944	489305000	28.0713	9.23653
789	622521	491169000	28.0891	9.24043
790	624100	493038000	28.1069	9.24434
791	625681	494913000	28.1247	9.24824
792	627264	496793000	28.1425	9.25213
793	628849	498677000	28.1603	9.25602
794	630436	500567000	28.1780	9.25991
795	632025	502460000	28.1958	9.26380
796	633616	504358000	28.2135	9.26768
797	635209	506262000	28.2312	9.27156
798	636804	508170000	28.2489	9.27544
799	638401	510082000	28.2666	9.27931
800	640000	512000000	28.2843	9.28318

Figure M-7 Table of Number Functions
(continued)

NUMBER	SQUARE	CUBE	SQUARE ROOT	CUBE ROOT
801	641601	513923000	28.3019	9.28705
802	643204	515849000	28.3196	9.29091
803	644809	517781000	28.3373	9.29477
804	646416	519719000	28.3549	9.29862
805	648025	521661000	28.3725	9.30248
806	649636	523607000	28.3901	9.30633
807	651249	525558000	28.4077	9.31018
808	652864	527514000	28.4253	9.31402
809	654481	529475000	28.4429	9.31786
810	656100	531441000	28.4605	9.32170
811	657721	533412000	28.4781	9.32553
812	659344	535387000	28.4956	9.32936
813	660969	537367000	28.5132	9.33319
814	662596	539354000	28.5307	9.33702
815	664225	541343000	28.5482	9.34084
816	665856	543338000	28.5657	9.34466
817	667489	545339000	28.5832	9.34847
818	669124	547343000	28.6007	9.35229
819	670761	549354000	28.6182	9.35610
820	672400	551369000	28.6356	9.35990
821	674041	553387000	28.6531	9.36371
822	675684	555413000	28.6705	9.36750
823	677329	557442000	28.6880	9.37130
824	678976	559476000	28.7054	9.37510
825	680625	561516000	28.7228	9.37889
826	682276	563560000	28.7402	9.38268
827	683929	565610000	28.7576	9.38646
828	685584	567664000	28.7750	9.39024
829	687241	569723000	28.7924	9.39402
830	688900	571786000	28.8097	9.39780
831	690561	573857000	28.8271	9.40157
832	692224	575930000	28.8444	9.40534
833	693889	578009000	28.8617	9.40911
834	695556	580093000	28.8791	9.41287
835	697225	582182000	28.8964	9.41663
836	698896	584277000	28.9137	9.42039
837	700569	586376000	28.9310	9.42414
838	702244	588481000	28.9482	9.42789
839	703921	590591000	28.9655	9.43164
840	705600	592705000	28.9828	9.43539
841	707281	594823000	29.0000	9.43913
842	708964	596947000	29.0172	9.44287
843	710649	599077000	29.0345	9.44661
844	712336	601212000	29.0517	9.45034
845	714025	603352000	29.0689	9.45407
846	715716	605497000	29.0861	9.45780
847	717409	607645000	29.1033	9.46153
848	719104	609801000	29.1204	9.46525
849	720801	611962000	29.1376	9.46897
850	722500	614125000	29.1548	9.47268

Figure M-7 Table of Number Functions
(continued)

NUMBER	SQUARE	CUBE	SQUARE ROOT	CUBE ROOT
851	724201	616294000	29.1719	9.47639
852	725904	618470000	29.1890	9.48011
853	727609	620650000	29.2062	9.48381
854	729316	622836000	29.2233	9.48752
855	731025	625027000	29.2404	9.49122
856	732736	627222000	29.2575	9.49492
857	734449	629424000	29.2746	9.49862
858	736164	631629000	29.2916	9.50231
859	737881	633840000	29.3087	9.50600
860	739600	636056000	29.3258	9.50969
861	741321	638277000	29.3428	9.51337
862	743044	640504000	29.3598	9.51705
863	744769	642735000	29.3769	9.52073
864	746496	644973000	29.3939	9.52441
865	748225	647215000	29.4109	9.52808
866	749956	649462000	29.4279	9.53175
867	751689	651714000	29.4449	9.53542
868	753424	653972000	29.4618	9.53908
869	755161	656235000	29.4788	9.54274
870	756900	658502000	29.4958	9.54640
871	758641	660777000	29.5127	9.55006
872	760384	663055000	29.5297	9.55371
873	762130	665339000	29.5466	9.55736
874	763876	667627000	29.5635	9.56101
875	765625	669922000	29.5804	9.56466
876	767376	672221000	29.5973	9.56830
877	769129	674527000	29.6142	9.57194
878	770884	676836000	29.6311	9.57558
879	772641	679152000	29.6479	9.57921
880	774400	681472000	29.6648	9.58284
881	776161	683797000	29.6816	9.58647
882	777924	686128000	29.6985	9.59009
883	779689	688464000	29.7153	9.59372
884	781456	690808000	29.7321	9.59734
885	783225	693155000	29.7490	9.60096
886	784996	695505000	29.7658	9.60457
887	786769	697864000	29.7825	9.60818
888	788544	700227000	29.7993	9.61179
889	790321	702596000	29.8161	9.61540
890	792100	704969000	29.8329	9.61900
891	793882	707348000	29.8496	9.62260
892	795664	709732000	29.8664	9.62620
893	797449	712121000	29.8831	9.62980
894	799237	714518000	29.8998	9.63339
895	801025	716918000	29.9166	9.63698
896	802816	719324000	29.9333	9.64057
897	804609	721734000	29.9500	9.64416
898	806404	724151000	29.9667	9.64774
899	808201	726573000	29.9833	9.65132
900	810000	729000000	30.0000	9.65489

Figure M-7 Table of Number Functions
(continued)

NUMBER	SQUARE	CUBE	SQUARE ROOT	CUBE ROOT
951	904402	860087000	30.8383	9.8339
952	906304	862801000	30.8545	9.8374
953	908209	865524000	30.8707	9.8408
954	910116	868251000	30.8869	9.8443
955	912025	870984000	30.9031	9.8477
956	913936	873723000	30.9192	9.8511
957	915849	876467000	30.9354	9.8546
958	917764	879220000	30.9516	9.8580
959	919681	881975000	30.9677	9.8614
960	921600	884735000	30.9839	9.8648
961	923521	887504000	31.0000	9.8683
962	925444	890276000	31.0161	9.8717
963	927369	893057000	31.0322	9.8751
964	929296	895841000	31.0484	9.8785
965	931225	898632000	31.0645	9.8819
966	933156	901429000	31.0805	9.8854
967	935089	904231000	31.0966	9.8888
968	937024	907039000	31.1127	9.8922
969	938961	909853000	31.1288	9.8956
970	940900	912673000	31.1448	9.8990
971	942841	915498000	31.1609	9.9024
972	944784	918330000	31.1769	9.9058
973	946729	921168000	31.1930	9.9092
974	948676	924012000	31.2090	9.9126
975	950625	926859000	31.2250	9.9160
976	952576	929715000	31.2410	9.9194
977	954529	932575000	31.2570	9.9227
978	956485	935442000	31.2730	9.9261
979	958442	938314000	31.2890	9.9295
980	960400	941193000	31.3050	9.9329
981	962361	944077000	31.3209	9.9363
982	964324	946966000	31.3369	9.9396
983	966289	949862000	31.3528	9.9430
984	968256	952764000	31.3688	9.9464
985	970225	955673000	31.3847	9.9497
986	972196	958587000	31.4006	9.9531
987	974169	961504000	31.4166	9.9565
988	976144	964429000	31.4325	9.9598
989	978122	967363000	31.4484	9.9632
990	980100	970297000	31.4643	9.9666
991	982082	973244000	31.4802	9.9699
992	984064	976192000	31.4960	9.9733
993	986050	979149000	31.5119	9.9766
994	988036	982107000	31.5278	9.9800
995	990025	985047000	31.5436	9.9833
996	992016	988047000	31.5595	9.9866
997	994009	991028000	31.5753	9.9900
998	996005	994013000	31.5911	9.9933
999	998001	997003000	31.6070	9.9967
1000	1000000	1000000000	31.6228	10.0000

Computer Program (Figure M-8)

The computer program is divided into sections so that the user may copy any part separately. If a part is used alone, without the main menu, the four lines pertaining to returning to it should be omitted.

Figure M-8 Math Tables Computer Program

```
 10 PRINT
 20 PRINT"COMPUTERIZED MATH TABLES"
 30 PRINT
 40 PRINT"MAIN MENU:"
 50 PRINT
 60 PRINT"ENTER ITEM NUMBER OF DESIRED TABLE"
 70 PRINT
 80 PRINT"1. LOGARITHMS TO ANY BASE"
 90 PRINT"2. ANTILOGARITHMS TO ANY BASE"
100 PRINT"3. SINE, COSINE & TANGENT"
110 PRINT"4. INVERSE SINE, COSINE & TANGENT"
120 PRINT"5. SECANT, COSECANT & COTANGENT"
130 PRINT"6. INVERSE SECANT, COSECANT & COTANGENT"
140 PRINT"7. HYPERBOLIC SINE, COSINE & TANGENT"
150 PRINT"8. INVERSE HYPERBOLIC SIN, COS & TAN"
160 PRINT"9. HYPERBOLIC SEC, CSC & COT"
170 PRINT"0. INVERSE HYPERBOLIC SEC, CSC & COT"
180 INPUT F
190 IF F=1 THEN 1000
200 IF F=2 THEN 2000
210 IF F=3 THEN 3000
220 IF F=4 THEN 4000
230 IF F=5 THEN 5000
240 IF F=6 THEN 6000
250 IF F=7 THEN 7000
260 IF F=8 THEN 8000
270 IF F=9 THEN 9000
280 IF F=0 THEN 10000
```

Figure M-8 Math Tables Computer Program
(continued)

```
1000 PRINT
1010 PRINT"LOGARITHMS TO ANY BASE"
1020   REM:BASIC gives natural logarithms.
1030   REM:This program converts them to
1040   REM:logarithms with any other base.
1050 PRINT
1060 PRINT"ENTER BASE (ENTER 'E' FOR NATURAL LOG)"
1070 INPUT B$
1080 IF B$<>"E"THEN 1170
1090 PRINT
1100 PRINT"ENTER NUMBER FOR WHICH YOU WANT THE LOG"
1110 INPUT N
1120 LET J=LOG(N)
1130   REM: LOG gets natural log of N.
1140 PRINT
1150 PRINT"LOG ";N;" = "J
1160 GOTO 1270
1170 PRINT
1180 PRINT"ENTER NUMBER FOR WHICH YOU WANT THE LOG"
1190 INPUT X
1200 LET B=VAL(B$)
1210   REM: VAL converts B$ to a number.
1220 LET L=LOG(X)/LOG(B)
1230   REM: This algorithm converts the
1240   REM: natural log to the base B.
1250 PRINT
1260 PRINT"LOG ";X;" = ";L
1270 PRINT
1280 PRINT"DO YOU WANT TO CONTINUE (Y/N)?"
1290 INPUT Y$
1300 IF Y$="Y"THEN 1050
1310 PRINT
1320 PRINT"RETURN TO MAIN MENU (Y/N)?"
1330 INPUT Z$
1340 IF Z$="Y"THEN 30
1350 END
```

Figure M-8 Math Tables Computer Program
(continued)

```
2000 PRINT
2010 PRINT TAB(6)"ANTILOGARITHMS OF LOGS TO ANY BASE"
2020   REM: This program converts logs of
2030   REM: any base to natural logs, for
2040   REM: which BASIC gives the antilog.
2050 PRINT
2060 PRINT"ENTER BASE (ENTER 'E' FOR NATURAL LOG)"
2070 INPUT B$
2080 IF B$<>"E"THEN 2170
2090 PRINT
2100 PRINT"ENTER LOG FOR WHICH YOU WANT THE ANTILOG"
2110 INPUT L
2120 LET A=EXP(L)
2130   REM: EXP gets antilog of natural log.
2140 PRINT
2150 PRINT"ANTILOG ";L;" = ";A
2160 GOTO 2250
2170 PRINT
2180 PRINT"ENTER LOG FOR WHICH YOU WANT THE ANTILOG"
2190 INPUT L
2200 LET B=VAL(B$)
2210   REM: VAL converts B$ to a number.
2220 LET A=EXP(L*LOG(B))
2230 PRINT
2240 PRINT"ANTILOG ";L;" = ";A
2250 PRINT
2260 PRINT"DO YOU WANT TO CONTINUE (Y/N)?"
2270 INPUT Y$
2280 IF Y$="Y"THEN 2050
2290 PRINT
2300 PRINT"RETURN TO MAIN MENU (Y/N)?"
2310 INPUT Z$
2320 IF Z$="Y"THEN 30
2330 END
```

Figure M-8 Math Tables Computer Program
(continued)

```
3000 PRINT
3010 PRINT TAB(8)"SINE, COSINE & TANGENT"
3020    REM: BASIC requires angles in
3030    REM: radians. The program will
3040    REM: convert degrees to radians
3050    REM: if required.
3060 PRINT
3070 PRINT"DEGREES OR RADIANS (D/R)?"
3080 INPUT A$
3090 PRINT"ENTER ANGLE"
3100 INPUT A
3110 IF A$="R"THEN 3140
3120 LET A=A/57.29578
3130    REM: A is converted radians.
3140 PRINT"SINE, COSINE, OR TANGENT (S/C/T)?"
3150 INPUT B$
3160 IF B$<>"S"THEN 3210
3170 LET B=SIN(A)
3180    REM: SIN gets sine of A.
3190 PRINT"SIN (";A;" RAD) = ";B
3200 GOTO 3320
3210 IF B$="C"THEN 3280
3220 IF B$="T"THEN 3230
3230 LET B=TAN(A)
3240    REM: TAN gets tangent of A.
3250 PRINT
3260 PRINT"TAN (";A;" RAD) = ";B
3270 GOTO 3320
3280 LET B=COS(A)
3290    REM: COS gets cosine of A.
3300 PRINT
3310 PRINT"COS (";A;" RAD) = ";B
3320 PRINT
3330 PRINT"DO YOU WANT TO CONTINUE (Y/N)?"
3340 INPUT Y$
3350 IF Y$="Y"THEN 3040
3360 PRINT
3370 PRINT"RETURN TO MAIN MENU (Y/N)?"
3380 INPUT Z$
3390 IF Z$="Y"THEN 30
3400 END
```

Figure M-8 Math Tables Computer Program
(continued)

```
4000 PRINT
4010 PRINT TAB(5)"INVERSE SINE, COSINE & TANGENT"
4020   REM: BASIC uses radians. The program
4030   REM: converts radians to degrees as
4040   REM: required.
4050 PRINT
4060 PRINT"DEGREES OR RADIANS (D/R)?"
4070 INPUT A$
4080 PRINT"ENTER INVERSE FUNCTION"
4090 INPUT A
4100 PRINT"ARC SIN, ARC COS, OR ARC TAN (S/C/T)?"
4110 INPUT B$
4120 IF B$="T"THEN 4370
4130 IF B$="C"THEN 4190
4140 LET B=ATN(A/SQR(-A*A+1))
4150   REM: This algorithm gives arcsin A.
4160 IF A$<>"D"THEN 4240
4170 LET B=B*57.29578
4180 GOTO 4280
4190 LET B=1.5707963-ATN(A/SQR(-A*A+1))
4200   REM: This algorithm gives arccos A.
4210 IF A$<>"D"THEN 4310
4220 LET B=B*57.29578
4230 GOTO 4340
4240 PRINT
4250 PRINT"ARCSIN ";A;" = ";B;" RAD."
4260 GOTO 4470
4270 IF B$="C"THEN 4310
4280 PRINT
4290 PRINT"ARCSIN ";A;" = ";B;" DEG."
4300 GOTO 4470
4310 PRINT
4320 PRINT"ARCCOS ";A;" = ";B;" RAD."
4330 GOTO 4470
4340 PRINT
4350 PRINT"ARCCOS ";A;" = ";B;" DEG."
4360 GOTO 4470
4370 LET B=ATN(A)
4380   REM: This gets arctan A.
4390 IF A$<>"D"THEN 4420
4400 LET B=B*57.29578
4410 GOTO 4450
4420 PRINT
4430 PRINT"ARCTAN ";A;" = ";B;" RAD."
4440 GOTO 4470
4450 PRINT
4460 PRINT"ARCTAN ";A;" = ";B;" DEG."
4470 PRINT
4480 PRINT"DO YOU WANT TO CONTINUE (Y/N)?"
4490 INPUT X$
4500 IF X$="Y"THEN 4050
4510 PRINT
4520 PRINT"RETURN TO MAIN MENU (Y/N)?"
4530 INPUT Z$
4540 IF Z$="Y"THEN 30
4550 END
```

Figure M-8 Math Tables Computer Program
(continued)

```
5000 PRINT
5010 PRINT TAB(6)"SECANT, COSECANT & COTANGENT"
5020   REM: These functions are the
5030   REM: reciprocals of cosine,
5040   REM: sine & tangent respectively.
5050 PRINT
5060 PRINT"DEGREES OR RADIANS (D/R)?"
5070 INPUT A$
5080 PRINT"ENTER ANGLE"
5090 INPUT A
5100 IF A$="R"THEN 5130
5110 LET A=A/57.29578
5120   REM: Converts degrees to radians.
5130 PRINT"SECANT, COSECANT OR COTANGENT (S/C/T)?"
5140 INPUT B$
5150 IF B$<>"S"THEN 5210
5160 LET B=1/COS(A)
5170   REM: This algorithm gives sec A.
5180 PRINT
5190 PRINT"SEC (";A;" RAD) = ";B
5200 GOTO 5310
5210 IF B$="C"THEN 5270
5220 LET B=1/TAN(A)
5230   REM: This algorithm gives cot A.
5240 PRINT
5250 PRINT"COT (";A;" RAD) = ";B
5260 GOTO 5310
5270 LET B=1/SIN(A)
5280   REM: This algorithm gives csc A.
5290 PRINT
5300 PRINT"CSC (";A;" RAD) = ";B
5310 PRINT
5320 PRINT"DO YOU WANT TO CONTINUE (Y/N)?"
5330 INPUT Y$
5340 IF Y$="Y"THEN 5050
5350 PRINT
5360 PRINT"RETURN TO MAIN MENU (Y/N)?"
5370 INPUT Z$
5380 IF Z$="Y"THEN 30
5390 END
```

Figure M-8 Math Tables Computer Program
(continued)

```
6000 PRINT
6010 PRINT"INVERSE SECANT, COSECANT & COTANGENT"
6020    REM: BASIC uses radians. The program
6030    REM: converts radians to degrees as
6040    REM: required.
6050 PRINT
6060 PRINT"DEGREES OR RADIANS (D/R)?"
6070 INPUT A$
6080 PRINT"ENTER INVERSE FUNCTION"
6090 INPUT A
6100 PRINT"ARC SEC, ARC COSEC, OR ARC COT (S/C/T)?"
6110 INPUT B$
6120 IF B$="T"THEN 6370
6130 IF B$="C"THEN 6190
6140 LET B=ATN(SQR(A*A-1))
6150    REM: This algorithm gives arcsec A.
6160 IF A$<>"D"THEN 6240
6170 LET B=B*57.29578
6180 GOTO 6280
6190 LET B=ATN(1/SQR(A*A-1))
6200    REM: This algorithm gives arccsc A.
6210 IF A$<>"D"THEN 6310
6220 LET B=B*57.29578
6230 GOTO 6340
6240 PRINT
6250 PRINT"ARCSEC ";A;" = ";B;" RAD."
6260 GOTO 6470
6270 IF B$="C"THEN 6310
6280 PRINT
6290 PRINT"ARCSEC ";A;" = ";B;" DEG."
6300 GOTO 6470
6310 PRINT
6320 PRINT"ARCCSC ";A;" = ";B;" RAD."
6330 GOTO 6470
6340 PRINT
6350 PRINT"ARCCSC ";A;" = ";B;" DEG."
6360 GOTO 6470
6370 LET B=ATN(1/A)
6380    REM: This algorithm gets arccot A.
6390 IF A$<>"D"THEN 6420
6400 LET B=B*57.29578
6410 GOTO 6450
6420 PRINT
6430 PRINT"ARCCOT ";A;" = ";B;" RAD."
6440 GOTO 6470
6450 PRINT
6460 PRINT"ARCCOT ";A;" = ";B;" DEG."
6470 PRINT
6480 PRINT"DO YOU WANT TO CONTINUE (Y/N)?"
6490 INPUT X$
6500 IF X$="Y"THEN 6050
6510 PRINT
6520 PRINT"RETURN TO MAIN MENU (Y/N)?"
6530 INPUT Z$
6540 IF Z$="Y"THEN 30
6550 END
```

Figure M-8 Math Tables Computer Program
(continued)

```
7000 PRINT
7010 PRINT"HYPERBOLIC SINE, COSINE & TANGENT"
7020   REM: This program gives sinh, cosh,
7030   REM: or tanh for values of x from
7040   REM: 0.00 through 10.00
7050 PRINT
7060 PRINT"ENTER X"
7070 INPUT A
7080 PRINT
7090 PRINT"SINH, COSH, OR TANH (S/C/T)?"
7100 INPUT B$
7110 IF B$="T"THEN 7230
7120 IF B$="C"THEN 7180
7130 LET B=(EXP(A)-EXP(-A))/2
7140   REM: This algorithm gives sinh A.
7150 PRINT
7160 PRINT"SINH ";A;" = ";B
7170 GOTO 7270
7180 LET B=(EXP(A)+EXP(-A))/2
7190   REM: This algorithm gives cosh A.
7200 PRINT
7210 PRINT"COSH ";A;" = ";B
7220 GOTO 7270
7230 LET B=(EXP(A)-EXP(-A))/(EXP(A)+EXP(-A))
7240   REM: This algorithm gives tanh A.
7250 PRINT
7260 PRINT"TANH ";A;" = ";B
7270 PRINT
7280 PRINT"DO YOU WANT TO CONTINUE (Y/N)?"
7290 INPUT Y$
7300 IF Y$="Y"THEN 7050
7310 PRINT
7320 PRINT"RETURN TO MAIN MENU (Y/N)?"
7330 INPUT Z$
7340 IF Z$="Y"THEN 30
7350 END
```

Figure M-8 Math Tables Computer Program
(continued)

```
8000 PRINT
8010 PRINT"INVERSE HYPERBOLIC SIN, COS & TAN"
8020    REM: This program gives the value
8030    REM: of x for values of sinh, cosh,
8040    REM: or tanh.
8050 PRINT
8060 PRINT"ENTER VALUE OF HYPERBOLIC FUNCTION"
8070 INPUT A
8080 PRINT
8090 PRINT"SINH, COSH, OR TANH (S/C/T)?"
8100 INPUT B$
8110 IF B$="T"THEN 8230
8120 IF B$="C"THEN 8180
8130 LET B=LOG(A+SQR(A*A+1))
8140    REM: This gives X for sinh A.
8150 PRINT
8160 PRINT"X FOR SINH ";A;" = ";B
8170 GOTO 8270
8180 LET B=LOG(A+SQR(A*A-1))
8190    REM: This gives X for cosh A.
8200 PRINT
8210 PRINT"X FOR COSH ";A;" = ";B
8220 GOTO 8270
8230 LET B=.5*(LOG(1+A))-.5*(LOG(1-A))
8240    REM: This gives X for tanh A.
8250 PRINT
8260 PRINT"X FOR TANH ";A;" = ";B
8270 PRINT
8280 PRINT"DO YOU WANT TO CONTINUE (Y/N)?"
8290 INPUT Y$
8300 IF Y$="Y"THEN 8050
8310 PRINT
8320 PRINT"RETURN TO MAIN MENU (Y/N)?"
8330 INPUT Z$
8340 IF Z$="Y"THEN 30
8350 END
```

Figure M-8 Math Tables Computer Program
(continued)

```
9000 PRINT
9010 PRINT"HYPERBOLIC SEC, CSC & COT"
9020   REM: This program gives sech,
9030   REM: csch, or coth for values
9040   REM: of x from 0.00 thru 10.00.
9050 PRINT
9060 PRINT"ENTER X"
9070 INPUT A
9080 PRINT
9090 PRINT"SECH, COSH, OR COTH (S/C/T)?"
9100 INPUT B$
9110 IF B$="T"THEN 9230
9120 IF B$="C"THEN 9180
9130 LET B=1/((EXP(A)+EXP(-A))/2)
9140   REM: This algorithm gives sech A.
9150 PRINT
9160 PRINT"SECH ";A;" = ";B
9170 GOTO 9270
9180 LET B=1/((EXP(A)-EXP(-A))/2)
9190   REM: This algorithm gives csch A.
9200 PRINT
9210 PRINT"CSCH ";A;" = ";B
9220 GOTO 9270
9230 LET B=1/((EXP(A)-EXP(-A))/(EXP(A)+EXP(-A)))
9240   REM: This algorithm gives coth A.
9250 PRINT
9260 PRINT"COTH ";A;" = ";B
9270 PRINT
9280 PRINT"DO YOU WANT TO CONTINUE (Y/N)?"
9290 INPUT Y$
9300 IF Y$="Y"THEN 9050
9310 PRINT
9320 PRINT"RETURN TO MAIN MENU (Y/N)?"
9330 INPUT Z$
9340 IF Z$="Y"THEN 30
9350 END
```

Figure M-8 Math Tables Computer Program
(continued)

```
10000 PRINT
10010 PRINT"INVERSE HYPERBOLIC SEC, CSC & COT"
10020    REM: This program gives values
10030    REM: of x for values of sech,
10040    REM: csch, and coth.
10050 PRINT
10060 PRINT"ENTER VALUE OF HYPERBOLIC FUNCTION"
10070 INPUT A
10080 PRINT
10090 PRINT"SECH, CSCH, OR COTH (S/C/T)?"
10100 INPUT B$
10110 IF B$="T"THEN 10230
10120 IF B$="C"THEN 10180
10130 LET B=LOG(1/A+SQR(1/(A*A)-1))
10140    REM: This gives X for sech A.
10150 PRINT
10160 PRINT"X FOR SECH ";A;" = ";B
10170 GOTO 10270
10180 LET B=LOG(1/A+SQR(1/(A*A)+1))
10190    REM: This gives X for csch A.
10200 PRINT
10210 PRINT"X FOR CSCH ";A;" = ";B
10220 GOTO 10270
10230 LET B=.5*(LOG(1+A))-.5*(LOG(A-1))
10240    REM: This gives X for coth A.
10250 PRINT
10260 PRINT"X FOR COTH ";A;" = ";B
10270 PRINT
10280 PRINT"DO YOU WANT TO CONTINUE (Y/N)?"
10290 INPUT Y$
10300 IF Y$="Y"THEN 10050
10310 PRINT
10320 PRINT"RETURN TO MAIN MENU (Y/N)?"
10330 INPUT Z$
10340 IF Z$="Y"THEN 30
10350 END
```

Maximum Working Voltage *See* specific device.

MEASUREMENT

Direct-Reading Meters

Direct-reading meters operate by drawing current from the circuit being measured. Therefore they have a loading effect upon the circuit which may actually change the value of the quantity being measured. The most widely used type of meter has the permanent-magnet moving-coil (PMMC) movement diagrammed in Figure M-9. The characteristics of this type of meter are as follows:

Figure M-9 Permanent-Magnet Moving-Coil Meter Movement—[6]

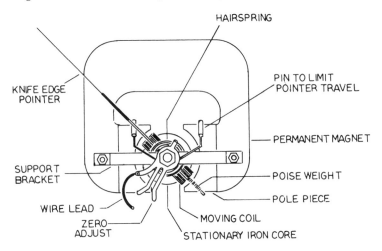

Accuracy is the measure of how close the meter reading is to the true value of the quantity being measured. This is usually given as a percentage of the full-scale reading. If the scale does not have zero at one end, then "full scale" means the total value of the range of the scale from one end to the other, regardless of sign.

Repeatability is the measure of the meter's ability to give the same reading every time for the same input. This also is given as pecentage of full scale.

Friction means the maximum percentage of full scale that the pointer may move if you tap the meter after the pointer comes to rest.

Damping Factor is the ratio obtained when a current is applied suddenly to a meter, so that the pointer deflects to full scale before dropping back to a steady reading, and is given by:

$$DF = SR/(FS - SR)$$

where:

$$DF = \text{damping factor.}$$

$$SR = \text{steady reading.}$$

$$FS = \text{full-scale value.}$$

Response Time is the time taken for the pointer to settle down to a new reading after an abrupt change in the applied energy.

Overshoot is the amount by which the pointer overshoots the correct reading when the applied energy is changed, and is given as the percentage of the deflection after the pointer comes to rest.

Tracking is the ability of the meter to indicate correctly at each scale division.

Temperature Influence is any variation in meter readings due to temperature alone.

Symmetry applies to *off-set* meters, in which the zero is not at the end of the scale, and refers to the ability of the meter to give readings with equal accuracy on both sides of zero.

Frequency Influence is a change in the reading due solely to a change in frequency. It applies only to AC meters.

Position Error means the change, if any, in the reading when the meter is operated in different positions.

Applications of Direct-Reading Meters

Current Meters are PMMC-movement meters in which the desired range of the meter is obtained with a shunt resistance. The value of the shunt resistance is given by:

$$R_S = R_{\text{meter}}/N - 1$$

where:

$R_S = $ the required resistance, in ohms.

$R_{\text{meter}} = $ the meter resistance, in ohms.

$N = $ full-scale reading desired, divided by the full-scale reading without the shunt.

The meter resistance, if not known, may be obtained by connecting it in series with a battery and a rheostat. The latter is adjusted until the meter reads full scale. A second rheostat is then connected in parallel with the meter and is adjusted until the meter reads half scale. The resistance of the second rheostat will then be equal to that of the meter. Do not attempt to measure the meter resistance directly with an ohmmeter, as the movement may be burnt out.

DC voltmeters are PMMC-movement meters in which the desired range of the meter is obtained with a series resistance. The value of the series resistance is given by:

$$R = V/I - R_M$$

where:

R = value of series resistance, in ohms.

V = full-scale reading desired, in volts.

I = full-scale current of meter, in amperes.

R_M = meter resistance, in ohms (usually negligible).

An important parameter of direct-reading voltmeters is the loading effect, mentioned above, given in ohms per volt:

$$\text{Ohms per volt} = 1/I$$

where:

I = full-scale current of meter, in amperes.

An *ohmmeter* consists in essence of a PMMC-movement meter with a battery and range resistance in series. When connected across an unknown resistance, the battery current flows through all four, and the reading on the meter is greater for lower unknowns. Consequently, an ohmmeter usually has zero on its scale at the opposite end to that of current meters and voltmeters. However, this does not apply to the less common shunt ohmmeter, in which the resistance is connected in parallel with the meter, as in a current meter.

The *AC voltmeter* is basically the same as the DC voltmeter above, except that a rectifier is included in the circuit to change the AC to DC. Direct-reading instruments usually give accurate readings up to about 10 kilohertz. Deflection of the pointer is proportional to the *average* value of a sine wave. However, the dial is calibrated in RMS values by making the divisions 1.11 times larger than they would be for average values. This meter can only give accurate values for *sine waves*.

Electronic Meters

Electronic meters are either analog or digital. Analog meters employ a meter movement similar to those used by direct-reading instruments, but since the electronic meter is much more sensitive, an amplifier is required. The amplifier used mostly is the operational amplifier, and DC inputs are usually chopped for greater stability.

Digital Voltmeters

The principal characteristics of *digital voltmeters* are summarized in Table M-1.

TABLE M-1   Digital Voltmeter Characteristics

Operating principle	Number of digits in display	Lowest range*	Accuracy ±ppm of max readg.	Input Z MΩ
Linear ramp	3	0.10 V	5000	10
Integration	4	0.10 V	300	10
Integration	6	0.02 V	40	10
Integration/successive approx.	7	1.00 V	60	10
Dual slope	7	1.00 V	10	10

*Highest range in all cases is 1 kV.

Digital Multimeters

A *digital multimeter (DMM)* typically has the characteristics shown in Table M-2.

TABLE M-2   Digital Multimeter Characteristics

Parameter	Typical characteristic
Operating principle	dual slope
Number of digits	4
Voltage range	0.2 V–1 kV (500 V for AC)
Current range	200μ A–2 A
Resistance range	0.2–2000 kΩ
Maximum frequency (AC)	20 kHz

Temperature Measurements

Temperature measurements are done with *thermocouples.* Characteristics of the principal types are given in Table M-3.

TABLE M-3   Thermocouple Characteristics

Materials	μV/°C	Temperature range °C
Chromel/Eureka	41	0 to +1000
Iron/Eureka	59	−200 to +1382
Chrome/Alumel	40	−200 to +1200
Platinum/Platinum-Rhodium	6.5	0 to +1450
Copper/Constantan	42	−200 to +300
Carbon/Silicon-Carbide	292*	0 to +2000

*In the range 1210°C to 1450°C

Sensitivity up to 1000 μV/°C can be achieved when one element is a *thermistor*.

Thermistors

Thermistors are made from sintered compounds of the metallic oxides of copper, manganese, nickel, and cobalt. They are formed into beads, rings, or disks and are enclosed in glass or epoxy resin. Beads can be as small as 0.1 mm in diameter.

They are made with resistance values from 1 ohm to several megohms at 20°C. Their outstanding property is a negative temperature coefficient of about −4% per °C. Appreciable current, even of a few milliamperes, must be avoided. The thermal properties of some materials commonly used in thermo-resistive devices are given in Table M-4.

TABLE M-4 Thermistor Characteristics

Material	Coefficient of thermal expansion $\times 10^{-6}$	Resistivity in ohm-meters $\times 10^{-8}$	Resistance/ temperature coefficient $\times 10^{-3}$	Melting point °C
Aluminum	28.7	2.82	3.9	660
Advance, Constantan, Eureka	14.8	49.1	0.2	1210
Brass	20.2	6.72	2.0	920
Copper (annealed)	16.1	1.72	3.93	1083
Iron (pure)	12.1	9.65	5.2–6.2	1535
Manganin		44.8	0.02	910
Mercury		96.0	0.89	−38.87
Molybdenum	6.0	5.7	4.5	2630
Nichrome		112.0	0.17	1350
Platinum	9.0	10.6	3.0	1774
Tungsten	4.6	5.6	4.5	3370

Metal-Film Resistors *See* Resistors.

Metal-Oxide Semiconductor Field-Effect Transistor (MOSFET) *See* Transistors.

Meters *See* Measurement.

Mica Capacitor *See* Capacitors.

Microphone *See* Transducers.

MICROPROCESSOR

A microcomputer *system* is generally built around a microprocessor, which contains within it most of the control and arithmetic functions of a digital computer. The microprocessor is also augmented by internal memory and peripheral drivers, which may be on the same chip, or in other chips on the system board. The microprocessor, therefore, consists of:

A control unit

An arithmetic logic unit (ALU)

An internal memory

An input-output system

Control Unit

The control unit consists of a group of flip-flops and registers that regulate the operation of the computer itself. It is responsible for causing the proper sequence of events to occur during the execution of each instruction. It contains the memory address register and the memory data register, the instruction register, the instruction decoder, and the accumulator.

The control unit alternates between the *fetch mode* and the *execute mode.* It starts by fetching the instruction; it then executes the instruction. It then returns to the fetch mode and reads the next instruction from memory, and so on. The fetch and execute flip-flops determine its current mode of operation. (*See* Logic Circuits for an explanation of flip-flops.)

Arithmetic Logic Unit (ALU)

The ALU performs all the arithmetic and logical operations required by the computer. The microprocessor inputs two operands to the ALU, which then carries out the operation. The operation may be:

Addition

Subtraction

Logical OR

Logical AND

Exclusive OR

Complementation

Shifting

Other operations, such as multiplication, division, extracting square roots, logarithms, trigonometrical functions, and so on, are usually done as software routines that use a series of the above ALU operations to achieve the desired result.

Attached to the ALU is the *condition-code* register, which indicates the status of the last operation of the microprocessor. The condition codes are called *flags*. These tell the microprocessor whether some further step is required as a result of the operation just performed. The most common flags are:

C = the arithmetic operation produced a carry.

Z = the last result was zero.

N = the last result was negative (S is also used).

V = the last operation resulted in an overflow.

P = the parity of the result is even.

H = used for carries in decimal arithmetic.

I = indicates the computer's decision to interrupt the current sequence in favor of a higher priority requirement.

Internal Memory

The internal memory consists of two kinds:

RAM = read and write memory

ROM = read only memory

The data is usually stored in *words* of 8 or 16 bits each. Each instruction or data word is written into a specific *address*, where it can be read at a later time when the information is needed. As mentioned above (Control Unit), the memory address register (MAR) holds the address of the word currently being accessed, and the memory data register (MDR) holds the information being written into or read out of that location. A *write* command causes the data in the MDR to be stored at the location indicated by the address in the MAR. A *read* command causes the data at the location indicated by the MAR to be transferred to the MDR. The data stored in memory is not destroyed by being read, but any data that was previously in a location into which new data is written is destroyed.

RAM is used to store variable data; ROM is used to store constant data. Data in RAM is lost when power is removed, but ROM is permanent. Permanent storage of data in RAM is achieved by transferring it to an external memory. (*See* Magnetic Storage.)

Input/Output System

The input/output system controls communication between the computer and its external devices. Such external devices include the keyboard, monitor, printer, and disk or tape units. (*See* Peripheral Devices.)

There are two types of input/output systems:

Port input/output

Memory-mapped input/output

In port I/O, the peripheral devices are connected to various *ports*. These are either input or output ports. The microprocessor selects the port by means of an IN or OUT instruction and a code designating the port. While this port is selected, all others are deselected.

In memory-mapped I/O, each peripheral device has an address in memory, and no IN or OUT command is required.

Microprocessor Types in Common Use

Some widely used microprocessors are listed in Table M-5. These include those with word sizes from 8 through 32.

TABLE M-5   Popular Microprocessor Integrated Circuits

Manufacturer	IC number	Number of pins	Data word size
Intel	8080	40	8
	8085	40	8
	8086	40	8/16
	8088	40	8/16
	80286	40	8/16
	80386	64	32
Motorola	M6800	40	16
	M68000	64	16
Zilog	Z80	40	8
	Z8000	48	16

Microwave Electromagnetic wave with wavelength in the centimeter range. *See* Waveguides and Cavities.

Miniature Lamps *See* Lamps.

Modulation *See* AM, FM, or PM.

MOTORS

The main types of electric motors are listed in Table M-6. Their schematic diagrams are given in Figures M-10 through M-17. (The motors themselves will generally have many more coils, commutator segments, rotor bars, and so on, than those shown in these simplified diagrams.)

TABLE M-6   Main Types of Electric Motors

Type	Voltage	φ	Use	Diagram
Commutator AC/DC ("Universal")	120	1	Electric drills, etc.	Fig. M-10
Shaded-pole	120	1	Fans, etc.	Fig. M-11
Capacitor start; and capacitor start, capacitor run	120/240	1	Small pumps, etc.	Fig. M-12 Fig. M-13
Induction, (squirrel-cage, wound, or solid armature) Synchronous	240 & up	3*	Industrial	Fig. M-14
Direct current	Various	—	General	Fig. M-15 Fig. M-16 Fig. M-17

*The most common; others are possible.

Figure M-10 Universal AC/DC Motor

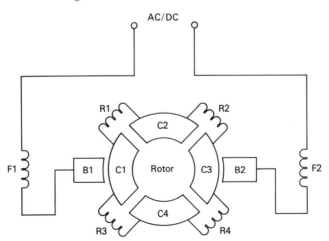

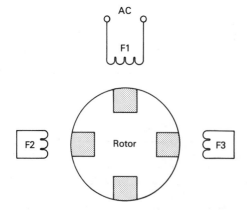

Figure M-11 Shaded Pole Motor

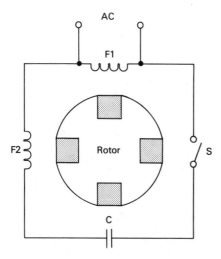

Figure M-12 Capacitor Start Motor

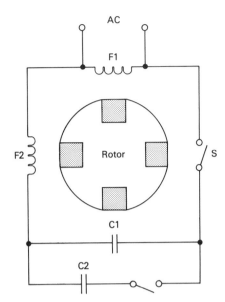

Figure M-13 Capacitor Start, Capacitor Run Motor

Figure M-14 Three-Phase Motor

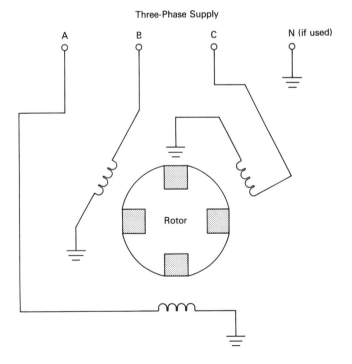

Figure M-15 Shunt-Wound DC Motor

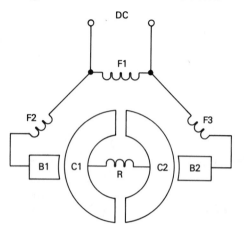

Figure M-16 Series-Wound DC Motor

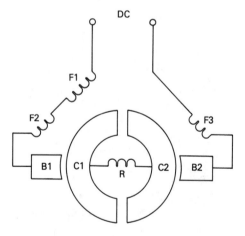

Figure M-17 Compound DC Motor

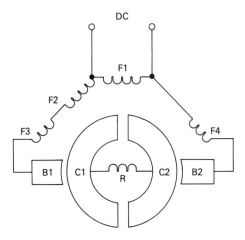

Motor starting currents in kilovolt-amperes per horsepower with locked rotor are given in Table M-7, and NEC full-load motor running currents in amperes (usual conditions and speeds) are given in Table M-8.

TABLE M-7 Motor Starting Currents per Horsepower with Locked Rotor

NEC code letter	kVA
A	0–3.14
B	3.15–3.54
C	3.55–3.99
D	4.00–4.49
E	4.50–4.99
F	5.00–5.59
G	5.60–6.29
H	6.30–7.09
J	7.10–7.99
K	8.00–8.99
L	9.00–9.99
M	10.00–11.19
N	11.20–12.49
P	12.50–13.99
R	14.00–15.99
S	16.00–17.99
T	18.00–19.99
U	20.00–22.39
V	22.40–up

TABLE M-8 NEC Full-Load Motor Running Currents in Amperes (Usual Conditions and Speeds)

HP	Single-phase AC		3-phase AC*			DC	
	115 V	230 V†	115 V	230 V†	460 V	120 V	240 V
1/6	4.4	2.2	—	—	—	—	—
1/4	5.8	2.9	—	—	—	3.1	1.6
1/3	7.2	3.6	—	—	—	4.1	2.0
1/2	9.8	4.9	4	2	1	5.4	2.7
3/4	13.8	6.9	5.6	2.8	1.4	7.6	3.8
1	16	8	7.2	3.6	1.8	9.5	4.7
1 1/2	20	10	10.4	5.2	2.6	13.2	6.6
2	24	10	13.6	6.8	3.4	17	8.2
3	34	17	—	9.6	4.8	25	12.2
5	56	28	—	15.2	7.6	40	20
7 1/2	80	40	—	22	11	58	29
10	100	50	—	28	14	76	38

*Induction type, with squirrel-cage and wound rotor.
†For 208 V, multiply by 1.1; for 200 V, multiply by 1.15.

N

Natural Logarithms *See* Mathematical Data.

Neon Lamps *See* Lamps.

Noise Noise level at a receiver is defined by:

$$f_a = P_n/kT_0B = T_a/T_0$$

where:

f_a = effective antenna noise factor.

P_n = noise power available from equivalent loss-free antenna, in watts.

k = Boltzman's constant (1.38×10^{-23} J/K).

T_0 = reference temperature (290 K).

B = effective receiver noise bandwidth, in hertz.

T_a = effective antenna temperature in the presence of external noise, in kelvins.

Figure N-1 shows the average values for noise power from various sources for an omnidirectional antenna near the surface.

Figure N-1 Sources of Noise

Atmospheric noise, with figures given for New York City, are approximately the same throughout the U.S. Rural man-made noise is less than galactic noise.

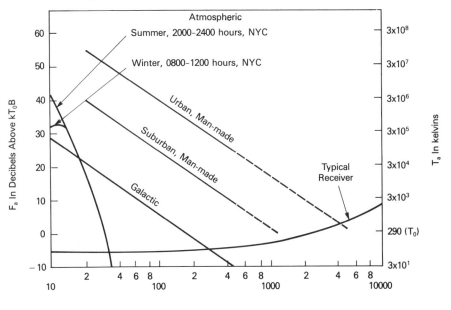

Frequency in Megahertz

Norton's Theorem *See* Electric Circuit Theory.

NPN Transistor *See* Transistors.

NUMBER SYSTEMS

General Representation of Numbers

Any number system can represent the integer number N, as:

$$N = a_{n-1}r^{n-1} + a_{n-2}r^{n-2} + \cdots + a_1r^1 + a_0r^0$$

where:

r = radix, or base.

r^i = digit weighting value.

a_i = value of the digit in the ith position, where $0 \le a_i \le r - 1$. Thus a radix k number system requires k different symbols to represent the digits 0 to $k - 1$.

n = number of digits in the representation of the number.

Decimal Numbers

In the above format, the decimal number 1983 is represented by:

$$1983 = (1 \times 10^3) + (9 \times 10^2) + (8 \times 10^1) + (3 \times 10^0)$$

where:

r = 10, with ten digit values 0, 1, 2, 3, 4, 5, 6, 7, 8, and 9.

Binary Numbers

The binary (base 2) number system is used in digital systems, and consists of two digits, 0 and 1. A number N in the binary system may be represented as:

$$N = b_{n-1}2^{n-1} + b_{n-2}2^{n-2} + \cdots + b_1 2^1 + b_0 2^0$$

where:

r = 2, and the digit values are either 0 or 1 (known as bits).

In this format, the decimal number 1983 is represented by:

$$11110111111$$

which is equivalent to:

$$1983 = (1 \times 2^{10}) + (1 \times 2^9) + (1 \times 2^8) + (1 \times 2^7)$$
$$+ (0 \times 2^6) + (1 \times 2^5) + (1 \times 2^4) + (1 \times 2^3)$$
$$+ (1 \times 2^2) + (1 \times 2^1) + (1 \times 2^0)$$

$$= 1024 + 512 + 256 + 128 + 32 + 16 + 8 + 4 + 2 + 1$$

Octal Numbers

The octal system, to the base 8, is used to simplify the handling of binary numbers. To convert binary numbers into octal numbers, divide the binary digits into 3-bit groups, as in:

$$1100110101010$$

which, when divided into 3-bit groups, becomes:

001   100   110   101   010

The "decimal" equivalent of each 3-bit group is:

1   4   6   5   2

but these are actually octal numbers.

Hexadecimal Numbers

The hexadecimal number system has a base of 16, with digits 0, 1, 2, 3, 4, 5, 6, 7, 8, 9, A, B, C, D, E, F.

To convert binary numbers to hexadecimal, divide the binary digits into 4-bit groups. For instance:

1011010011101

becomes:

0001   0110   1001   1101

The "decimal" equivalents of these groups are:

1   6   9   13(D)

so the hexadecimal number is 169D.

The foregoing numbers are summarized in Table N-1.

TABLE N-1   Decimal, Hexadecimal, Octal, and Binary Number Equivalents

Dec	Hex	Octal	Binary	Dec	Hex	Octal	Binary
0	0	0	0	8	8	10	1000
1	1	1	1	9	9	11	1001
2	2	2	10	10	A	12	1010
3	3	3	11	11	B	13	1011
4	4	4	100	12	C	14	1100
5	5	5	101	13	D	15	1101
6	6	6	110	14	E	16	1110
7	7	7	111	15	F	17	1111

Excess-3 Code

This code is designed for applications where zero is represented by the absence of a signal. The binary number 0000 cannot be distinguished from no signal. This is avoided by adding the binary notation for 3 to each binary group of 4 digits, as shown in Table N-2.

TABLE N-2   Equivalent Numerical
Representations in Decimal, Binary,
Excess-3, and Gray Codes

Decimal	Binary	Excess-3	Gray
0	0000	0011	0000
1	0001	0100	0001
2	0010	0101	0011
3	0011	0110	0010
4	0100	0111	0110
5	0101	1000	0111
6	0110	1001	0101
7	0111	1010	0100
8	1000	1011	1100
9	1001	1100	1101

Gray or Reflected Binary Code

This code is used for inputting mechanical data (such as angle of rotation of a shaft) into a computer where it is desirable that one, and only one, digit of the code changes in proceeding to or from the next higher or lower number. Thus there is no intermediate instant which can be interpreted as a number which is in error by more than one unit in the least significant position.

Ohm, Ohm's Law *See* Resistance.

Operational Amplifier *See* Amplifiers.

OSCILLATORS

Colpitts Oscillator

In Figure O-1, the resonant circuit consists of L1 with C1 and C2. Frequency of oscillation is given by:

$$f = 1/6.28 \times \sqrt{LC}$$

Figure O-1 Colpitts Oscillator—[3]

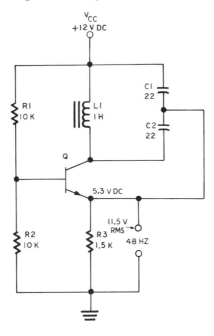

where:

f = frequency, in hertz.

L = inductance of L, in henries.

C = total capacitance of $C1$ and $C2$, in farads.

$C = C1C2/(C1 + C2)$

Hartley Oscillator

In Figure O-2, the resonant circuit consists of $L1$ and $C1$. Frequency of oscillation is given by:

$$f = 1/6.28 \times \sqrt{LC}$$

Figure O-2 Hartley Oscillator—[3]

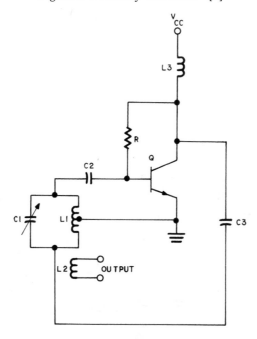

where:

f = frequency, in hertz.

L = inductance of $L1$, in henries.

C = capacitance of $C1$, in farads.

Clapp Oscillator

Figure O-3 shows that a Clapp oscillator is a Colpitts oscillator with the addition of $C5$. Frequency of oscillation is given by:

$$f = 1/6.28 \sqrt{LC}$$

Figure O-3 Clapp Oscillator—[2]

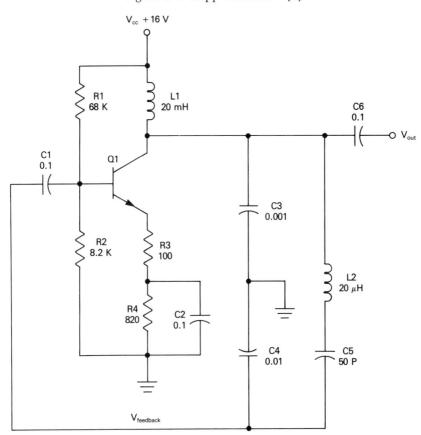

where:

$\quad f$ = frequency, in hertz.

$\quad L$ = inductance of $L2$, in henries.

$\quad C$ = total capacitance of $C3$, $C4$, and $C5$, in farads.

$\qquad C = 1/(1/C3 + 1/C4 + 1/C5)$

Pierce Oscillator

In Figure O-4, this oscillator is shown with a crystal, its usual configuration. Frequency depends upon the crystal used. A Pierce oscillator with a resonant circuit in its output is a *Miller oscillator*. The output resonant circuit is tuned to the second or third harmonic of the fundamental frequency generated by the crystal.

Figure O-4 Pierce Oscillator—[2]

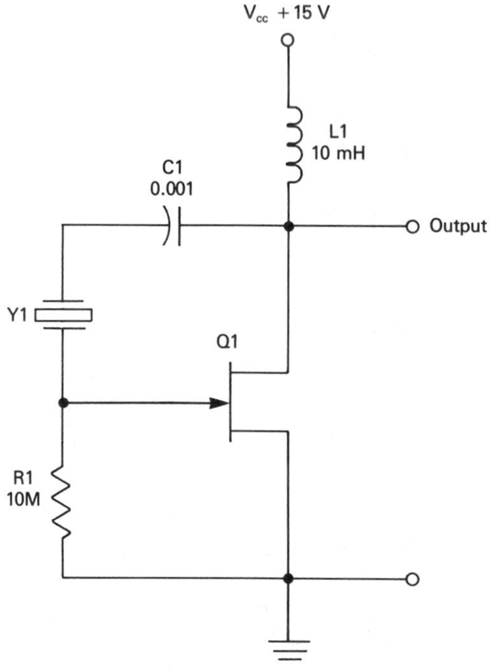

Unijunction Oscillator

The frequency of the unijunction oscillator shown in Figure O-5 is given by:

$$f = 1/[R \times C \times \ln (1/1 - \eta)]$$

Figure O-5 UJT Oscillator

    C1 charges from *V* via *R1* until the voltage on the emitter makes *Q1*'s emitter-*B1* junction forward-biased. *C1* then discharges via this junction and *R3*. *Q1* then turns off, and *C1* charges again. The charge-discharge cycle repeats itself as long as power is applied, resulting in the waveforms shown. — [2]

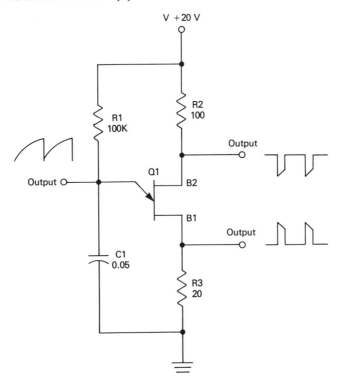

where:

f = the frequency, in hertz.

R = resistance of *R1*, in ohms.

C = capacitance of *C1*, in farads.

η = intrinsic standoff ratio of UJT.

Astable Multivibrator

The time period taken to switch by $Q2$ in an astable multivibrator, such as that in Figure O-6, is given by:

$$T_1 = 0.68 \times C1 \times R3$$

Figure O-6 An Astable Multivibrator
　　　The two transistors take turns conducting, switching each other on and off. The collector of $Q2$ alternates between 12 V when the transistor is off to approximately 0 V when it is on, giving the square-wave output shown. — [2]

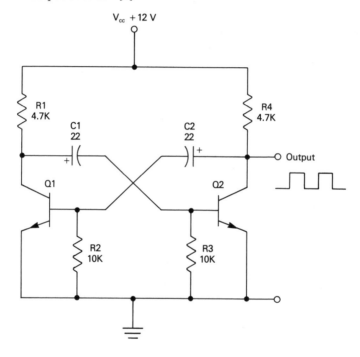

where:

T_1 = time period, in seconds.

$C1$ = capacitance of $C1$, in farads.

$R3$ = resistance of $R3$, in ohms.

The transistor switching factor 0.68 is close enough for practical purposes in all circuits of this type.

Assuming $C1 = C2$ and $R1 = R3$, the time period T_2 for $Q1$ to switch must be the same. The time for one complete cycle of operation is therefore $T_1 + T_2$. The pulse repetition rate is its reciprocal, or $PRR = 1/(T_1 + T_2)$.

Phase-Shift Oscillator

Figure O-7 shows a phase-shift oscillator. To obtain a particular frequency of oscillation, the RC product is given by:

$$RC = 1/(2.45 \times 2\pi f)$$

Figure O-7 Phase-Shift Oscillator

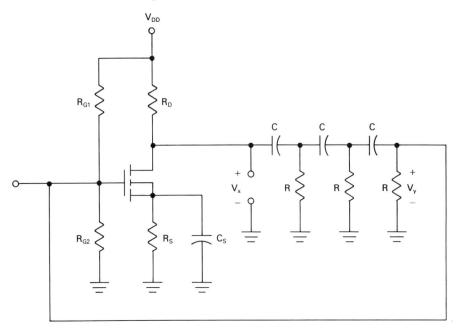

The values of R (in ohms) and C (in farads) may then be selected.

C_S must be large enough to bypass the oscillator frequency, and the value of R_{G1} in parallel with R_{G2} must be very much larger than R. The ratio V_y/V_x must be real.

P

Peak, Peak-to-Peak *See* Alternating Current.

Peak Inverse, Peak Reverse Voltage *See* Rectifiers.

PERIPHERAL DEVICES

Peripheral devices are the means by which a computer communicates with the outside world, or by which the outside world communicates with the computer. The main ones are:

Monitor
Printer
Modem
Keyboard

A *monitor* is similar to a television receiver, but instead of tuning in broadcast channels, it gets its signal from the computer. This enables the computer to display on the monitor's screen whatever it is instructed to print.

A *printer* provides a paper output from the computer. Printers are of the following types:

Dot matrix
Thermal
Ink jet
Daisy wheel
Laser

A *dot matrix* printer has seven needles held in a vertical plane in the head assembly. Each needle can be individually driven by a solenoid to contact the paper through an ink or carbon ribbon interposed between it and the paper. A complete character is formed by stepping the head through five positions horizontally and energizing the appropriate solenoids at each position.

A *thermal* printer uses the same method, except that no ink is used. The needles are heated, and the paper is sensitized to mark with the application of heat.

An *ink jet* device uses ink squirted from fine tubes when they are squeezed by their piezoelectric transducer sleeves.

A *daisy wheel* printer uses a plastic or metal wheel with spokes radiating from a hub. Each spoke is terminated in a character slug. The wheel is rotated to bring the desired character into position, and a solenoid driven hammer then strikes it against the paper through a carbon or ink ribbon. This printer, and the next to be described, give the highest quality results.

The *laser* printer is similar to a xerographic copier. A laser places a charge on a rotating drum, which passes through a dry bath of carbon-plastic powder that has been oppositely charged. The drum attracts powder to those places where the laser has "printed" characters. The drum is next pressed against the paper under bonding temperature so that the image is fixed.

Other peripheral devices include plotters, direct-input devices (such as optical character readers), and modems (interface with a telephone line for networking).

The *keyboard* has all the usual keys of a typewriter, plus some additional ones for special computer purposes. The names of the special keys are not the same on all models. Entries made via the keyboard are "echoed" to the monitor. A small flashing indicator on the monitor screen, called a cursor, shows where the next item typed will appear. The cursor may be moved to various positions by means of special keys on the keyboard. With some keyboards, you can use an auxiliary device called a *mouse*. This is a small control that rolls around, and in doing so moves the cursor on the screen to various positions. It is particularly useful in computer graphics.

Permeability Permeability is the ratio between the magnetizing field (H) produced by electric-current flow in an air-core coil and the magnetic flux density (B) inside a material when it is substituted for air as the core of the coil, given by $\mu = B/H$ (assuming the permeability of air to be the same as a vacuum, equal to 1). *See* Properties of Materials.

Phase In wave motion, phase is the fraction of time that has elapsed, measured from a reference or zero position. This fraction is generally given in degrees of arc (phase angle), a full cycle being 360 degrees (2 π radians). Symbol, ϕ (Greek letter phi).

Pin Numbering *See* Integrated Circuits.

Plug *See* Jacks and Plugs.

PM *See* Pulse Modulation.

PNP Transistor *See* Transistors.

Potentiometer *See* Resistors.

POWER

Power is the rate at which electric energy is delivered to or absorbed by a circuit, expressed in watts (W). In a DC circuit, power (P) is given by $V \times I$, where V = voltage in volts, and I = current in amperes. In an AC circuit, $P = VI \cos \theta$, where $\cos \theta$ is the power factor. *See* Power Factor.

Power Factor

Ratio of power consumed to apparent power, usually expressed as percentage, given by:

$$PF = VI \cos \theta / VI = \cos \theta$$

where:

$$PF = \text{circuit load power factor.}$$

$$VI \cos \theta = \text{true power, in watts.}$$

$$VI = \text{apparent power, in volt-amperes.}$$

$$V = \text{applied potential, in volts.}$$

$$I = \text{load current, in amperes.}$$

$$\theta = \text{phase angle.}$$

Power Gain

1. Of an antenna, ratio of power required to produce a given field strength with an isotropic or half-wave dipole to the power required to produce the same field strength with a specified type in its most favorable direction, expressed in decibels.

2. In an amplifier, ratio of output signal power to input signal power. *See* Amplifiers.

Powers of Numbers *See* Mathematical Data.

POWER SOURCES

Batteries—Primary Cells

The *Leclanché (zinc carbon) cell* is available in two forms: the round cell and the layer cell. The former (Figure P-1) is marketed both as single unit and a multicell battery; the latter is sold only as a multicell battery (Figure P-2).

Figure P-1 Leclanché Cell

The positive electrode is made from a mixture of manganese dioxide (the electrode material) and carbon black or graphite (for conductivity), packed around a carbon rod (the current collector). The electrode material is also mixed with the electrolyte (ammonium chloride and zinc chloride in a gel). The foregoing materials are surrounded by an absorbent paper-lining impregnated with the electrolyte; its purpose is to separate the positive electrode material from the negative electrode. The latter is a zinc cup which holds everything else. A metal jacket is crimped on to the outside of the cell, and this in turn is surrounded by a thick paper tube. The ends of the cell are sealed to keep its contents from leaking out and to centralize the positive electrode.

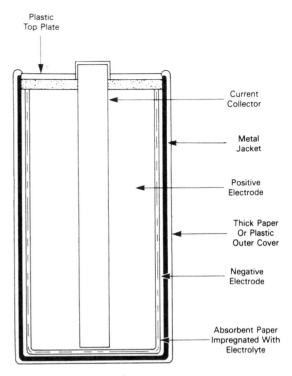

The Leclanché cell has electrodes of zinc and manganese dioxide. These are immersed in an electrolyte of ammonium chloride and zinc chloride. This mixture does not react with atmospheric oxygen.

The initial voltage of a new cell is 1.55–1.6 V. This drops during the life of the cell to 1.2–1.4 V for a fully discharged cell. The life of the cell depends upon its size, rate of discharge, duty cycle, age of cell, temperature, manufacturer, and end-point voltage. The last named means the final voltage, when its life is finished.

The Leclanché cell will store satisfactorily at 20°C. It will have a longer shelf life if kept between −10°C and +10°C, but should be in sealed containers and kept in them while being warmed to ambient temperature to avoid condensation.

The *zinc chloride cell* is similar to the Leclanché cell, except that the electrolyte consists of zinc chloride only. It has the advantage of operating below freezing, an area where the Leclanché cell is weak, and it also has a higher capacity. Zinc chloride without ammonium chloride reacts with oxygen from the air, so these cells must be well sealed if shelf life is not to be affected.

The *mercury cell* has a zinc anode and a cathode of a compressed mixture of mercuric oxide, manganese dioxide, and graphite. The electrolyte is a solution of an alkali metal hydroxide, whose ions act as carriers for the chemical reactions in the cell, but is not part of the reaction.

271

Figure P-2 Layer-cell battery. A layer-cell battery consists of several Leclanché cells in the form of flat rectangular "cakes." In each cell, an absorbent paper tray holds the positive electrode and electrolyte material. The tray rests on a zinc plate, which is coated with carbon on its under side. This provides for the connection between adjacent cells and the current collector for the positive electrode of the next cell. Each cake and its tray are banded with a plastic strip, and the complete stack is enclosed in a wax coating to seal the contents. The battery is contained in a metal case, with a metal bottom plate and a plastic top plate. The latter closes the top of the battery and carries the terminals.

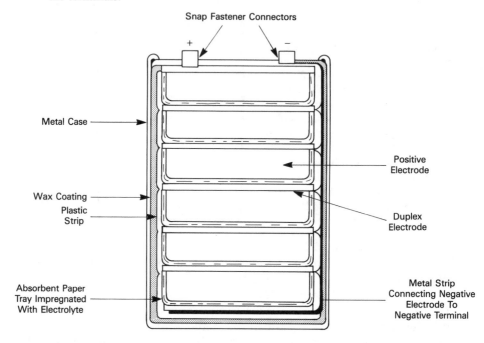

The effective voltage of the cell is typically 1.3 V down to 1.0 V depending on load and temperature. Voltage stability is excellent over the temperature range − 30 to + 70°C. A regulation within one percent can be sustained over long periods. Rest periods, as for ordinary cells, are not required. Shelf life is up to three years. The cell can is made from nickel-plated steel, which is resistive to corrosion.

Alkaline cells have a zinc anode, a strong alkaline electrolyte, and a manganese dioxide cathode. The operating voltage range is from 1.3 V, when new, to 0.8 V end voltage, with a maximum open-circuit voltage of 1.56 V. The alkaline cell is capable of sustaining heavier currents than ordinary cells, as much as 2 A intermittently. Its temperature operating range is from − 30 to + 70°C. It has a long shelf life, with typical capacity retention of over 85% after two and a half years at 20°C.

Lithium cells have a lithium anode, with a cathode of manganese dioxide, thionyl chloride, or other material that works well with lithium.

The electrolyte is either a nonaqueous organic or inorganic substance. Lithium is highly reactive with water, so all moisture must be kept away from it.

For much of their life, the voltages in lithium cells remain relatively flat, falling sharply only near the end of life. The open-circuit and operating voltages of various types of lithium cell are given in Table P-1. The lithium silver chromate cell is particularly noteworthy, since it has two operating voltages. The first, 3.1 V, is its nominal operating voltage, but toward the end of its life, it drops to 2.6 V. This is used as a battery status indication, giving advance notice when replacement must be carried out. For this reason, this battery is employed in cardiac stimulators ("pacemakers").

TABLE P-1   Voltages of Lithium Batteries

Battery anode/cathode	Open-circuit volts	Nominal operating volts
Lithium/copper oxide	2.4	1.5
Lithium/copper sulfide	2.1	1.5
Lithium/iron sulfide	1.8	1.5
Lithium/lead copper sulfide	2.2	1.5
Lithium/bismuth trioxide	2.04	1.5
Lithium/lead bismuthate	1.8	1.5
Lithium/carbon monofluoride	3.1	2.8
Lithium/manganese dioxide	3.7	3.0
Lithium/silver chromate	3.45	3.1 (2.6)
Lithium/sulfur dioxide	3.0	2.85
Lithium/thionyl chloride	3.65	3.5
Lithium/iodine	3.1	2.8

The shelf life of lithium cells is up to 10 years with over 80% retained capacity. High reliability is epitomized by the lithium/iodine and lithium/silver chromate cells used in the medical industry, in which the reliability level is greater than 0.7×10^{-7}, and increasing.

The *zinc-air cell* uses zinc as the anode and oxygen from the air as the cathode material. The aqueous electrolyte contains potassium hydroxide. Air is let into the cell through a hole or holes and diffuses into the electrolyte through a thin plastic film (which also prevents the electrolyte from escaping), so that oxygen combines with the hydroxide to form water and frees electrons to flow to the anode.

The no-load voltage of the cell is 1.4 V, and it is used in applications requiring high current for long periods. Its operating temperature range is from -40 to $+60°C$. Its shelf life is very good, with an average loss of capacity of about 2% per year. In use, it can be affected adversely by extremes of atmospheric humidity. The water vapor pressure in the cell is equivalent to 55% relative humidity, so that very dry or very damp conditions can cause it to lose or gain moisture, affecting the aqueous electrolyte.

Batteries—Secondary Cells

The most popular type of secondary (rechargeable) cell is the *lead-acid cell*, used in automobile batteries. Both anode and cathode are constructed of lead in the form of a grid. The positive plate is filled with lead dioxide; and the negative, with spongy lead. These thin plates are interleaved with porous separators. The electrolyte is a dilute solution of sulfuric acid. During discharge, the spongy lead in the negative plate and the lead dioxide in the positive plate react with the sulfuric acid to give lead sulfate crystals and water. The lead sulfate crystals grow on the lead dioxide, and if they are excessive, the operation of the cell will slow down. The water increases the dilution of the electrolyte so that the status of the cell can be determined by measuring its specific gravity.

The nominal cell voltage is 2.1 V, and the specific gravity of battery acid for automotive use is 1.280. In Table P-2, the volts per cell and the specific gravity of the electrolyte are shown during charging. Values during discharging would be in the reverse order.

**TABLE P-2   Charging
a Lead-Acid Battery**

Volts per cell	Specific gravity
1.8	1.120
1.9	1.140
2.0	1.160
2.1	1.180
2.2	1.200
2.3	1.220
2.4	1.240

A 12-V automotive battery in good condition and under no load will show a voltage of over 14 V when fully charged.

The current capacity of a lead-acid cell can withstand high charge and discharge rates. It can deliver even larger currents for a short time, as in starting an engine.

Temperature range for a lead-acid battery is -60 to $+60°C$, but the optimum temperature is $+20°C$. Shelf life depends on temperature. A nearly discharged cell loses 0.01% charge per day at 0°C, but rises to 2% per day for a fully charged cell at 45°C.

Nickel-cadmium cells have a negative electrode of cadmium hydroxide and a positive of nickel hydroxide in an electrolyte of potassium hydroxide. The characteristics of cylindrical sealed cells are given in Table P-3.

TABLE P-3   Nickel-cadmium
Cylindrical Sealed Cells

Size	Nominal capacity (Ah)	Charge rate for 16 hrs (mA)
AAA	0.18	18
AA	0.50	50
C	2.20	220
D	4.00	400
F	7.00	700
Super F	10.00	1000

Nickel-cadmium batteries operate best at about 25°C. Their shelf life is longest at 0°C.

Nickel-cadmium cells can be recharged from 500 to 1000 times at normal temperatures and conditions.

Silver-zinc cells are made in sealed button form. The positive electrode consists of a silver mesh coated with silver oxide. The negative electrode consists of a silver, or silver-coated copper, plate covered with zinc oxide. The electrolyte is potassium hydroxide.

These cells have more than double the capacity of nickel-cadmium cells of the same size. Their voltage when fully charged is 1.85, which falls to 1.5 V in operation. The discharge curve is almost flat. The number of charge cycles is approximately the same as the nickel-cadmium cell.

Dry Cells

Early batteries had "wet" cells, with the electrolyte in aqueous form. The requirement of portability led to the development of "dry" cells, in which the electrolyte is made in the form of a gel. Even lead-acid batteries can be obtained in this form. Dry cells are sealed to prevent the exudation of the electrolyte, but high temperature, and in some cases excessive current, can break down the seal. Attempts to recharge primary batteries can also have this effect. Electrolytes have a corrosive effect on electronic circuitry, so care should be taken to avoid leakage.

Electronic Power Supplies

The most convenient source of electrical power is the utility company's 120-volt, 60-hertz line. However, this must be changed to DC at other voltages for most purposes in electronic equipment. Transformers are used to adjust the voltage. (*See* Transformers.) Rectifiers are used to turn the AC to pulsating DC, and filters then smooth the latter until it is as close to pure DC as necessary for the equipment concerned.

Rectifiers today are mostly solid-state devices using the rectifying properties of semiconductors such as silicon, germanium, selenium, and copper oxide. However, electron-tube rectifiers are also used for some purposes. For the majority of uses, the silicon rectifier is preferred. (*See* Diodes.)

Figure P-3 shows a single-phase half-wave rectifier circuit. The diode conducts only on positive-going excursions of the input AC; therefore the output of the circuit consists of only half of the input, resulting in low efficiency.

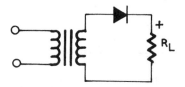

Figure P-3 Single-Phase Half-Wave Rectifier—[6]

Figure P-4 shows a single-phase full-wave center-tap rectifier circuit. The efficiency is good since both excursions of the AC are used. However, it requires a larger transformer with the added complication of a center tap.

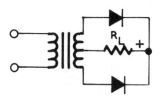

Figure P-4 Single-Phase Full-Wave Center-Tap Rectifier—[6]

Figure P-5 shows a single-phase full-wave bridge rectifier circuit. This is equally efficient, requires a simpler transformer and, with low-cost solid-state rectifier diodes, is cheaper to make than the center-tap rectifier circuit.

Figure P-5 Single-Phase Full-Wave Bridge Rectifier—[6]

Figure P-6 shows a conventional voltage-doubler rectifier circuit. There is no transformer. Capacitors $C1$ and $C2$ are each charged during alternate half-cycles to the peak value of the alternating input voltage. The capacitors discharge in series into the load R_L, so their individual voltages add together.

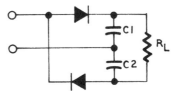

Figure P-6 Voltage-Doubler Rectifier — [6]

Figure P-7 shows a cascade voltage-doubler circuit. In this circuit, the capacitor $C1$ is charged to the peak value of the AC input via $D2$ during one half-cycle. During the other half-cycle, it discharges in series with the AC input through $D1$ to charge $C2$ to twice the AC peak voltage.

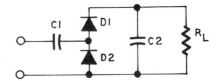

Figure P-7 Cascade Voltage-Doubler Rectifier — [6]

Figure P-8 shows how cascade voltage-doublers can be added to obtain further voltage multiplication. The number of stages is limited, however, by the load current, which must be small, and by deterioration in regulation as the number of stages increases.

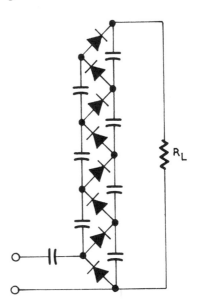

Figure P-8 Cascade Voltage-Doublers Combined to Make a Voltage-Quadrupler — [6]

The three types of rectifier filters are shown in Figure P-9.

Figure P-9 Rectifier Filters (a) Inductor-input filter (one section
shown) (b) Capacitor-input filter
(pi, or π filter) (c) Resistor-input filter—[6]

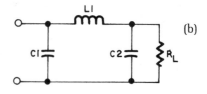

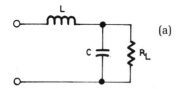

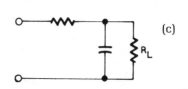

The percentage ripple from a single-section filter, as in Figure P-9(a),
is made up of any values of inductance and capacitance and may be
determined closely enough for practical purposes for a full-wave rectifier
from $100/LC$, where L is in henries and C in microfarads. In the case of
a half-wave rectifier, the values of inductance and capacitance must be
doubled. The minimum value of the choke in henries is determined by
dividing the maximum-load resistance in ohms by 1000, so once this is
known, the value of C can easily be calculated.

Because the value of the choke is mathematically related to the total-
load resistance, which may vary considerably, it is wiser to use chokes
with twice the calculated value. Alternatively, a swinging choke may be
used. This will have the lower value of inductance ($R_L/1000$) when there
is no load (or only a bleeder resistor), and about twice this value at full
load. Conversely, the bleeder resistor should have a resistance in ohms
equivalent to 1000 times the maximum inductance of the swinging choke
in henries.

Additional filter sections identical to Figure P-9(a) may be cascaded,
and each will reduce the ripple at its input in accordance with the factor
$100/LC$ given above.

The value of C1 in a capacitor-input filter for a full-wave rectifier is
determined from:

$$r = 0.00188/C_1R_L$$

where:

r = degree of filtering required.

C_1 = capacitance of C1 in microfarads.

R_L = value of total load resistance in megohms.

$$r = V_r/V_{dc}$$

where:

$$V_r = \text{maximum ripple voltage across } C1.$$

$$V_{\text{dc}} = \text{DC voltage across } C1.$$

The maximum value of $C1$ is limited by the maximum allowable peak-current rating of the rectifier. For this reason, a series resistor is usually connected between the rectifier and a capacitor-input filter to limit the input current when power is first applied.

Greater filtering is obtained by adding the inductor $L1$ and capacitor $C2$ as shown. Their values are calculated in the same way as for the inductor-input filter section, and the reduction of ripple is given by the same factor, $100/LC$.

Since a resistor presents the same opposition to DC that it does to AC, resistor-input filters are suitable only for low-current applications. The value of the resistor ideally should be about the same as the reactance of a choke in the same position in the circuit, but a lower-value compromise is often made so as not to reduce the output voltage unduly. This usually means that the resistor will be about one-tenth of the output load.

Power supply circuits frequently contain regulation circuits that ensure a constant output regardless of variations in load or line voltage. If the output voltage should begin to rise or fall from the value set by the adjustment of the voltage-adjust potentiometer (*see* Figure P-10), the change is sensed by the comparator, which monitors it constantly against the voltage reference (frequently a zener diode). An error voltage is gen-

Figure P-10 Series Regulator—[1]

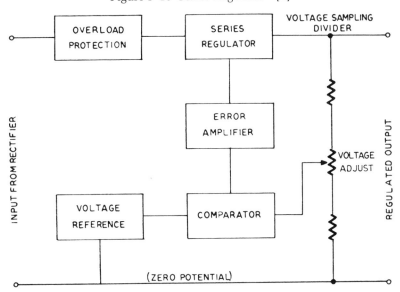

erated, amplified, and used to adjust the bias on the series regulator to restore the original level.

This type of regulator represents the class of *linear* regulators. In these, the input power increases as the input voltage increases. Since the output power is constant, the power supply must dissipate more power at higher input voltages, and this decreases its efficiency. A power supply that delivers 100 watts to the load may dissipate 200 watts in heat.

A switching power supply achieves high efficiency by minimizing internal power losses and holding input power relatively constant as input voltage increases. Such power supplies used to be complex and expensive, but have become more popular since ICs have come into general use.

As shown in Figure P-11, a switching power supply has the usual input from the powerline, and a transformer and rectifier network, just like other power supplies. There is also a filter capacitor, followed by a power transistor that regulates the flow of current to the load. Finally, there are a choke and capacitor that look like a low-pass filter.

Some of the output voltage is fed back to a *pulse-width modulator*. The widths of the pulses generated by this IC vary according to the feedback voltage. If the output voltage begins to rise, it causes the width of the pulses to start to narrow, and vice versa. These pulses turn $Q1$ on and off. If the pulses get narrower, $Q1$ conducts for periods that are shorter than the periods when it is not conducting. The opposite happens, of course, when the output voltage starts to fall.

Figure P-11 Switching Regulator
  A switching regulator uses an IC called a pulse-width modulator. Changes in the output voltage V_o cause changes in the width of the pulses applied to $Q1$'s base. —[2]

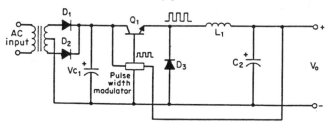

$D3$ is provided to clamp the pulses to zero volts. It shunts any negative component to ground.

The output from $Q1$ is a series of pulses. The low-pass filter $L1$ and $C2$ smooths them to give a DC output.

Bleeder Resistor

A resistor is sometimes placed across the output of a power supply to stabilize the voltage. To do this, it must draw a current heavy enough to swamp variations in the load resistance, which requires that it be a wirewound resistor. The same resistor also serves to discharge the filter capacitors when power is turned off.

Power Supply *See* Power Sources.

Power Transformer *See* Transformers.

PREFERRED VALUES

In order to limit the quantities of parts that must be stocked and to standardize their values, preferred values are used. These are calculated according to their tolerances, each nominal value being separated from the next by a constant multiplier. For small electronic components, such as fixed composition resistors and fixed ceramic, mica, and molded capacitors, the values in Table P-4 are used.

TABLE P-4   ANSI Standard C83.2-1971 — [6]

±20%	±10%	±5%
10	10	10
		11
	12	12
		13
15	15	15
		16
	18	18
		20
22	22	22
		24
	27	27
		30
33	33	33
		36
	39	39
		43
47	47	47
		51
	56	56
		62
68	68	68
		75
	82	82
		91
100	100	100

A slightly different set of preferred values is used for fixed wire-wound, power-type resistors, and for time-delay fuses, as shown in Table P-5.

TABLE P-5   ANSI Standard
Z17.1-1973 — [6]

Series "5" (±24%)	Series "10" (±12%)
10	10
	12
16	16
	20
25	25
	32
40	40
	50
63	63
	80
100	100

These tables give two significant figures for each value, which could therefore be, for example, 33, 330, 3300, 33,000, 330,000, or 3,300,000, and so on. Those values that appear in more than one column are values available in more than one tolerance, the tolerance of each column in which they appear.

PRINTED CIRCUITS

Rigid printed-circuit base materials (laminates) are manufactured in thicknesses ranging from 1/64 to 1/2 inch. Important properties of the usual materials are given in Table P-6. Other materials that may be used are:

>   Glass-cloth teflon (polytetrafluorethylene, PTFE),
>   Kel-F (polymonochlorotrifluoroethylene),
>   Silicone rubber,
>   Glass-mat-polyester-resin,
>   Teflon film,
>   Ceramic.

TABLE P-6   Printed-Circuit Base Materials

Material	Max. temp °C	Insulation	Strength
NEMA XXXP paper-base phenolic	105	Good	Good
NEMA XXXPC paper-base phenolic	105	Good	Good
NEMA FR-2 paper-base phenolic, flame-resistant	105	Good	Very good
NEMA FR-3 paper-base epoxy, flame-resistant	105	Very good	Very good
NEMA FR-4 glass-fabric-base epoxy, flame-resistant	130	Excellent	Excellent
NEMA FR-5 glass-fabric-base temperature-, and flame-resistant	155	Excellent	Excellent
NEMA G-10 glass-fabric-base epoxy, general purpose	130	Excellent	Excellent
NEMA G-11 glass-fabric-base epoxy, temperature-resistant	155	Excellent	Excellent
Glass-fabric-base fluorinated ethylene propylene	150	Excellent	Good
Glass-fabric-base PTFE	150	Excellent	Good

Conductor material is almost exclusively copper foil, in thicknesses of 0.0014 inch (1 oz/sq ft) and 0.0028 inch (2 oz/sq ft). The usual width of the conductor is 0.060 inch. With 1 oz/sq ft foil, a conductor of this width can carry a maximum current of 8 A, if the allowable temperature rise does not exceed 75°C. The normal ambient temperature surrounding the board plus the allowable temperature rise should not exceed the maximum safe operating temperature of the board material given in Table P-6. The minimum spacing between conductors for voltages up to 100 V should be 0.025 inches for uncoated boards.

Holes are punched in all paper-base boards, but many glass-fabric-base boards require drilling to avoid crazing or separation of the laminate layers. All holes (and other features) should be arranged to be centered at the intersections of a 0.100-, 0.050-, or 0.025-inch rectangular grid with preference in that order. Many components (ICs, for instance) have pins spaced to match the standard grids. Hole sizes should not exceed by more than 0.020 inch the diameter of the wire or pin to be inserted in the hole.

PROPAGATION

The atmosphere at great heights above the ground is very thin, merging imperceptibly into space itself. At these levels, it is exposed to the full force of the sun's radiation. High-energy ultraviolet rays strike atmospheric molecules and knock electrons out of their atoms. Although recombination takes place continuously, the liberation of other electrons maintains an electron density that varies with the intensity of the radiation. Since this increases with sunspot activity (and some other phenomena to be discussed later), it is not always the same and disappears gradually during the hours of darkness.

There are actually several ionized layers in the atmosphere, as shown in Figure P-12. The F2 layer, during the day, is between 250 and 400 kilometers above the Earth. Because it is the most exposed layer, it stores more solar energy than the lower layers, and since its molecules are more dispersed, the recombination rate is slower, so it remains ionized for many hours after dark. The F1 layer below it exists only during daylight.

Figure P-12 Ionized Layers in the Upper Atmosphere — [6]

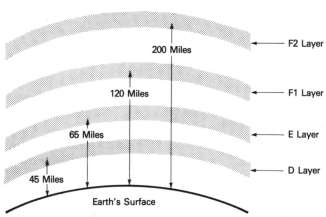

Lower yet is the E layer. Its ionization density corresponds closely with the elevation of the sun. Its molecules are not as thinly scattered, and it has another phenomenon, called sporadic E, in which irregular cloud-like areas of unusually high ionization occur, up to more than 50 percent of the time on certain days or nights. Sporadic-E ionization is ascribed to visible and subvisible wavelength bombardment of the atmosphere.

The lowest layer, extending down to 50 kilometers above the surface, is the D layer. It exists only during daylight hours, and its ionization density corresponds with the elevation of the sun.

The ionization of these layers increases with height, and the ability of radio waves to pass through these layers varies according to their wavelength, only the shortest wavelengths being able to penetrate the upper layers. Each layer has a *critical frequency*, which is that frequency above which waves can pass through. Waves at or below the critical frequency are reflected back to earth just as if the ionized layer were a solid object.

Very low-frequency waves (3–30 kHz) and low-frequency waves (30–300 kHz) (see Figure P-13) have wavelengths from 1 to 100 km, so they have no chance of passing through the ionized layers. However, since the ground and the ionosphere act very much like a waveguide to the lower frequencies, they can travel a long way and follow the curvature

Figure P-13 Electromagnetic Spectrum—[6]

Frequency (hertz)		Wavelength (meters)		Radioactive and Radio Waves	Ultraviolet, Visible, Infrared and Audio Waves
100 EHz	($\times 10^{18}$)	3 pm	($\times 10^{-12}$)	Gamma rays	
10 EHz	"	30 pm	"	(hard)	
1 EHz	"	300 pm	"	X rays	
100 PHz	($\times 10^{15}$)	3 nm	($\times 10^{-9}$)	(soft)	Ultraviolet rays
10 PHz	"	30 nm	"		
1 PHz	"	300 nm	"		
100 THz	($\times 10^{12}$)	3 μm	($\times 10^{-6}$)		Visible light rays
10 THz	"	30 μm	"		Infrared rays
1 THz	"	300 μm	"	12	
100 GHz	($\times 10^{9}$)	3 mm	($\times 10^{-3}$)	EHF - 11	
10 GHz	"	30 mm	"	SHF - 10	
1 GHz	"	300 mm	"	UHF - 9	
100 MHz	($\times 10^{6}$)	3 m	($\times 10^{0}$)	VHF - 8	
10 MHz	"	30 m	"	HF - 7	
1 MHz	"	300 m	"	MF - 6	
100 kHz	($\times 10^{3}$)	3 km	($\times 10^{3}$)	LF - 5	
10 kHz	"	30 km	"	VLF - 4	
1 kHz	"	300 km	"	VF - 3	
100 Hz	($\times 10^{0}$)	3 Mm	($\times 10^{6}$)	ELF - 2	Audio waves
10 Hz	"	30 Mm	"		
1 Hz	"	300 Mm	"		

of the earth. Since the conductivity of sea water is very high, their range over the ocean is even greater. Consequently, maritime and aircraft stations use these frequencies for navigational purposes, although they are now being superseded by satellite navigation stations.

Medium-frequency waves (0.3–3 MHz) include the standard AM broadcast band, and in this range both surface waves and waves reflected from the ionosphere (sky waves) are important. During the day, the sky waves are absorbed by the D and E layers, so propagation is almost entirely by the surface wave (ground wave) for distances between 25 and 100 miles. At night, when the D and E layers have disappeared, sky-wave reflection takes place from the F layer also. This is illustrated in Figure P-14. The fading area is the region where both ground and sky waves are received, but because of the different lengths of the paths traveled, they may not always have the same phase, especially at sunset, when electron density and layer height are changing rapidly. This effect also varies seasonally and with changes in sunspot activity.

Figure P-14 Nighttime Reception Conditions for Broadcast Stations — [6]

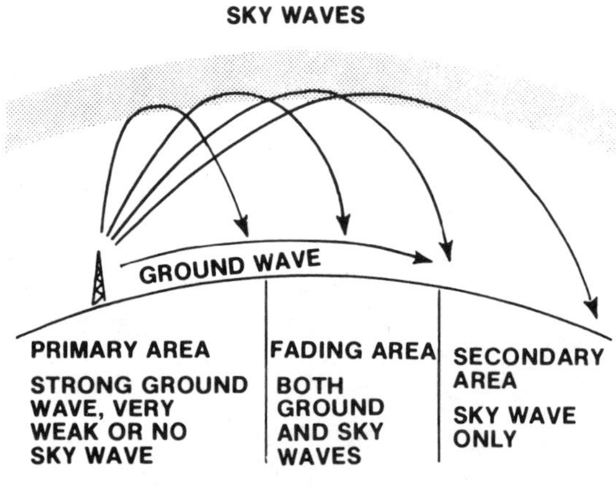

SKY WAVES

GROUND WAVE

PRIMARY AREA	FADING AREA	SECONDARY AREA
STRONG GROUND WAVE, VERY WEAK OR NO SKY WAVE	BOTH GROUND AND SKY WAVES	SKY WAVE ONLY

High-frequency waves (3–30 MHz) are the most interesting and variable part of the radio spectrum, since this segment contains the bands most used for short-wave listening and, because it uses sky waves to a much greater extent, may be received over very great distances if conditions are favorable. The angle at which the wave encounters the reflecting layer determines the distance, as shown in Figure P-15.

Figure P-15 Reception of High-Frequency Signals, Showing Skip Zone—[6]

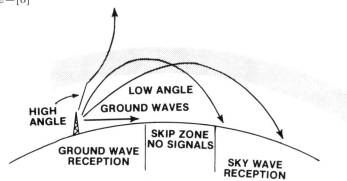

The short-wave band can be divided into three sections, as follows:

3–10 MHz   For daytime operation, the low end of this band, between 3 and 7 MHz, is excellent for transmission or reception up to a few hundred miles. The nighttime range can be a thousand or more miles. At the high end of this band, between 7 and 10 MHz, the daytime range can often extend to almost a thousand miles, while at night, especially in winter, coverage can be thousands of miles. In this range, the E layer dominates in the daytime, while at night the signals are reflected by the F layer.

10–20 MHz   This range of frequencies is used by most of the international broadcast stations. The frequency, high enough to penetrate the E layer, is reflected from the F layer during daylight hours. By using a low-wave angle at the transmitter and by controlling the direction of transmission, signals can be beamed to other parts of the world over great distances. This is enhanced during periods of sunspot activity; during a sunspot minimum, the nighttime performance is more limited because the F layer is thinner and radiation escapes into space instead of being reflected.

20–30 MHz   This section is suitable for both local and long-distance work. Local communication is very good by ground wave up to about 20 miles and is used largely by the lower-frequency CB channels (26.96–27.23 MHz). Long-distance communication is limited to times when the F layer is most dense, which is when sunspot activity is greatest. At other times, it is poor or impossible.

Very high-frequency waves (30–300 MHz) and ultra-high-frequency waves (0.3–3 GHz) normally are not reflected by the ionosphere, although low-channel television signals (54–88 MHz) may be reflected by a very intense F layer during exceptional sunspot activity. This is most unusual, however. Sporadic E propagation can also give a longer-than-usual range.

As a general rule, though, propagation at these frequencies is very nearly in a straight line, much the same as a beam of light. It is not entirely straight because of the refractive index of the atmosphere. This decreases with height so that waves near the ground travel more slowly and are bent downwards slightly. This extends the distance the wave can travel beyond the "line-of-sight" distance by about one-third, under average conditions in temperate climates. It does vary, however, with weather and atmospheric conditions, such as temperature, barometric pressure, and water vapor content in the air. The effect is more pronounced with VHF signals, less so with UHF; the higher the frequency, the more nearly radio waves approach light in their behavior. Another effect of the lower atmosphere, as opposed to the ionosphere, on VHF, UHF and SHF waves, is called tropospheric scatter, in which weak but reliable fields are propagated several hundred miles beyond the horizon.

Signals above 30 MHz are readily reflected by objects on the ground, such as tall buildings, hills, or the ground itself. The reflected signal travels a longer path than the direct one and so may arrive out of phase with it. The receiver than receives two identical signals one after the other. This will cause "ghosts" in a television picture or degraded audio in a radio. Reflection from airplanes causes a television picture to flutter.

Television and FM stations transmit horizontally polarized waves, whereas AM stations send out vertically polarized waves. This is because, at TV and FM frequencies, a vertical antenna would also pick up a lot of noise from electrical apparatus at these frequencies (or harmonics of them). By using a horizontal antenna, the noise is reduced by about 20 dB.

The atmosphere will only allow waves of certain frequencies to pass through it. Figure P-16 shows that "windows" exist for some frequencies, though not all can be used. For instance, the window for visible light can be used only when the sky is clear and not obscured by clouds. But below 50 gigahertz, the atmosphere is transparent to radio waves down to about 10 megahertz, below which transmission is severely affected by the ionosphere. Frequencies above 10 gigahertz are also attenuated by rain. As a result, satellites at first were using frequencies between 3.7 and 4.2 gigahertz only; and their earth stations, with much higher power, were operating between 5.925 and 6.425 gigahertz.

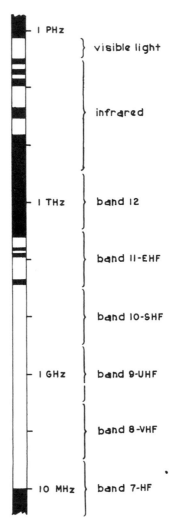

Figure P-16 Windows into Space—
[6]

PROPERTIES OF MATERIALS USED IN ELECTRONICS

The tables appearing in this section, and listed below, give the properties of materials commonly used in electronics:

TABLE P-7   Metals Commonly Used in Electronics

Metal	Density at 20°C g/cm^3	Melting point °C	Coefficient of linear expansion at 20°C × 10^{-6}/°C	Resistivity $\mu\Omega$/cm	Modulus of elasticity kg/mm^3	Thermal conductivity at 20°C W/cm/°C/s
Aluminum	2.70	660	22.90	2.62	7 250	2.18
Beryllium	1.82	1 278	12.00	10.00	30 000	1.64
Brass	8.55	900	18.77	3.90	13 200	*
Bronze	8.15	1 040	18.45	6.50	16 500	*
Copper	8.96	1 083	16.50	1.67	11 000	3.94
Gold	19.30	1 063	14.20	2.19	7 300	2.96
Iridium	22.40	2 410	6.50	5.30	52 500	1.40
Iron (wrought)	7.87	1 535	11.70	9.71	20 000	0.79
Lead	11.34	327	28.70	21.90	1 800	0.35
Magnesium	1.74	651	25.20	4.46	4 600	1.55
Manganese	7.44	1 244	23.00	5.00	16 000	
Mercury	13.55	−39		95.80		0.08
Molybdenum	10.20	2 610	4.90	4.90	35 000	1.46
Monel	8.90	1 400		42.00		
Nickel	8.90	1 453	13.30	6.84	21 000	0.90
Osmium	22.48	3 000	5.00	9.50	57 000	0.61
Palladium	12.00	1 552	11.80	10.80	12 000	0.70
Platinum	21.45	1 769	8.90	9.83	15 000	0.69
Rhodium	12.00	1 966	8.10	4.51	30 000	1.50
Ruthenium	12.20	2 250	9.10	7.60	42 000	
Silver	10.49	961	18.90	1.59	7 200	4.08
Tantalum	16.60	2 996	6.60	12.40	19 000	0.54
Tin	7.30	232	23.00	11.40	41 100	0.64
Titanium	4.54	1 675	8.50	80.00	8 500	0.20
Tungsten	19.30	3 410	4.30	5.50	35 000	1.99
Zinc	7.14	419	29.39	6.00	8 400	1.10
Zirconium	6.40	1 852	5.60	41.00	7 500	1.40

*Varies with composition, somewhat lower than copper

TABLE P-8 Electrical Properties of Commonly Used Insulators

Material	Resistivity (ohm/cm)	Dielectric constant
Air, dry	very high	1.0
Bakelite	10^{11}	4.4–5.4
Cellulose acetate	very high	3.3–3.9
Formica	very high	4.6–4.9
Window glass	10^{12}–10^{14}	7.6–8.0
Pyrex glass	10^{12}–10^{14}	4.8
Mica	10^{13}	5.4
Neoprene	10^{12}	6.7
Paper	high	3.0
Plexiglass	very high	2.8
Polyethylene	10^{18}	2.3
Polystyrene	10^{18}	2.6
Porcelain	very high	5.1–5.9
Rubber	10^{15}	2.4–2.9
Shellac	10^{16}	3.8
Sillca (quartz)	$> 10^{19}$	3.8
Teflon	10^{17}	2.1

See also under *Capacitors.*

TABLE P-9 Standard Annealed Bare Copper Wire Using American Wire Gauge (B&S)—[6]

Gauge (AWG) or (B&S)	Diameter inches Min.	Nom.	Max.	Area Circular Mils	Weight Pounds per M	Length Feet per Lb.	Resistance at 68°F Ohms per M	Feet per Ohm	Ohms per lb.	Current* capacity (Amps) Rubber Insulated
0000	.4554	.4600	.4646	211600.	640.5	1.561	0.4901	20400.	.00007652	225
000	.4055	.4096	.4137	167800.	507.9	1.968	.06180	16180.	.0001217	175
00	.3612	.3648	.3684	133100.	402.8	2.482	.07793	12830.	.0001935	150
0	.3217	.3249	.3281	105500.	319.5	3.130	.09827	10180.	.0003076	125
1	.2864	.2893	.2922	83690.	253.3	3.947	.1239	8070.	.0004891	100
2	.2550	.2576	.2602	66370.	200.9	4.977	.1563	6400.	.0007778	90
3	.2271	.2294	.2317	52640.	159.3	6.276	.1970	5075.	.001237	80
4	.2023	.2043	.2063	41740.	126.4	7.914	.2485	4025.	.001966	70
5	.1801	.1819	.1837	33100.	100.2	9.980	.3133	3192.	.003127	55
6	.1604	.1620	.1636	26250.	79.46	12.58	.3951	2531.	.004972	50
7	.1429	.1443	.1457	20820.	63.02	15.87	.4982	2007.	.007905	
8	.1272	.1285	.1298	16510.	49.98	20.01	.6282	1592.	.01257	35
9	.1133	.1144	.1155	13090.	39.63	25.23	.7921	1262.	.01999	
10	.1009	.1019	.1029	10380.	31.43	31.82	.9989	1001.	.03178	25
11	.08983	.09074	.09165	8234.	24.92	40.12	1.260	794.	.05053	
12	.08000	.08081	.08162	6530.	19.77	50.59	1.588	629.6	.08035	20
13	.07124	.07196	.07268	5178.	15.68	63.80	2.003	499.3	.1278	
14	.06344	.06408	.06472	4107.	12.43	80.44	2.525	396.0	.2032	15
15	.05650	.05707	.05764	3257.	9.858	101.4	3.184	314.0	.3230	
16	.05031	.05082	.05133	2583.	7.818	127.9	4.016	249.0	.5136	6
17	.04481	.04526	.04571	2048.	6.200	161.3	5.064	197.5	.8167	
18	.03990	.04030	.04070	1624.	4.917	203.4	6.385	156.5	1.299	3
19	.03553	.03589	.03625	1288.	3.899	256.5	8.051	124.2	2.065	
20	.03164	.03196	.03228	1022.	3.092	323.4	10.15	98.5	3.283	

continued

TABLE P-9   Standard Annealed Bare Copper Wire Using American Wire Gauge (B&S) (cont.)

Gauge (AWG) or (B&S)	Diameter inches			Area	Weight	Length	Resistance at 68°F			Current* capacity (Amps)
	Min.	Nom.	Max.	Circular Mils	Pounds per M'	Feet per Lb.	Ohms per M'	Feet per Ohm'	Ohms per lb.	Rubber Insulated
21	.02818	.02846	.02874	810.1	2.452	407.8	12.80	78.11	5.221	
22	.02510	.02535	.02560	642.4	1.945	514.2	16.14	61.95	8.301	
23	.02234	.02257	.02280	509.5	1.542	648.4	20.36	49.13	13.20	
24	.01990	.02010	.02030	404.0	1.223	817.7	25.67	38.96	20.99	
25	.01770	.01790	.01810	320.4	.9699	1031.	32.37	30.90	33.37	
26	.01578	.01594	.01610	254.1	.7692	1300.	40.81	24.50	53.06	
27	.01406	.01420	.01434	201.5	.6100	1639.	51.47	19.43	84.37	
28	.01251	.01264	.01277	159.8	.4837	2067.	64.90	15.41	134.2	
29	.01115	.01126	.01137	126.7	.3836	2607.	81.83	12.22	213.3	
30	.00993	.01003	.01013	100.5	.3042	3287.	103.2	9.691	329.2	
31	.008828	.008928	.009028	79.7	.2413	4145.	130.1	7.685	539.3	
32	.007850	.007950	.008050	63.21	.1913	5227.	164.1	6.095	857.6	
33	.006980	.007080	.007180	50.13	.1517	6591.	206.9	4.833	1364.	
34	.006205	.006305	.006405	39.75	.1203	8310.	260.9	3.833	2168.	
35	.005515	.005615	.005715	31.52	.09542	10480.	329.0	3.040	3448.	
36	.004900	.005000	.005100	25.00	.07568	13210.	414.8	2.411	5482.	
37	.004353	.004453	.004553	19.83	.06001	16660.	523.1	1.912	8717.	
38	.003865	.003965	.004065	15.72	.04759	21010.	659.6	1.516	13860.	
39	.003431	.003531	.003631	12.47	.03774	26500.	831.8	1.202	22040.	
40	.003045	.003145	.003245	9.888	.02993	33410.	1049.	0.9534	35040.	
41	.00270	.00280	.00290	7.8400	.02373	42140.	1323.	.7559	55750.	
42	.00239	.00249	.00259	6.2001	.01877	53270.	1673.	.5977	89120.	
43	.00212	.00222	.00232	4.9284	.01492	67020.	2104.	.4753	141000.	
44	.00187	.00197	.00207	3.8809	.01175	85100.	2672.	.3743	227380.	
45	.00166	.00176	.00186	3.0976	.00938	106600.	3348.	.2987	356890.	
46	.00147	.00157	.00167	2.4649	.00746	134040.	4207.	.2377	563900.	

*Note: Values from National Electrical Code.

TABLE P-10 Properties of Ferromagnetic Materials: Representative Core Materials—[6]

Material	Permeability Initial	Permeability Maximum	Coercivity (A/m)	Rententivity (T)
Ferroxcube 3 (Mn-Zn-Ferrite)	1.26×10^{-3}	1.88×10^{-3}	7.96×10^{-2}	0.10
Ferroxcube 101 (Ni-Zn-Ferrite)	1.38×10^{-3}		1.43×10^{-1}	0.11
HyMu 80 (Ni 80%, Fe 20%)	2.51×10^{-2}	1.26×10^{-1}	3.98×10^{-2}	
Iron, silicon (transformer) (Fe 96%, Si 4%)	6.28×10^{-4}	8.80×10^{-3}	2.39×10^{-1}	0.70
Mumetal (Ni 77%, Fe 16%, Cu 5%, Cr 2%)	2.51×10^{-2}	1.26×10^{-1}	3.98×10^{-2}	0.60
Permalloy 45 (Fe 55%, Ni 45%)	3.14×10^{-3}	3.14×10^{-2}	2.39×10^{-1}	
Permendur 2V (Fe 49%, Co 49%, V 2%)	1.01×10^{-3}	5.65×10^{-3}	1.59×10^{0}	1.40
Rhometal (Fe 64%, Ni 36%)	1.26×10^{-3}	6.28×10^{-3}	3.98×10^{-1}	0.36
Sendust (high-frequency powder) (Fe 85%, Si 10%, Al 5%)	3.77×10^{-2}	1.51×10^{-1}	3.98×10^{-2}	0.50
Supermalloy (Ni 79%, Fe 16%, Mo 5%)	1.26×10^{-1}	1.26×10^{0}	1.59×10^{-3}	

TABLE P-11 Properties of Ferromagnetic Materials: Representative Permanent Magnetic Materials—[6]

Material	External energy $(B_d H_d)$	Coercivity (A/m)	Retentivity (T)
Alnico V (Fe 51%, Co 24%, Ni 14%, Al 8%, Cu 3%)	35 810	45 757	1.20
Alnico VI (Fe 48.75%, Co 24%, Ni 15%, Al 8%, Cu 3%, Ti 1.25%)	27 852	59 683	1.00
Carbon steel (Fe 98.5%, C 1%, Mn 0.5%)	1 432	3 820	0.86
Chromium steel (Fe 95.5%, Cr 3.5%, C 1%)	2 308	5 013	0.90
Cobalt steel (Co 36%, Cr 35%, Fe 25.15%, W 3%, C 0.85%)	7 448	16 711	0.90
Cunife I (Cu 60%, Ni 20%, Fe 20%)	15 597	4 775	0.58
Iron oxide powder (4.96 g/cm^3) (Fe_3O_4 92%, Fe_2O_3 8%)	—	31 433	0.75
Platinum alloy (Pt 77%, Co 23%)	30 239	159 155	0.45
Tungsten steel (Fe 94%, W 5%, C 1%)	2 546	5 570	1.03
Vectolite (sintered) (Fe_3O_4 44%, Fe_2O_3 30%, Co_2O_3 26%)	4 775	79 577	0.16

TABLE P-12   Principal Semiconductors—[6]

Semiconductor	Density (g/cm³)	Melting point (°C)	Coefficient of linear expansion (× 10⁻⁶/°C)	Energy band gap at 300K (eV)	Electron mobility (cm³/V.s) Light mass	Heavy mass	Hole mobility (cm³/V.s) Light mass	Heavy mass
AlSb	4.28	1 065		1.60		180–230		420–500
B	2.34	2 075		1.40	1	1		2
C (diamond)	3.51	3 800	1.18	5.30	1 800	1 800		1 600
GaAs	5.32	1 238	5.70	1.43	8 600–11 000	1 000	3 000	426–500
GaSb	5.62	706	6.90	0.70	5 000–40 000	1 000	7 000	700–1 200
GaP	4.13	1 450	5.30	2.25		120–300		420–500
Ge	5.32	937	6.10	0.66	3 900	3 900	14 000	1 860
InAs	5.67	942	5.30	0.33	33 000–40 000		8 000	450–500
InP	4.79	1 062	4.50	1.27	4 800–6 800			150–200
InSb	5.78	530	5.50	0.17	78 000		12 000	750
Se (amorphous)	4.82			2.30	0.005			0.15
Se (hexagonal)	4.79	217	36.9	1.80				1
Si	2.33	1 417	4.20	1.09	1 500	1 500	1 500	480
Te	6.25	432	16.80	0.38	1 100	1 100	10 000	700

Carrier mobilities are at 300 K

TABLE P-13 Galvanic Series in Seawater—[6]

If any two metals from the following list are connected by a conductor and immersed in sea water they form a galvanic cell. If they are in different groups the metal coming first in the list will be corroded by the other metal. It is therefore described as anodic. The other metal is therefore cathodic, or most noble. If the two metals are in the same group corrosion will be negligible.

Magnesium
Magnesium alloys

Zinc
Galvanized steel
Galvanized wrought iron

Aluminum:
  52SH, 4S, 3S, 2S, 53ST
  Aluminum clad

Cadmium

Aluminum:
  A17ST, 17ST, 24ST

Mild Steel
Wrought iron
Cast iron

Ni-resist

13% chromium stainless steel
50-50 lead-tin solder
18-8 stainless steel (active)
18-8-3 stainless steel (active)

Lead
Tin

Muntz metal
Manganese bronze
Naval brass

Nickel (active)
Inconel (active)

Yellow brass
Admiralty brass
Aluminum bronze
Red brass
Copper
Silicon bronze
Ambrac
70-30 copper nickel
Comp. G bronze
Comp. M bronze

Nickel (passive)
Inconel (passive)

Monel

18-8 stainless steel (passive)
18-8-3 stainless steel (passive)

PULSE MODULATION

In pulse modulation, the carrier is transmitted as a series of pulses instead of as a continuous wave, as in AM and FM. The modulating signal is sampled at regular intervals, and the samples are used to modulate the pulses in various ways, as shown in Figure P-17. The modulating waveform is sampled at a rate higher than twice the highest significant modulating signal frequency.

Figure P-17 Types of Pulse Modulation—[6]

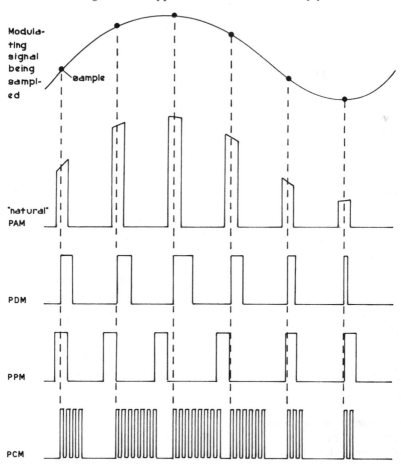

Pulse-amplitude modulation (PAM)

Height of the pulse is varied in accordance with the amplitude of the modulating signal. The type illustrated is called "natural" because the pulse tops follow the amplitude variation of the modulating signal during the sampling interval. In "square-topped" or "instantaneous" PAM, the pulse tops are flat and correspond to the instantaneous value of the modulating signal amplitude at the center or edge of the pulse.

In the type illustrated, the pulses are all positive going, and it is therefore called single-polarity PAM. In another type, the pulses also go negative when the modulating signal does, and it is called double-polarity PAM.

Pulse-Coded Modulation (PCM)

In this type, the modulating signal is sampled uniformly, and the sampled values are converted to code groups of pulses according to the amplitude of the modulating signal.

Pulse-Duration Modulation (PDM)

In this type, the width or duration of the pulses is proportional to the amplitude of the modulating signal. Like PAM, sampling may be "natural," the samples coinciding with the pulses, but as the pulses vary in width; the sampling intervals are not constant. In "uniform" sampling, the samples are uniformly spaced. PDM is also called *pulse-length* or *pulse-width* modulation (PLM or PWM).

Pulse-Position Modulation (PPM)

In this type, the occurrence of each pulse in time is advanced or retarded in accordance with the amplitude of the natural or uniform sample of the modulating signal. This is also called pulse-time modulation (PTM), or pulse-phase modulation (PPM). Pulse-frequency modulation (PFM) varies the rate of occurrence of the pulse in proportion to the amplitude of the modulating signal.

Q

Q

1. Quantity of electric charge, expressed in coulombs.

2. Quality of a reactive circuit, given by the ratio of the reactance of the circuit to the total resistance of the circuit, or $Q = X/R$.

R

Reactance Measure of the imaginary part of the impedance of a circuit or component to an alternating current, expressed in ohms. Inductive reactance (X_L) is given by:

$$X_L = 2\pi f L$$

where:

f is the frequency, in hertz.

L is the inductance, in henries.

Capacitive reactance (X_C) is given by:

$$X_C = 1/2\pi f C$$

where:

f = the frequency, in hertz.

C = the capacitance, in farads.

Rectifiers *See* Power Sources.

Regulation *See* Power Sources.

RELAYS

A relay is an electromechanical device in which switch contacts are closed or opened by an electromagnet. The switching contacts may be normally open, or normally closed. Upon energization, they go to the opposite of their normal position and are held in that condition as long as current flows in the electromagnet. However, some have a means of latching so that they will remain in the new condition when current is removed. Contacts may be single-throw, double-throw, or multiple. They are made of gold, silver, palladium, and alloys of these metals.

Dust-protected relays are inside a case which is open to the air at gaps around tags and join lines. Fumes generated in the case can escape and do not contaminate the contacts.

Hermetically-sealed relays have metal covers sealed to a glass base, through which the leads pass. Air is replaced with nitrogen.

Reed relays have their contacts sealed in a glass capsule. The contacts are long thin nickel-iron rods, flattened at the ends, overlapping, and separated by a small gap. By passing current through a surrounding coil, the reeds are magnetized, and attracted to each other. When the current ceases, the contacts spring apart. The capsule is filled with an inert gas.

Mercury-wetted contact relays are similar, with contacts wetted with a film of mercury. The capsule is filled with hydrogen under pressure.

Diaphragm relays have a metal core. At the end of the core is a glass capsule sealed to it, containing a thin nickel-iron diaphragm. A coil is wound around the core. When current flows in the coil, the core is magnetized, attracting the diaphragm, which closes the contacts. Those are also in the glass capsule.

Table R-1 shows a comparison of these relay types. On a scale of 4, the higher the number, the better the relay for that parameter.

TABLE R-1   Comparison of Relay Types

Parameter	Dust-protected	Hermetically-sealed	Reed	Mercury-wetted	Diaphragm
Reliability	1	3	2	4	4
Life	2	1	2	4	3
Resistance to external forces	4	3	3	1	2
Maximum contact load	4	3	3	1	2
Sealing	—	4	3	3	2
Position sensitive	no	no	no	yes	no
Price	4	2	4	1	2
Multiple contacts	3	2	1	1	1

Series or shunt resistors, diodes, and capacitors may be used to suppress contact erosion resulting from initial heavy currents associated with capacitive and inductive loads.

Reluctance Measure of the opposition encountered by magnetic flux in a magnetic circuit is given by:

$$\mathscr{R} = M/\Phi$$

where:

$\mathscr{R}$ = reluctance, in ampere-turns/webers.

M = magnetomotive force, in ampere-turns.

Φ = induction flux, in webers.

RESISTANCE

The resistance of a material is given by:

$$R = \rho l/A$$

where:

R = resistance, in ohms.

ρ = resistivity of the material, in ohm-meters.

l = length, in meters.

A = cross-sectional area, in square meters.

Resistivities of various materials are given in Table R-2.

TABLE R-2   Typical Resistivities of Materials* at 20°C

Material	Resistivity ρ (ohm-meters)	Material	Resistivity ρ (ohm-meters)
Aluminum	2.83×10^{-8}	Graphite	8×10^{-6}
Antimony	4.17×10^{-7}	Iron	9.8×10^{-7}
Bakelite plastic resins	$1 \times 10^{+10}$	Lead	2.2×10^{-7}
and compounds		Manganin alloy	4.4×10^{-7}
Brass	7×10^{-8}	Mercury	9.6×10^{-7}
Carbon	3.5×10^{-5}	Mica	$1 \times 10^{+14}$
Constantan alloy	4.9×10^{-7}	Nichrome	1×10^{-6}
Copper	1.7×10^{-8}	Rubber (hard)	$1 \times 10^{+16}$
German silver	3.3×10^{-7}	Silicon	$1.3 \times 10^{+3}$
Germanium	0.45	Silver	1.6×10^{-8}
Glass	$1 \times 10^{+12}$	Steel (4% Si)	5×10^{-7}
Gold	2.4×10^{-8}	Tungsten	5.2×10^{-8}

*Values may vary with purity of material.

Conductance

Conductance (the reciprocal of resistance) is given by:

$$G = 1/R$$

where:

G = conductance, in siemens.

R = resistance, in ohms.

Ohm's Law

Resistance is directly proportional to the voltage across a resistance, and inversely proportional to the current flowing through it:

$$R = V/I$$

Power is directly proportional to the square of the current, and directly proportional to the resistance:

$$P = I^2 R$$

where:

R = resistance, in ohms.

V = voltage across resistance, in volts.

I = current through resistance, in amperes.

P = power dissipated in resistance, in watts.

Equivalent Resistance

Equivalent resistance of resistances in series is given by:

$$R_{EQ} = R_1 + R_2 + R_3 + \cdots + R_n$$

Equivalent parallel resistance is given by:

$$R_{EQ} = 1/[(1/R_1) + (1/R_2) + (1/R_3) + \cdots + (1/R_n)]$$

Except that in the case of two resistances, it is given by:

$$R_{EQ} = R_1 R_2/(R_1 + R_2)$$

See also Electric Circuit Theory.

RESISTORS

Composition resistors are made by embedding particles of carbon in a clay binder in the form of a slug. The resistor's two leads are also embedded in the opposite ends of the slug, and this assembly is enclosed in a molded body. Nominal values of resistance and tolerance are indicated by colored bands. These are placed closer to one end of the body than the other. Reading from the nearer end, the first band gives the first digit of the value, the second band gives the second digit, the third band gives the multiplier, and the fourth band the tolerance. The color code is given in Table R-3.

TABLE R-3—[7]

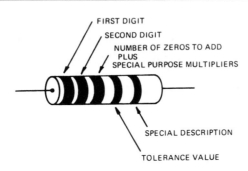

Color	1st color digit value	2nd color digit value	3rd color # o's	4th color tolerance	5th color special
Black	0	0	0	20%	—
Brown	1	1	1	1%	1.0 / 1khr (M)*
Red	2	2	2	2%	0.1 / 1khr (P)*
Orange	3	3	3	3%	0.01 / 1khr (R)*
Yellow	4	4	4	4%	0.001 / 1khr (S)*
Green	5	5	5	GMV	tested after load cycle
Blue	6	6	6	6%	—
Violet	7	7	7	7%	—
Gray	8	8	8 (X0.01)	8%	—
White	9	9	9 (X0.1)	9%	solderable terminals**
Gold	—	—	X0.1	5%	—
Silver	—	—	X0.01	10%	—
No color	—	—	—	20%	—

  * Reliable types only
 ** Film types
  GMV—Guaranteed Minimum Value
  Note: You may find gray or silver and white or gold used in the third band. Gray = silver; white = gold in the third band.

Tolerance is indicated by a gold band for ±5 percent, a silver band for ±10 percent, and no band for ±20 percent. Preferred values for these tolerances are given in Table R-4.

The sizes of composition resistors determine the maximum power they can dissipate, and they are made for 1/8, 1/4, 1/2, 1 and 2 watts.

TABLE R-4—[7]

TOLERANCES	5%		10%		20%
Two U.S. Standard Multipliers (A) *Z17.1 (B) **C83.2	*1.58	**1.10	*1.26	**1.21	1.46
	10	10	10	10	10
	—	11	—	—	—
	—	12	12	12	—
	—	13	—	—	—
	—	15	—	15	15
	16	16	16	—	—
	—	18	—	18	—
	—	20	20	—	—
	—	22	—	22	22
	—	24	—	—	—
	25	—	25	—	—
	—	27	—	27	—
	—	30	—	—	—
	—	—	32	—	—
	—	33	—	33	33
	—	36	—	—	—
	—	39	—	39	—
	40	—	40	—	—
	—	43	—	—	—
	—	47	—	47	47
	—	—	50	—	—
	—	51	—	—	—
	—	56	—	56	—
	—	62	—	—	—
	63	—	63	—	—
	—	68	—	68	68
	—	75	—	—	—
	—	—	80	—	—
	—	82	—	82	—
	—	91	—	—	—
	100	100	100	100	100

NOTE:

(1) For resistances under 100 ohms, multiply by one.

(2) For resistances under 1000 ohms, multiply by ten. IE: 160 ohms may be bought having 5- and 10-percent tolerances.

(3) For resistances under 10,000 ohms, multiply by one hundred. IE: 2,200 ohms can be bought having 5-, 10-, and 20-percent tolerances.

(4) For resistances under 100,000 ohms, multiply by one thousand. IE: 62,000 ohms is available only in a 5-percent resistor.

(5) For resistances greater, multiply by 10k, 100k, etc.

Semi-precision resistors are made with a film of metal or carbon on a ceramic core. They are available with tolerances of 0.1, 0.25, 0.5, 1 and 2 percent. Their values are usually printed on their bodies, but may be indicated with the same color code as given in Table R-3.

Wirewound resistors are made by winding a nickel-chromium alloy wire on a ceramic tube, and covering it with a vitreous coating. These can stand more heat than other types, but their spiral winding generates a magnetic field that limits their use to frequencies below 1 MHz, unless they are made with two windings wound in opposite directions. Wirewound resistors are often made with a slider to allow the value to be adjusted or to provide a tap for voltage division.

Metal-film network resistors are also made in single inline packages (SIPs) for use in printed circuit boards.

Other less common types are high-voltage, high-resistance, and ultraprecision resistors.

The *temperature coefficient of resistance (TCR or tempco)* of a resistor represents a percentage change of the nominal resistance at 25°C, expressed in parts per million per degree Celsius (ppm/°C). It may be positive or negative.

The *rated continuous working voltage* of a resistor is the maximum voltage that can be safely applied to it without exceeding its power rating, and is given by:

$$V = \sqrt{PR}$$

Variable resistors, often called potentiometers, have additional parameters that should be taken into consideration:

1. Resolution, which is the smallest change in resistance that can be realized as the wiper arm is rotated.

2. Wiper current, which means the maximum current that can flow through the wiper terminal.

3. End resistance, which means how much resistance exists between the wiper arm and either end terminal when the wiper has been rotated all the way to either end.

4. Setting stability, or repeatability. (Does the variable resistor give the same resistance each time the wiper is reset to the same position?)

5. Maximum number of allowed rotations.

6. Number of turns.

7. Ability of the variable resistor shaft to operate a switch, as in many volume controls.

8. Taper or linearity. In some potentiometers, the value of resistance is linearly proportional to the rotation of the wiper; in other types, the change is logarithmic.

9. Whether the potentiometer can be ganged with any others, and the effect this may have on temperature derating.

A *rheostat* is a variable resistor with one end-terminal.

Resonance In an *LC* circuit, resonance is the condition when the inductive reactance is equal to the capacitive reactance ($X_L = X_C$). The frequency is given by:

$$f = 1/(2\pi\sqrt{LC})$$

where:

$$f = \text{frequency, in hertz.}$$
$$L = \text{inductance, in henries.}$$
$$C = \text{capacitance, in farads.}$$

If the frequency is known, L and C are given by:

$$L = 1/(4\pi^2 f^2 C)$$
$$C = 1/(4\pi^2 f^2 L)$$

The nomographs in Table R-5 may be used to save calculating these values.

To find the resonant frequency, lay a ruler across the appropriate nomograph with its edge connnecting the values of inductance and capacitance, and read the frequency where the ruler's edge cuts the frequency column. To find reactance, lay the ruler across the appropriate nomograph so that its edge connects the value of inductance or capacitance to the frequency value, and read the reactance where the ruler's edge cuts the reactance column.

See also Oscillators.

Rheostat *See* Resistors.

Ripple *See* Power Sources.

TABLE R-5   Nomographs for Inductance, Reactance,
Capacitance, and Frequency.—[6]

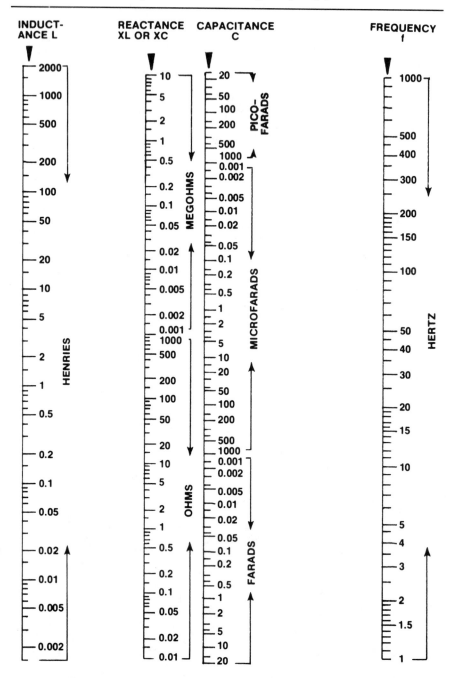

TABLE R-5 Nomographs for Inductance, Reactance,
Capacitance, and Frequency. (*Cont.*)

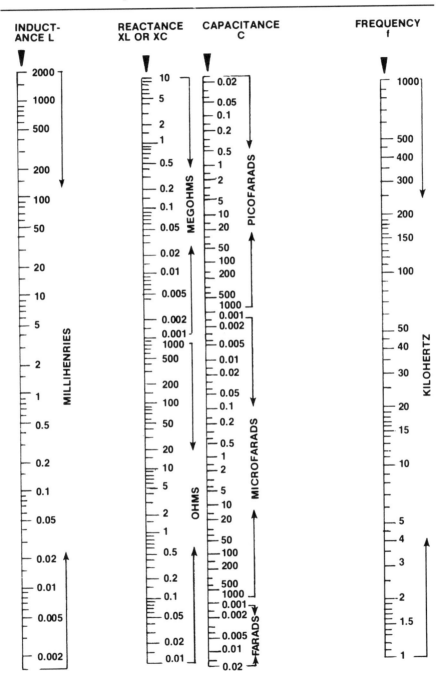

| INDUCT-ANCE L | REACTANCE XL OR XC | CAPACITANCE C | FREQUENCY f |

TABLE R-5 Nomographs for Inductance, Reactance, Capacitance, and Frequency. (*Cont.*)

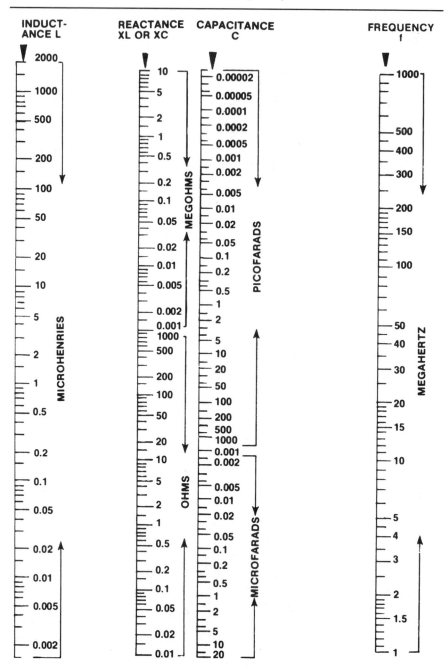

S

Satellites Frequency data for satellites:

Frequency (GHz)	Allocated for:
250–275	Satellites, space research, radio astronomy
220–240	Satellites, space research, radio astronomy
170–200	Satellites, space research, radio astronomy
84–152	Satellites, space research, radio astronomy
50–51	Satellites, space research
40–48	Satellites
29.50–31.00	Fixed satellite (up)
27.50–29.50	Fixed satellite (up)
21.20–22.00	Earth exploration satellite (down)
17.70–21.20	Fixed satellite (down)
14.00–14.50	Fixed satellite (up)
12.50–12.75	Fixed satellite (up)
11.45–12.20	Fixed satellite (down)
10.95–11.20	Fixed satellite (down)
5.925–8.400	Fixed satellite (up)
4.400–4.700	Fixed satellite (up)
3.400–4.200	Fixed satellite (down)
2.500–2.690	Fixed satellite (down)
1.770–1.790	Meteorological satellite (down)
1.690–1.700	Meteorological satellite (down)
1.645–1.660	Aeronautical mobile satellite
1.6365–1.644	Maritime mobile satellite
1.5425–1.5435	Aeronautical and maritime mobile satellites
1.535–1.5425	Maritime mobile satellite
1.525–1.535	Earth exploration satellite (down)
0.460–0.470	Meteorological satellite (down)
0.400–0.403	Meteorological satellite (up)
0.137–0.138	Meteorological satellite (down)

Schottky Diode *See* Diodes.

Semiconductors *See* Diodes, Transistors.

Silicon Controlled Rectifier (SCR) *See* Transistors.

Speaker *See* Transducers.

Solid State *See* Diodes, Transistors.

Sound *See* Audio.

Source *See* Transistors.

Standing-Wave Ratio *See* Transmission Lines.

Star Network *See* Tee or Wye Network.

T

Tee or Wye Network Three-phase AC is more efficient than single-phase. For example, single-phase motors are not inherently self-starting. There-

Figure T-1 Sinusoidal Waves of Voltage Produced by a Three-Phase Generator

The phases are designated red (R), yellow (Y), and blue (B).

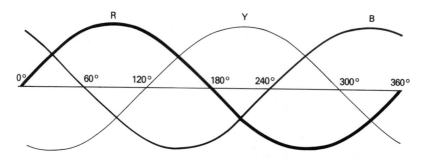

Figure T-2 Star or Wye Configuration
How a three-phase generator is connected to a three-phase load.
The currents in each leg, referenced to I_R, are given by:

$$i_R = (V/Z) \sin (\omega t - \theta)$$

$$i_Y = (V/Z) \sin (\omega t - \theta)$$

$$i_B = (V/Z) \sin (\omega t - \theta)$$

where θ = the phase shift caused by the load impedance.

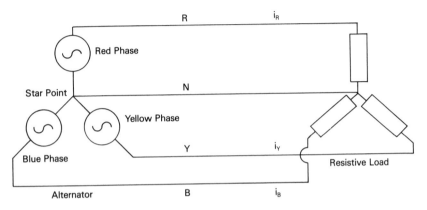

fore, three-phase AC is used extensively in industrial and other large-scale operations. In a three-phase system, there are three voltages, each separated by a phase difference of 120 degrees, as shown in Figure T-1. These are carried from the generator to the load by four wires, as shown in Figure T-2. Such an arrangement is known as a star, wye, or tee connected system. An alternative arrangement is shown in Figure T-3. This requires only three wires, and is called a delta connected system.

Three-phase transformers may be connected in either a star (wye) or a delta configuration. The primary and the secondary need not be the same. Formulas for determining the voltage across the secondary winding for each of the four possible configurations are as follows:

Δ to Y:

$$V_s = V_p \times N \times \sqrt{3}$$

Y to Δ:

$$V_s = (V_p \times N)/\sqrt{3}$$

Figure T-3 Three-Phase Generator Connected in the Delta Configuration

$$Y_{R\text{delta}} = Y_{R\text{star}}Y_{Y\text{star}}/(Y_{R\text{star}} + Y_{Y\text{star}} + Y_{B\text{star}})$$

and similarly for $Y_{Y\text{delta}}$ and $Y_{B\text{delta}}$.

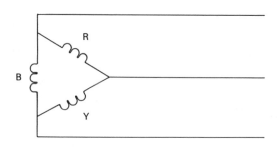

Δ to Δ:

$$V_s = V_p \times N$$

Y to Y:

$$V_s = V_p \times N$$

where:

V_s = secondary voltage, in volts.

V_p = primary voltage, in volts.

N = turns ratio.

Temperature Effects *See* device.

Thermocouples *See* Transducers.

Thevenin's Theorem *See* Electric Circuit Theory.

TIME-CONSTANT

A circuit consisting of a resistor and a capacitor in series is called an *RC* circuit. If a DC voltage is applied across them so that a constant current flows through the resistor into the capacitor until the latter is charged to the applied voltage, the time taken will be given by:

$$T = RC$$

A circuit consisting of a resistor and an inductor is called an *LC* circuit. If a DC voltage is applied across them so that the current flowing through the resistor and the inductor increases at a constant rate, until the current reaches a maximum value, the time taken will be given by:

$$T = L/R$$

where:

$T =$ time, in seconds.

$R =$ resistance, in ohms.

$C =$ capacitance, in farads.

$L =$ inductance, in henries.

In reality, this does not happen. The current flowing into the capacitor depends upon the voltage difference between the charge on the capacitor and the source voltage. As this gets less and less, the current decreases also. In the case of an inductor, the self-induced voltage subtracts from the source voltage to produce a similar effect.

This is illustrated in Figure T-4, which graphs the voltage build-up in a 100-microfarad capacitor in series with a 220 kilohm resistor when a 9-volt source is applied to them. If $T = LC$, the voltage rise on the capacitor would be as shown by the straight sloping line, and would reach 9 volts in 22 seconds ($100 \times 10^{-6} \times 220 \times 10^3$). But, in fact, the voltage on the capacitor after 22 seconds is only 5.69 V, which is 63.2 percent of 9 V. This is nevertheless called the *RC* time-constant. Another 22 seconds is a second *RC* time-constant. At 44 seconds, the charge on the capacitor is 7.78 V. This is 5.69 V + 63.2 percent of the remaining difference. After a third *RC* time-constant (66 s), the charge has become 8.55 V [7.78 + 0.632(9.00 − 7.79)]; after a fourth (88 s), 8.84 V [8.55 + 0.632(9.00 − 8.55)]; and after a fifth (110 s), 8.94 V [8.84 + 0.632(9.00 − 8.84)]. At this point (five time-constants), the capacitor is considered to be fully charged, although in theory it never is.

The build-up of current in an *LC* circuit has the same profile as that in an *RC* circuit (A in Figure T-4), and both also have the same profile when discharging under similar conditions (B).

Figure T-4 Time-Constant (*T*) of an *RC* Circuit

The solid curve *A* shows how the voltage on a capacitor of 100 μF rises as a current flows from a 9-V battery into it through a 220-kΩ resistor. At first, the difference between the battery and the capacitor is 9 V, but as the capacitor voltage increases, the difference gets less, and so the current decreases. Consequently, curve *A* is steep at first, but subsequently flattens out. If the capacitor charged at an even rate (sloping straight line), it would be fully charged after 22 s. This is the time-constant (*T*).—[2]

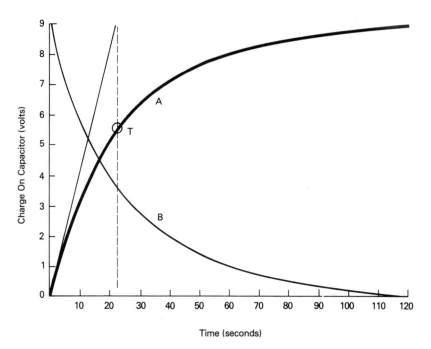

If *C* or *L* is in:	and *R* is in:	*T* is in:
microfarads	megohms	seconds
microhenries	megohms	seconds
microfarads	ohms	microseconds
picofarads	megohms	microseconds
microhenries	ohms	microseconds

TRANSDUCERS

Distance Transducers

Transducers for measuring linear or angular movement convert the movement to an electrical quantity. They include:

Resistance transducers

Strain gages

Capacitive transducers

Inductive transducers

Optical encoders

Resistance transducers use a linear or rotating potentiometer, in which change of distance causes change of resistance. This is supplied with an AC input to overcome DC bias and to facilitate amplification. The potentiometer can be molded or wirewound. The use of a wirewound track is limited by the winding density (turns per mm) and the dimensions of the wiper contact; therefore molded tracks are normally used. These give a resolution up to 0.0035 percent, with a linearity of ± 0.2 percent over distances in excess of 1 m. A typical standard resistance of 40 Ω per mm at an operating voltage of 10 V is used.

Strain gages utilize the change of resistance of an electrical conductor that occurs when a stress is applied. The sensitivity of a strain gauge along its axes of measurement is given by:

$$K = (\Delta R/R)/(\Delta l/l)$$

where:

$$K = \text{the gauge factor.}$$

$$\Delta R/R = \text{electrical strain.}$$

$$\Delta l/l = \text{mechanical strain.}$$

For alloy strain gauges, $2 < K < 5$, while for semiconductor gauges, $K > 100$.

The change in resistance of a strain gauge is directly proportional to the strain, and is measured with the strain gauge acting as one arm of a Wheatstone bridge. The bridge is balanced when:

$$R_1/R_2 = R_3/R_4$$

Capacitive transducers employ two plates in which the distance or the permittivity between them varies. The permittivity may be varied by having a dielectric that moves in or out, to a greater or lesser extent. Since they are most accurate when the separation between the plates is very small, the first type is only used for very small distance measurements of less than 1 mm. However, in this range, resolution is almost infinite. The capacitance between two parallel plates is given by:

$$C = (\epsilon_o \epsilon_r) A / d$$

Another type of capacitive transducer consists of a rod inside a concentric tube, separated from it by a small gap. Its capacitance varies linearly with distance, and it is capable of measurements up to 0.4 m with a resolution of 10^{-4} mm. The capacitance of this capacitor is given by:

$$C = (2\pi \epsilon_o \epsilon_r) / \ln (b/a)$$

where:

C = capacitance, in farads.

ϵ_o = permittivity of free space.

ϵ_r = relative permittivity.

A = effective area of the plates.

d = separation between the plates.

b = internal diameter of tube.

a = diameter of rod.

Inductive transducers work by having the reluctance of a magnetic circuit change in accordance with the distance. A typical arrangement has two coils connected in anti-phase with a common magnetic core. A high-frequency voltage is applied to the coils, and the core positioned so that the output voltage is at a null. Movement of the core will then result in a reading proportionate to the distance. Typical ranges of measurement are 0.125 mm to 75 mm, with a sensitivity of 0.25 mV per mm. Resolution is virtually infinite.

Optical encoders consist of a glass disk in the case of a rotary encoder, or a strip in the case of a linear encoder, with accurately generated lines at regular intervals. A narrow beam of light passes through the encoder, and the relative movement between the encoder and the light source produces pulses that are detected by a photoelectric detector and amplified to give a square-wave output.

Two glass disks or plates are used to measure absolute distance. These can be tilted with respect to each other to give a moiré effect, resulting in a high degree of accuracy. Resolution up to 1/40,000 of a revolution is possible.

Interferometers using lasers are also used in applications such as precision machining and calibration. These can measure distances over several meters to within 0.1 μm.

Velocity Transducers

The simplest and most well-known velocity transducer is the automobile speedometer. In it, a flexible shaft driven by gears at the rear of the transmission rotates a circular permanent magnet 1000 times every mile. This magnet is positioned within a movable metal drag cup made of a light nonmagnetic metal that is attached to the shaft carrying the dial pointer. Eddy currents induced in the cup provide an electromagnetic torque, proportional to the relative speed, that tends to drag the cup around with it, against the resistance of a spiral spring. The faster the magnet rotates, the greater is the pull on the cup and the pointer, giving a reading on the dial in miles or kilometers per hour.

If stationary coils are positioned around the rotating magnet instead of a drag cup, the device is called an AC tachogenerator. The rotating magnet field generates an AC current in the coils with a frequency proportional to the speed of rotation.

A DC tachogenerator is similar in construction, except that the coils rotate within a stationary magnet. This has the disadvantage that a commutator and carbon brushes are required to make contact with the coils.

Linear velocity transducers use a magnet coupled to the moving object. The magnet moves along the axis of a solenoid, generating an e.m.f. proportional to the velocity. However, it is limited to relatively short path lengths.

Transducers for Force and Pressure

Piezoelectric elements are used in transducers for force or pressure. The material may be quartz or a ferroelectric ceramic, such as barium titanate. The transducer acts as a capacitor of varying charge whose output is expressed either in terms of charge as C/g or voltage V/g sensitivity. As such a transducer has a very high output impedance, its output must be coupled into an amplifier with very high input impedance (of the order of 10^{14} ohms) to limit discharge of the capacitor, which typically has a capacitance of 20 picofarads.

Accelerometers

A seismic accelerometer (see Figure T-5) has a known mass supported by a spring that compresses in accordance with the acceleration. The resulting displacement of the mass actuates a distance transducer, such as a potentiometer, to give an electrical output proportional to the acceleration. A damping mechanism has to be provided to eliminate oscillation at the resonant frequency of the system.

Figure T-5 Seismic Accelerometer—[6]

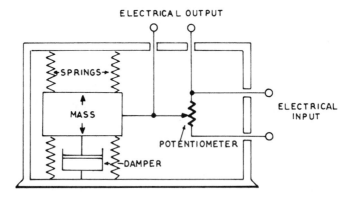

The principle of operation of the seismic accelerometer is given by:

$$ma = kx$$

where:

m = the seismic mass.

a = the acceleration.

x = the deflection of the spring.

k = the force due to the deflection.

A piezoelectric transducer similar to those used for force or pressure may also be used for sensing acceleration.

Vibration

Vibration may be measured using a seismic accelerometer or a stroboscope. The vibration level is expressed as:

$$\text{vibration level} = 20 \log_{10}(A_1/A_0) \text{ dB}$$

where:

A_1 = acceleration (ms^{-2}) or velocity (ms^{-1}).

A_0 = acceleration reference $(10^{-5} \text{ ms}^{-2})$, or velocity reference $(10^{-3} \text{ ms}^{-1})$.

Temperature

Since the resistance of most conductors varies with temperature, *resistance thermometers* made of platinum, copper, tungsten, or nickel are used for precision measurements of temperature in laboratory and industrial work. Platinum is most generally used. The resistance–

temperature relationship for platinum is:

$$T = [100(R_T - R_0)/(R_{100} - R_0)] + \partial(T/100 - 1)(T100)$$

where:

$$T = \text{temperature in °C.}$$

$$R_T = \text{resistance at } T.$$

$$R_0 = \text{resistance at 0°C}$$

$$R_{100} = \text{resistance at 100°C.}$$

$$\partial = \text{Callender constant (approximately 1.5).}$$

Thermistors are semiconductors whose resistance varies with temperature. The resistance at any temperature T is given by:

$$R_T = R_0 \exp \beta(1/T - 1/T_0)$$

where:

$$R_T = \text{thermistor resistance at temperature } T \text{ (K).}$$

$$R_0 = \text{thermistor resistance at temperature } T_0 \text{ (K).}$$

$$\beta = \text{a constant determined by calibration.}$$

At high temperatures, this reduces to:

$$R_T = R_0 \exp (\beta/T)$$

Thermocouples consist of pairs of dissimilar metals that generate a small voltage at their junction. The most popular is the chromel-alumel thermocouple, which is used for temperatures up to about 1300°C. Above this temperature, thermocouples of platinum/platinum-rhodium alloy and tungsten/tungsten-rhenium alloy are used. Characteristics of commonly used thermocouples are listed in Table T-1.

Comparison of Temperature Transducers

Table T-2 shows how the three types of temperature transducer compare with each other.

Sound Transducers

Microphones are electroacoustic devices that, when actuated by sound waves, deliver essentially equivalent electrical waves. The principal types are:

Dynamic	Electrostatic	Electrostrictive
Magnetic	Piezoelectric	Carbon

TABLE T-1   Commonly Used Thermocouples

Thermocouple	Max continuous operating temp (°C)	Typical output ($\mu V°C^{-1}$)	Comments
Platinum-rhodium:			
$Pt-Pt_{87}Rh_{13}$ (Type R)	1500	12(1600)	Stable, resists corrosion
$Pt_{94}Rh_6-Pt_{70}Rh_{30}$	1600	11.6(1600)	
$Pt_{80}Rh_{20}-Pt_{60}Rh_{40}$	1700	4.5(1600)	
Palladium:			
$Pt_{90}Ir_{10}-Pd_{40}Au_{60}$	1000	60(800)	Resists corrosion
$Pt_{12.5}Pd-Au_{54}Pd_{46}$	1200	35(400)	Resists corrosion
Iridium:			
$Ir-Ir_{40}Rh_{60}$	2100	6.6(2000)	Fragile at high temperatures
Tungsten-Rhenium:			
$W-W_{74}Re_{26}$	2700		Inert atmosphere only
$W_{95}Re_5-W_{14}Re_{26}$	2700		Vacuum only
Chromel-Alumel (Type K):			
$Ni_{90}Cr_{10}-Ni_{94}$, A1, Si, Mn	1300	25(150–1300)	Generally up to 1100°C
Iron-constantan (Type J):			
$Fe-Cu_{57}Ni_{35}$	800	63(800)	High output
Copper constantan	350	60(350)	
Chromel constantan	700	81(500)	High output

TABLE T-2   Comparison of Temperature Transducers

Parameter	Platinum resistance thermometer	Thermistor	Thermocouple
Repeatability	0.03°C–0.05°C	0.1°C–1°C	1°C–10°C
Stability	<0.1% drift in 5 years	0.1°C–2.5°C drift per year	0.5°C–1°C drift per year
Sensitivity	$0.2–10\Omega°C^{-1}$	$100–1000\Omega°C^{-1}$	$10–50\ \mu V°C^{-1}$
Temperature range	$-120°C–850°C$	$-100°C–350°C$	$-200°C–1600°C$
Signal output	1–6 V	1–3 V	0–60 mV
Minimum size	7.5 mm dia. × 6 mm long	0.44 mm dia.	0.4 mm dia.
Linearity	good	poor	good
Special features	greatest accuracy over wide range; high stability	greatest sensitivity; high impedance (minimizes lead effects)	widest operating range

In a *dynamic microphone*, a movable conductor is positioned in a magnetic field. The conductor may be in the form of a coil, a straight wire, or a ribbon. Sound waves impinging on a diaphragm, or on the ribbon in a ribbon type, move the conductor in the magnetic field, generating a current in proportion to the amplitude and velocity of movement. The impedance of the voice coil may vary from 1 to 30 ohms. A small transformer is included to step up the impedance to any of the standard values used for transmission over a line: 30, 150, 250 ohms; or high impedance (25,000 ohms) for direct feed to an amplifier.

This moving-coil type of microphone is also called a pressure microphone. The straight-wire type is similar, the coil being replaced by a single wire attached to a V-shaped diaphragm.

The ribbon microphone consists of a metallic ribbon positioned in a magnetic field. It is held at its ends, but is free to move because it is corrugated. Movement in the magnetic field caused by sound waves induces currents in the ribbon. A small transformer is also included to match its impedance to the line.

A special form of ribbon microphone has a bundle of small tubes or pipes of different lengths with their open ends equally spaced along the axis of the bundle, and their other ends connected at a common junction in front of the ribbon. This microphone is highly directional in the voice-frequency range and is much used for picking up speech at long range under conditions of high ambient noise.

A *magnetic microphone* has a diaphragm that is moved by the sound waves, but it is attached to an armature which varies the reluctance in a magnetic field surrounded by a coil. This induces currents in the coil. Thus it is like the dynamic microphone, but because of the greater mass of the armature, the diaphragm has to be made stiffer, and so the magnetic microphone is not as sensitive.

An *electrostatic microphone* is also called a *condenser microphone* because it consists of one fixed plate and one movable plate that is moved by the sound waves. This causes it to vary in distance from the fixed plate, so varying the capacitance between them. The capacitance of the diaphragm and fixed plate is part of the resonant circuit of an oscillator so that the frequency of oscillation is made to vary in accordance with the sound waves. The capacitance of the diaphragm and fixed plate is from 50 to 300 picofarads, so the oscillator must be as close to it as possible since any additional capacitance introduced by shielded cables, and the like, will reduce the sensitivity of the microphone.

A *piezoelectric* or *crystal microphone* consists of a diaphragm actuating an element constructed by cementing together two crystals of Rochelle salt or ammonium dihydrogen phosphate (ADP). The capacitance of the unit is from 1000 to 2000 picofarads, so the signal can be transmitted over several feet of low-capacitance cable with negligible attenuation. No impedance-matching transformer is required.

An *electrostrictive microphone* is also called a *ceramic* microphone because it uses a ceramic such as barium titanate. It is constructed in the same way as a crystal microphone and has a similar performance.

The *carbon microphone* is widely used in telephones. The diaphragm is connected to a movable electrode which forms the "lid" of a small metal cup containing carbon granules. As the sound waves move the diaphragm, the latter causes the lid to press with varying force on the carbon granules. This varies their resistance (100 to 200 ohms), so varying the current flowing through them. The carbon microphone requires a source of direct current and a matching transformer.

Directivity

The response of a microphone is nondirectional (omnidirectional), bidirectional, or cardioid (unidirectional). Pressure microphones (dynamic, magnetic, electrostatic, crystal, ceramic, and carbon) are generally nondirectional because air pressure is nondirectional. The exception is the ribbon, or velocity microphone. The ribbon has the most sensitivity to sound waves reaching it from in front or behind (bidirectional). This microphone can be made unidirectional by blocking the sound waves from reaching the ribbon from behind, except through apertures (ports) positioned so that the phase of these sounds is shifted and is very low.

Similar arrangements can be provided for other types of microphone, of course. However, the greater sensitivity of the ribbon microphone gives the best results, as was seen in the description of the line-type microphone already mentioned.

For television and motion picture sound, two dynamic microphones mounted in tandem on the same axis (and in one enclosure, with front and connector screens) are used. This is a comparatively large and heavy device that is therefore mounted on a boom. Its response to random sounds is only one-eighth that of a nondirectional microphone, and its pick-up distance is about three times as great.

Parabolic reflectors are also used to enhance directivity and sensitivity of microphones. The microphone is placed at the focus of the reflector. Its directivity increases with frequency.

Comparison of Microphone Types

Table T-3 compares the characteristics of the principal types of microphone.

A *loudspeaker* is a device that converts an electrical audio signal into sound waves. In this, it is the opposite of a microphone, and in some cases is interchangeable with one. There are two types in general use:

Moving coil

Electrostatic

TABLE T-3 Types of Microphones Compared

Type	Directivity	Operating impedance*
Carbon	Nondirectional	*L,M,H* (resistive)
Magnetic		*L,M,H* (inductive)
Dynamic		*L,M,H* (resistive)
Ribbon		*L,M,H* (resistive)
Condenser		*H* (capacitive)
Crystal		*H* (capacitive)
Ceramic		*H* (capacitive)
Ribbon	Bidirectional	*L,M,H* (resistive)
Ribbon	Unidirectional	*L,M,H* (resistive)
Dynamic		*L,M,H* (resistive)
Condenser		*H* (capacitive)
Ribbon (line)	Highly directional	*L,M,H* (resistive)
Dynamic (line)		*L,M,H* (resistive)
Dynamic (reflector)		*L,M,H* (resistive)

*Impedance at output terminals: includes transformer, if any. L = low impedance (<100 ohms); M = medium impedance (100 to 1000 ohms); H = high impedance (>1000 ohms).

The construction of a moving coil speaker is shown in Figure T-6. Because it radiates sound from both front and back, it will normally be mounted in an enclosure to prevent sound from the back getting around to the front and interfering destructively with sound radiating to the front. In some cases, however, the enclosure is designed so that low-frequency sounds are emitted through a port in the front, shifted in phase to reinforce the front radiation (bass reflex).

In order to give the equal coverage to the entire audio spectrum required in high fidelity reproduction, it is usual to mount three speakers with different ranges in the same enclosure. The largest, called a woofer, covers the range from 20 Hz to 800 Hz. The second speaker is frequently a midrange horn, with a range from 800 Hz to 8000 Hz. The smallest, called a tweeter, has range from 8000 Hz to 25,000 Hz. The frequency response of these speakers actually overlap, and a crossover network is provided to divide the audio signal among them. For stereo use, two of these "systems" are required, 6 to 10 feet apart.

A horn-type speaker also has a moving coil, but it is attached to a diaphragm positioned at the narrow end (throat) of a rigid horn. The horn is an acoustical "transmission line" that matches the high impedance of the diaphragm to that of the outside air. It may be straight, bent, or folded.

An *electrostatic* speaker is one in which the mechanical displacement is produced by the action of electrostatic fields. Structurally, it is a

Figure T-6 How a Loudspeaker Works

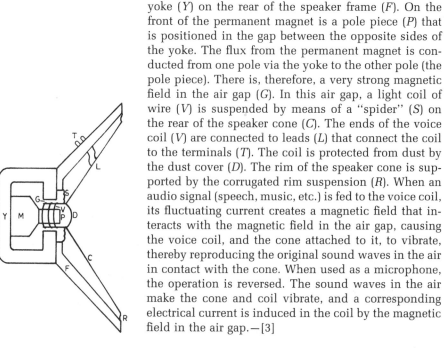

A strong permanent magnet (*M*) is mounted in a yoke (*Y*) on the rear of the speaker frame (*F*). On the front of the permanent magnet is a pole piece (*P*) that is positioned in the gap between the opposite sides of the yoke. The flux from the permanent magnet is conducted from one pole via the yoke to the other pole (the pole piece). There is, therefore, a very strong magnetic field in the air gap (*G*). In this air gap, a light coil of wire (*V*) is suspended by means of a "spider" (*S*) on the rear of the speaker cone (*C*). The ends of the voice coil (*V*) are connected to leads (*L*) that connect the coil to the terminals (*T*). The coil is protected from dust by the dust cover (*D*). The rim of the speaker cone is supported by the corrugated rim suspension (*R*). When an audio signal (speech, music, etc.) is fed to the voice coil, its fluctuating current creates a magnetic field that interacts with the magnetic field in the air gap, causing the voice coil, and the cone attached to it, to vibrate, thereby reproducing the original sound waves in the air in contact with the cone. When used as a microphone, the operation is reversed. The sound waves in the air make the cone and coil vibrate, and a corresponding electrical current is induced in the coil by the magnetic field in the air gap.—[3]

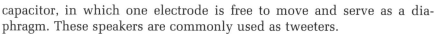

capacitor, in which one electrode is free to move and serve as a diaphragm. These speakers are commonly used as tweeters.

In small radios and similar equipment, only one speaker is provided. It is relatively small, and the frequency range is limited.

Earphones may be magnetic, dynamic, electrostatic, or piezoelectric. In the magnetic type, a permanently magnetized diaphragm is moved in and out by an electromagnet energized by the audio signal. The miniature magnetic type that fits inside the ear canal is similar.

The dynamic type is actually a small dynamic loudspeaker. A voice coil is attached to the membranous diaphragm and is positioned in the field of a permanent magnet. Audio signal currents in the coil cause it and the diaphragm to move. This type is standard for high fidelity headphones.

An electrostatic earphone contains a thin metallized plastic film with a large constant electrostatic charge, which is sandwiched between two perforated wire-mesh plates, on which the audio signal is impressed, so causing it to move and create sound pressure waves. In some models, the wire-mesh plates have been replaced by two electrets of fluorocarbon. This latter type is called a dynamic-electrostatic, or an orthodynamic earphone.

A piezoelectric earphone contains a crystal element coupled mechanically to the center of a small cone. The audio signal causes the crystal to expand and contract physically.

TRANSFORMERS

When an alternating voltage is applied to an inductance, an e.m.f. is induced by the varying magnetic field accompanying the flow of alternating current. If a second coil is brought into the same field, a similar e.m.f. will be induced in this coil as well. If a circuit is connected to the terminals of the second coil, a current will flow in it also. The coils are said to be coupled, and together they constitute a transformer. The input coil is called the primary coil or winding; the output coil, the secondary.

For a given alternating magnetic field, the voltage induced is proportional to the number of turns in the coil. Since the primary and secondary windings are in the same field, the voltages induced will be proportional to the number of turns on each coil. The induced voltage in the primary coil is practically the same, though opposite to the applied voltage, so:

$$V_s = \frac{n_s}{n_p} V_p$$

where:

V_p = induced voltage in the primary = input voltage.

V_s = induced voltage in the secondary.

n_p = number of turns in the primary.

n_s = number of turns in the secondary.

The ratio n_s/n_p is called the turns ratio of the transformer. Since the applied voltage and the induced voltage in the primary are equal and opposite, no current would flow at all in the primary if there were no losses, and no load on the secondary. In fact, there are losses, as already mentioned, and a small current does flow in the amount necessary to supply these losses and to overcome the resistance of the primary wiring. This current, which is so small it can be neglected for most purposes, is called the magnetizing current or exciting current (I_{ex}).

However, when current is drawn from the secondary by any load connected to it, the secondary current sets up a magnetic field of its own in the core. This reduces the strength of the original field because it is of opposite phase. But the original field must always be maintained, for otherwise the induced voltage will not equal the applied voltages. The current in the primary increases by the amount necessary to intensify the primary field so that the effect of the secondary field is completely canceled, and the primary field current is maintained at the original level.

This means that whatever power is taken from the secondary is made up by power taken by the primary from the source. Allowing for losses, the power output is given by:

$$P_o = \eta P_i$$

where:

P_o = power output from secondary.

P_i = power input to primary.

η = efficiency factor.

The efficiency factor is the full-load efficiency of the transformer and decreases with either higher or lower outputs. For small power transformers, such as are used in radio receivers and transmitters, η = 0.60 through 0.90 (60 to 90 percent).

Since the voltage in the primary is given by:

$$V_p = \frac{P_i}{I_p}$$

where:

V_p = induced voltage in primary = input voltage.

P_i = input power to primary.

I_p = primary current.

the voltage in the secondary is given by:

$$V_s = \frac{P_o}{I_s}$$

where:

V_s = induced voltage in secondary = input voltage.

P_o = output power from secondary.

I_s = secondary current.

Taking the last two equations and substituting them into the original equation

$$V_s = \frac{n_s}{n_p} V_p$$

gives

$$\frac{P_o}{I_s} = \frac{n_s}{n_p}\left(\frac{P_i}{I_p}\right)$$

Ignoring all losses, and assuming 100 percent efficiency, so that $P_o = P_i$, allows this expression to be simplified to:

$$I_p = \frac{n_s}{n_p} I_s$$

Hysteresis and *eddy currents* are core losses. Hysteresis is the flux that remains in the core when the magnetizing force returns to zero. If the voltage applied to the primary is in the form of a sine wave, the flux density increases as the voltage increases to a peak. In a perfect magnetic material, it would return to zero as the voltage fell back to its starting point. Then as the voltage rose to the opposite peak, the flux would increase again, but with the reverse polarity, and so on. But even the best magnetic materials cannot quite do this. Some of the magnetic domains are still in the former alignment at the moment the magnetizing force changes polarity so that additional power must be used to turn them around. This power is therefore wasted. The amount lost will depend on the material used. Best core materials require low coercive force, defined as the magnetizing force that must be applied in a direction opposite the residual flux in order to reduce it to zero. High-performance core materials, such as alloys of iron with nickel, silicon, molybdenum, cobalt or other substances, require a coercive force of between 0.16 and 40 amperes per meter (0.002 and 0.5 oersteds). [For contrast, silmanal, an alloy used for permanent magnets, has a coercivity of 4.8×10^5 amperes per meter (6000 oersteds).]

Eddy currents are currents induced in the core by the magnetic fields of the windings. To minimize the energy lost in this way, transformer cores are made of thin sheets called laminations, which are coated with shellac or some other nonconductive material, and are stacked as shown in Figure T-7. Although this does not entirely eliminate eddy-current losses, because some current paths are still present, it does reduce eddy-current losses to a low value.

Both hysteresis and eddy-current losses increase with frequency; hence even laminated iron cores are useless at radio frequencies. However, transformers for frequencies up to one megahertz are made with ferrite cores for use in the telephone carrier range, and i.f. transformers with cores of powdered iron alloy in a binder are used for frequencies as

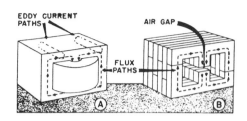

EDDY CURRENT PATHS

AIR GAP

FLUX PATHS

Ⓐ   Ⓑ

Figure T-7 Reducing Eddy Currents in a Transformer Core

If the core is solid, as at *A*, there are many eddy current paths in it. These can be reduced by making a laminated core, as at *B*, where the laminations are varnished to insulate them from each other.— [6]

high as 40–50 megahertz (television i.f.). The latter are tuned transformers, which means they are made for certain frequencies, and therefore they can handle higher frequencies as long as they are confined to a limited bandwidth. Pulse transformers are also of this type.

Another loss is due to the power lost in overcoming the DC resistance of the windings and is called *copper loss*, or I^2R loss (from $P = I^2R$). A typical winding of 3000 turns of AWG #28 wire might total 2000 feet. From the Copper Wire Table (*Properties of Materials* Table P-9), this would have a DC resistance of 129.8 ohms. Assuming a current of 0.5 ampere, the power dissipated in this winding would be $(0.5)^2 \times 129.8 = 32.45$ watts.

In a practical transformer, some of the flux is not common to both windings. It escapes and travels through the air surrounding the core; it is therefore called *leakage flux*. If the magnetic material in the core is near its saturation point, where it cannot hold much more flux, the leakage flux increases rapidly if the coil current increases further so that a much greater amount of power is wasted. Transformers should usually be operated well below the saturation level to minimize this, but even so there will always be some.

Leakage flux acts in the same way as flux about any coil that is not coupled to another coil. It generates a voltage in the coil by self-induction. Consequently there are small amounts of leakage inductance in both windings, but *not* common to them. These offer an equivalent amount of inductive reactance to the current flowing in the windings, a reactance called leakage reactance. Since it is no different from other inductive reactance, its value increases with frequency.

There is also *capacitance* between the turns of each winding, which has the effect of placing a capacitor in parallel with the winding. At low frequencies, the shunting effect is negligible because the reactance is high, but the reactance decreases as the frequency increases. Furthermore, there will be some frequency at which the inductive and capacitive reactances are equal so that the winding is self resonant. This will generally be of importance only at radio frequencies, however.

These various parameters of the transformer are shown schematically in the equivalent network in Figure T-8.

Another important characteristic of transformers is the way the impedance of a fixed load can be transformed to any desired value, within practical limits. A case in point is the use of an audio output transformer to couple the output of the final stage of an amplifier to a loudspeaker. For maximum power transfer, the load impedance should equal the output impedance of the amplifier.

To design or select a suitable transformer, the following formula is used, although it is an approximation that ignores all the losses:

$$N = \sqrt{\frac{Z_s}{Z_p}}$$

where:

N = required turns ratio, secondary to primary.

Z_s = impedance of load connected to secondary.

Z_p = impedance required by source.

Figure T-8 Equivalent Network of a Transformer

a = turns ratio = N_p/N_s
C_p = primary shunt capacitance*
C_s = secondary shunt capacitance*
E_g = generator voltage (rms)
E_o = output voltage = aE_g in iron-core transformer
k = coefficient of coupling (ignore in iron-core transformer)
L_p = primary inductance
  *Negligible at low frequencies—[6]

l_p = primary leakage inductance
l_s = secondary leakage inductance
R_c = core-loss shunt resistance
R_g = generator impedance
R_L = load impedance
R_p = primary winding resistance
R_s = secondary winding resistance

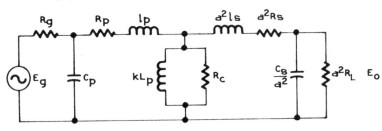

As mentioned already, r.f. transformers are generally air-core transformers. The permeability of air is thousands of times less than that of most core materials, so inductance is also much less, although there are no core losses. On the other hand, distributed capacitance has a much greater shunting effect, although this is reduced as much as possible by universal winding, in which the turns are crisscrossed.

In most cases, the secondary of the transformer, at least, is tuned by a variable capacitor to form a resonant circuit. This results in a resonant voltage step-up across the secondary, which is independent of the turns ratio.

Leakage flux is very considerable. Instead of being only 2 to 5 percent of the total magnetic flux, it may even exceed the mutual flux. However, the air core itself cannot saturate.

This makes the mathematical analysis of air-core transformers quite different from that of iron-core types. Iron-core transformers have a mutual flux of 95 to 98 percent. This is called their coefficient of coupling, or K. For air-core transformers, K is only 0.5 to 1.0 percent.

The coupling coefficient K can be calculated from

$$K = \frac{M}{\sqrt{L_p L_s}}$$

where:

M = the mutual inductance value (see below).

L_p = the primary inductance in henries.

L_s = the secondary inductance in henries.

The mutual inductance M is given by

$$M = \frac{L_A - L_o}{4}$$

where:

L_A = total inductance of L_p and L_s, with fields aiding.

L_o = total inductance of L_p and L_s, with fields opposing.

R.f. transformers with powdered-iron or ferrite cores behave much more like iron-core transformers, except that distributed capacitance has a more serious shunting effect. However, these are usually tuned to a frequency by a variable capacitor or by varying the core permeability (by moving the core) to obtain the resonant voltage step-up already mentioned. (See Figure T-9).

Figure T-9 Variable Transformer
   This type, widely used in the
i.f. amplifiers of older television receivers, has a powdered-iron slug
for a core. The position of the slug
is adjusted by means of the
threaded rod projecting from one
end. — [6]

   Many transformers are enclosed in metal shields which are either
conductive or magnetic. R.f. transformers are enclosed in conductive
shields of copper or aluminum. Currents induced in the shield oppose
the changing flux field and cancel it at external points. I.f. transformers
have shields of magnetic material that provide an easy path for flux immediately surrounding the transformer, so only a negligible external field
can exist. Any shield must be at a certain minimum distance from the
transformer for optimal operation.

TRANSISTORS

Transistors are of two main types: bipolar junction transistors (BJT) and
field-effect transistors (FET). The BJT is made of either germanium or
silicon. Each of these materials is "doped" to give both n-type (in which
electrons are the majority charge carriers) and p-type (in which holes are
the majority charge carriers). In a BJT, a thin region of n-type material is
sandwiched between two regions of p-type material to make a *pnp* transistor; or a thin region of p type material is sandwiched between two
regions of n-type material to make an *npn* transistor.
   The boundaries between the n- and p-type regions in a BJT are called
junctions. If voltages are arranged on either side of a junction such that
the n-type region is negative with respect to the p-type region (or the p-
type region is positive with respect to the n-type region, which amounts
to the same thing), majority carriers will flow across the junction from
the n-type region to the p-type region. Since majority carriers in n-type
material are electrons, the current will consist of electrons. This is the
same as what happens in a diode when it is forward biased.
   In a silicon BJT, the forward bias must exceed 0.7 V before current
will flow; in a germanium BJT, it must exceed 0.3 V.
   If the polarities are interchanged, majority carriers are unable to
cross the junction at all, because the "diode" is reverse biased.

Although electrons are majority carriers in an *n* region, they are minority carriers in a *p* region. Minority carriers can cross a reverse-biased junction.

In an *npn* BJT, one junction is forward biased, and the other is reverse biased. Electrons flow readily across the forward-biased junction into the *p* region, where they are now minority carriers. Because this region is thin, electrons find themselves close to the other reverse-biased junction, and they flow across it into the other *n* region.

If this were a *pnp* BJT, the same action would take place, except that the majority carriers would be holes. Of course, the biasing polarities would have to be reversed as well.

The region that supplies the majority carriers is called the *emitter*. The middle region, where they become minority carriers, is called the *base*, and the region into which they then go is called the *collector*. Each of these regions has a lead for connecting it to the outside world.

In any circuit, a transistor requires two input connections and two output connections. However, as it has only three leads, one of them has to be shared by both the input and the output, as shown in Figure T-10. The configuration of the transistor's circuit takes its name from which lead is common: common base, common emitter, or common collector. Transistors are connected mostly in the common-emitter configuration.

Common-emitter circuits have an input impedance of about 1 kilohm, and an output impedance of about 50 kilohms. The output signal is 180° out of phase with the input signal.

Common-base circuits have an input impedance of about 25–50 ohms and an output impedance of about 2 kilohms. The output signal is in phase with the input signal.

Common-collector circuits have a high input impedance and a low output impedance, and the signal phase is not reversed.

The way in which BJTs perform is defined by *hybrid parameters*. These are symbolized by the letter *h*, with subscripts as follows:

i = input impedance (with output short-circuited)

o = output admittance (with input open-circuited)

r = reverse open-circuit voltage amplification factor

f = forward short-circuit current amplification factor

Hybrid parameters also have a second subscript indicating which type of circuit the transistor is being used in:

b = common base

c = common collector

e = common emitter

Figure T-10 The Three Ways Transistor Circuits are Configured
(A) Common base; (B) common emitter; (C) common collector.
They get their names from which lead is connected to the low side of
the circuit (GG'), which is common to both the input (IG) and the
output (OG').—[3]

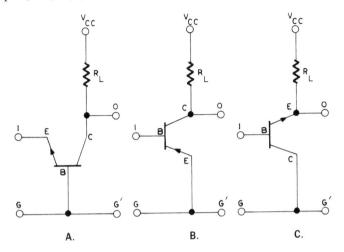

A.   B.   C.

For example, h_{fe} means "forward short-circuit current amplification
factor *in a common-emitter circuit.*"

The expressions "short circuit" and "open circuit" are intended
only for AC. Obviously, DC must not be blocked or cut off, or the transistor will not work. A large capacitor connected across the load resistor
would be an output short circuit for AC; disconnecting the signal source
would result in an open input circuit for AC.

You can convert hybrid parameters for one circuit configuration into
those for another as follows:

$$h_{ib} = h_{ie}/(1 + h_{fe})$$

$$h_{rb} = [h_{ie}h_{oe}/(1 + h_{fe})] - h_{re}$$

$$h_{fb} = -h_{fe}/(1 + h_{fe})$$

$$h_{ob} = h_{oe}/(1 + h_{fe})$$

$$h_{ic} = h_{ie}; \text{ also } h_{ic} = h_{ib}/(1 + h_{fb})$$

$$h_{rc} = 1 - h_{re} \approx 1 \quad (h_{rc} \cong 1)$$

$$h_{fc} = -(1 + h_{fe}); \text{ also } h_{fc} = -1/(1 + h_{fb})$$

$$h_{oc} = h_{oe}; \text{ also } h_{oc} = h_{ob}/(1 + h_{fb})$$

$$h_{ie} = h_{ib}/(1 + h_{fb})$$
$$h_{re} = [h_{ib}h_{ob}/(1 + h_{fe})] - h_{ib}$$
$$h_{fe} = -h_{fb}/(1 + h_{fb})$$
$$h_{oe} = h_{ob}/(1 + h_{fb})$$

In the common-emitter configuration, the parameter h_{fe} is also known as β (beta). In the common-base configuration, the parameter h_{fb} is also known as α (alpha). These are related to each other as follows:

$$\beta = \alpha/(1 - \alpha)$$
$$\alpha = \beta/(1 + \beta)$$

Where the suffix is given in upper-case letters (for instance, h_{FE}), a DC parameter is indicated. Lower-case letters always indicate an AC or a small-signal value.

The design of amplifiers using these parameters is explained under Amplifiers.

BJT parameters, with their symbols and meanings, are listed in Tables T-4 and T-5.

TABLE T-4   BJT Parameters

Parameter	Symbol	Meaning
Collector-base voltage, (emitter open)	V_{CBO}	Maximum allowable voltage between collector and base with emitter open
Collector-emitter voltage (base short-circuited to emitter)	V_{CES}	Maximum allowable voltage between collector and emitter with base short-circuited to emitter (approx. half V_{CBO})
Collector-emitter voltage (with specified resistor between base and emitter)	V_{CER}	Maximum allowable voltage between collector and emitter (greater than V_{CES}, but less than V_{CBO})
Emitter-base voltage (collector open)	V_{EBO}	Maximum allowable voltage between emitter and base with collector open
Collector saturation voltage	$V_{CE,sat}$	Collector-emitter voltage when fully conducting
Small-signal input resistance	h_{ib}, h_{ie}	Input resistance with output short-circuited for signals
Small-signal output admittance	h_{ob}, h_{oe}	Output admittance with input open for signals

TABLE T-4   BJT Parameters (*Cont.*)

Parameter	Symbol	Meaning
Small-signal reverse-voltage transfer ratio	h_{rb}, h_{re}	Ratio of input voltage to output voltage with input open-circuited for signals
Small-signal forward current gain	h_{fb}, h_{fe}	Ratio of output to input signal currents, output short-circuited
DC forward current gain	h_{FE}	Ratio of DC collector current to DC base current in common-emitter configuration
Collector dissipation	P_C	Product of DC collector-emitter voltage (V_{CE}) and DC collector current (I_C)
Gain-bandwidth product	f_T	Frequency at which forward current gain is unity (common-emitter configuration)
Cutoff frequency	f_{hfb}, f_{hfe}	Frequency at which h_{fb} or h_{fe} is 0.707 times its value at 1 kHz
Collector cutoff current (emitter open)	I_{CBO}, I_{CO}	Leakage current from collector to base with emitter open
Collector cutoff current (base open)	I_{CEO}	Leakage current from collector to emitter with base open
Collector-base capacitance	C_{ob}, C_{cb}	Internal capacitance between collector and base

Note: The parameters using the symbol *h* are called *h parameters*. The second subscript denotes the transistor configuration: *b* for common-base, and *e* for common-emitter.

TABLE T-5   Special Parameters for Switching BJTs

Parameter	Symbol	Meaning
Delay time	t_d	Time delay between beginning of input and output signal when transistor turns on
Rise time	t_r	Time for output signal to increase from 10% to 90% of final value when transistor turns on
Storage time	t_s	Time delay between trailing edges of input and output signal when transistor cuts off
Fall time	t_f	Time for output signal to decrease from 90% to 10% of final value when transistor cuts off
Turn-on time	t_{on}	Total time for transistor to become fully conducting ($\approx t_d + t_r$)
Turn-off time	t_{off}	Total time for transistor to become fully cut off ($\approx t_s + t_f$)
Stored charge	Q_T	Amount of charge carriers in transistor (indication of turn-off time)

JFETs and MOSFETs

Junction and insulated-gate field-effect transistors (the latter are also called metal-oxide field-effect transistors) are unipolar devices, in which only one type of charge carrier is used.

A JFET consists of a relatively low-conductivity semiconductor channel sandwiched between two layers of high-conductivity material of opposite type. As shown in Figure T-11, the opposite ends of the channel are connected to electrodes called the source and drain, which correspond to the emitter and collector of a BJT. However, unlike a BJT, both junctions are reverse biased, and as the bias voltage is increased, their depletion regions encroach on the channel, so reducing the flow of charge carriers through it until they are pinched off entirely. Thus the JFET is normally conducting, but may be switched off.

Figure T-11 Junction Field-Effect Transistor—[8]

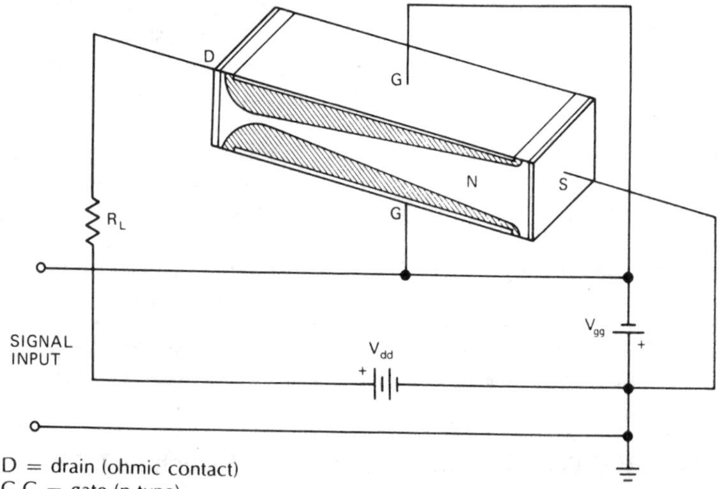

D = drain (ohmic contact)
G,G = gate (p-type)
N = channel (n-type)
S = source (ohmic contact)
Shaded area = depletion region. The depletion region becomes larger as V_{gg} increases. If V_{gg} increases enough the channel is "pinched off."

The source and drain of a MOSFET are formed by diffusing impurities into a substrate of one type to make regions of opposite type, as shown in Figure T-12. The gate consists of a layer of aluminum evaporated on to a very thin layer of silicon dioxide, which insulates it from the substrate.

When a voltage of proper polarity is applied to the gate, its electric field penetrates the insulating layer and the substrate, driving back charge carriers of opposite polarity, and so creating a channel between the source and drain regions that is of the same polarity as they are. Thus current can now flow between them. The size of the current depends upon

Figure T-12 A *p*-Channel MOSFET

The source and drain regions are made by diffusing *p*-type impurities into an *n*-type substrate. The gate is a layer of aluminum insulated from the substrate by a very thin layer of silicon dioxide. A negative voltage on the gate drives back electrons from under it, creating a *p*-channel connecting the source and drain, through which hole current can flow. When the gate voltage is withdrawn, the electrons return, changing the channel back to *n*-type, and so shutting off the current. An *n*-channel MOSFET is the same as a *p*-type, but with all the polarities reversed. — [8]

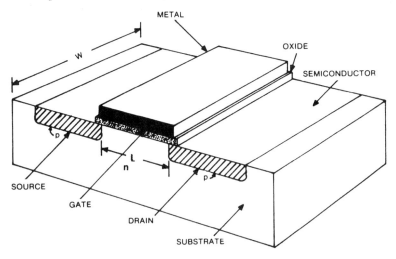

the depth of the channel, and therefore upon the voltage on the gate. A MOSFET is normally nonconductive, but is turned on by a voltage on its gate. A certain minimum voltage, called the threshold voltage, is required to turn it on.

JFET and MOSFET parameters are listed in Table T-6.

TABLE T-6 JFET and MOSFET Parameters

Parameter	Symbol	Meaning
Drain current for zero bias	I_{DSS}	Drain current flowing when gate is short-circuited to source ($V_{GS} = 0$)
Gate reverse current	I_{GSS}	Leakage current flowing between gate and source for a specified reverse bias across gate and source terminals
Drain cutoff current	I_D, off	Drain current flowing when device is biased in its OFF state
Gate-source breakdown voltage	BV_{GSS}	Maximum reverse voltage that may be impressed across gate and source terminals without damaging the device

TABLE T-6 JFET and MOSFET Parameters (*Cont.*)

Parameter	Symbol	Meaning
Gate-source pinchoff voltage	V_P	Gate-to-source voltage which reduces I_{DSS} to 1% or less of maximum value at a specified drain-to-source voltage
Small-signal forward transconductance	g_{fs}, g_m, y_{fs}	Ratio of a small change in signal gate-to-source voltage in common-source configuration. g_{fs} is an indication of gain for the device.
DC drain-source ON	r_{DS}	Ratio of drain-source voltage to DC drain current when $v_{GS} = 0$
Input capacitance	C_{iss}	When $V_{DS} = 0$ (common source)
Reverse transfer capacitance (drain-to-gate)	C_{rss}	When $V_{DS} = 0$ (common source)

Unijunction Transistor (UJT)

A unijunction transistor is really a tiny bar of silicon with leads attached at each end, called *base 1* and *base 2*. The bar of silicon is typically *n*-type, and offers a resistance of about 9 kilohms to current flowing from B1 to B2.

An aluminum wire called the emitter is welded to a point approximately halfway along the bar. The *n*-type material around this point is changed to *p*-type. This is the only junction, since B1 and B2 are ohmic connections.

If a positive voltage is applied to the emitter so that the emitter-B1 diode is forward biased, its conductivity increases sharply. Reducing the emitter voltage turns the diode off. The UJT can therefore be used as a switch.

Figure T-13 shows a typical static emitter characteristic curve for a UJT,

where:

$$V_p = \text{peak point emitter voltage.}$$

$$V_{EB1} = \text{emitter base 1 junction diode drop.}$$

At the "valley point" the current is 4 mA.

SCRs and Triacs

An SCR is a rectifier diode with a third lead for a gate. It will conduct the half-cycles of AC that give forward bias as long as I_{GT} is applied. By varying the time of application, a smaller or larger part of the half-cycle is passed.

A triac is a bidirectional device. It does not have an anode and a

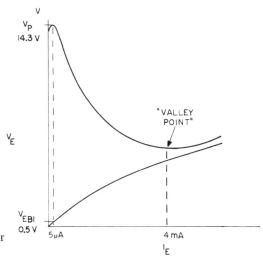

Figure T-13 UJT Static Emitter Characteristic Curve—[3]

cathode, its two main terminals being designated *main terminal 1 (MT1)* and *main terminal 2 (MT2)*. The third terminal is the gate. Trigger levels and polarities are given in reference to MT1. The device operates like an SCR, except that it passes both half-cycles of AC to the extent allowed by the gate trigger.

SCR and triac parameters are listed in Table T-7.

TABLE T-7   SCR and TRIAC Parameters

Parameter	Symbol	Meaning
Forward breakdown voltage	$V_{(br)F}$, V_{BO}	Forward voltage at which device fires
Reverse breakdown voltage	$V_{(br)R}$	Maximum reverse voltage causing avalanche
On-state voltage	V_T, V_F	Voltage across device when conducting
On-state current	I_T, I_F	Current flowing in device when conducting
Holding current	I_H	Minimum current for conduction
Latching current	I_L	Minimum current for conduction after trigger has been removed
Gate-trigger current	I_{GT}	Minimum current for turn-on
Gate-trigger voltage	V_{GT}	Voltage needed for I_{GT}
Gate turn-on time	t_{on}	Time for device to turn on
Commutated turn-off time	t_{off}, t_q	Time for device to turn off
Critical rate of rise	dv/dt	Maximum rate of voltage change that can be applied to anode or main terminal without turning device on

TRANSMISSION LINES

Transmission lines are used to transfer electrical energy at various frequencies below microwave frequencies, with minimum loss, generally between antennas and receivers or transmitters, and also in closed-circuit television and the like. They have inductance, capacitance, and resistance so that sections of transmission line can also be used as reactances.

Some representative types of transmission lines are given in Table T-8.

TABLE T-8 Transmission Line Velocity Factor

Type of line	Velocity factor
Coaxial (polyethylene dielectric)	0.66
300-ohm twin lead	0.82–0.84
150-ohm twin lead	0.76–0.77
75-ohm twin lead	0.68–0.71
Two-wire line in air	0.98

Transmission Time

The time for a signal to travel along a length of transmission line is given by:

$$t = d/kc$$

where:

t = time, in seconds.

d = distance, in meters.

k = velocity factor.

c = velocity in free space ($= 3 \times 10^8$ m/s).

When Is a Cable a Transmission Line?

A cable is a transmission line when the wavelength of the transmitted signal is smaller than the physical length of the line, or is of the same order of magnitude. The wavelength of the signal is given by:

$$\lambda = c/f$$

where:

λ = wavelength, in meters.

c = velocity in free space ($= 3 \times 10^8$ m/s).

f = frequency, in hertz.

Characteristic Impedance

A transmission line terminated by its characteristic impedance (Z_o) will have no standing waves. Z_o is given by:

$$Z_o = \sqrt{L/C}$$

where:

L = inductance per foot, in henries.

C = capacitance per foot, in farads.

See Table T-9 for typical values of inductance and capacitance of commonly-used transmission lines.

TABLE T-9 Typical Inductances and Capacitances per Foot for Common Transmission Lines

Transmission line type	Inductance per ft μH	Capacitance per ft pF
RG-8A/U	0.083	29.5
RG-11A/U	0.115	20.5
RG-59A/U	0.112	21.0
214-023	0.107	20.0
214-076	0.351	3.9

Characteristic impedance can also be calculated from the cable dimensions, and is given by:

$$Z_o = (138/\sqrt{K}) \log b/a$$

where:

K = dielectric constant of insulating material.*

b = inside diameter of outer conductor.

a = outside diameter of inner conductor.

TABLE T-10 Dielectric Constants of Commonly-Used Insulators

Insulating material	Dielectric constant	Insulating material	Dielectric constant
Air	1.0	Polyethylene	2.3
Bakelite	4.4–5.4	Polystyrene	2.6
Cellulose acetate	3.3–3.9	Porcelain	5.1–5.9
Formica	4.6–4.9	Pyrex glass	4.8
Mica	5.4	Quartz	3.8
Paper	3.0	Teflon	2.1
Plexiglass	2.8		

*See Table T-10.

Standing Waves

Standing waves are created when a transmission line is not terminated with its characteristic impedance. In this event, the incident waves are reflected, to some extent, back toward the generator. The *standing wave ratio (SWR)* is the ratio of maximum current or voltage along the line to minimum current or voltage along the line. Voltage *SWR* is given by:

$$VSWR = V_{rms,max}/V_{rms,min}$$

Current *SWR* is given by:

$$ISWR = I_{rms,max}/I_{rms,min}$$

$$SWR = VSWR = ISWR$$

SWR is also given by:

$$SWR = Z_o/R_L$$

or

$$SWR = R_L/Z_o$$

whichever gives a quantity greater than 1.

Reflection Coefficient

The reflection coefficient K_r is the ratio of reflected voltage to incident voltage, or reflected current to incident current, and is given by:

$$K_r = V_{refl}/V_{inc} = I_{refl}/I_{inc}$$
$$K_r = (Z_o - R_L)/(Z_o + R_L)$$
$$\text{(Use absolute value of } K_r)$$

Reflected Power

Reflected power (P_{refl}) is given by:

$$P_{refl} = K_r^2$$

Coaxial Cables

Table T-11 gives a listing of the dimensions of coaxial cables according to their characteristic impedances and maximum operating voltages.

See also Attenuators (minimum-loss matching pads).

TABLE T-11   Coaxial Cable Data—[7]

Impedance	RG/U#	Diameters Inch	Millimeter	Maximum Operating Voltage
25 ohms————	191	1.460	37.084	15,000 vrms
35 ohms————	83	0.405	10.287	—
48 ohms————	25	0.565	14.351	8,000 V peak
	25A	0.505	12.827	10,000 V peak
	25B	0.750	19.050	15,000 V peak
	26	0.525	13.335	8,000 V peak
	26A	0.505	12.827	10,000 V peak
	27	0.675	17.145	15,000 V peak
	27A	0.670	17.018	15,000 V peak
	28	0.805	20.447	15,000 V peak
	28B	0.750	19.050	15,000 V peak
	64	0.495	12.573	8,000 V peak
	64A	0.475	12.065	10,000 V peak
	77	0.414	10.516	—
	78	0.385	9.779	—
	88	0.515	13.081	10,000 Vrms
50 ohms————	5A	0.328	8.331	—
	9B	0.420	10.668	—
	55B	0.206	5.232	1,900 Vrms
	58A	0.195	4.953	—
	58C	0.195	4.959	1,900 Vrms
	60	0.425	10.795	—
	87	0.425	10.795	—
	115	0.375	9.525	—
	117	0.730	18.542	—
	119	0.470	11.938	—
	122	0.160	4.064	—
	126	0.290	7.366	—
	141	0.195	4.953	—
	141A	0.190	4.826	—
50 ohms————	142	0.206	5.232	—
	142B	0.195	4.953	—
	143	0.325	8.255	—
	156	0.540	13.716	10,000 Vrms
	157	0.725	18.415	15,000 Vrms
	158	0.725	18.415	15,000 Vrms
	174	0.100	2.540	—
	178B	0.075	1.905	1,000 Vrms
	179B	0.105	2.667	1,200 Vrms
	188A	0.102	2.591	—
	190	0.700	17.780	15,000 Vrms
	196A	0.080	2.032	1,000 Vrms
	211A	0.730	18.542	7,000 Vrms
	212	0.332	8.433	3,000 Vrms
	213	0.405	10.287	5,000 Vrms
	214	0.425	10.795	5,000 Vrms

Coaxial Cable Data (*Cont.*)

Impedance	RG/U#	Diameters Inch	Millimeter	Maximum Operating Voltage
	215	0.405	10.287	5,000 Vrms
	217	0.545	13.843	7,000 Vrms
	218	0.870	22.098	11,000 Vrms
	219	0.603	15.316	11,000 Vrms
	220	1.120	28.448	14,000 Vrms
	221	1.195	30.353	14,000 Vrms
	223	0.216	5.486	1,900 Vrms
	224	0.615	15.621	7,000 Vrms
	225	0.430	10.922	5,000 Vrms
	226	0.500	12.700	7,000 Vrms
	227	0.490	12.446	5,000 Vrms
	228A	0.795	20.193	7,000 Vrms
	301	0.245	6.223	3,000 Vrms
	303	0.170	4.318	1,900 Vrms
	304	0.280	7.112	3,000 Vrms
	316	0.102	2.591	1,200 Vrms
51 ohms———	9	0.420	10.668	4,000 Vrms
	9A	0.420	10.668	4,000 Vrms
	33	0.470	11.938	—
	8	0.405	10.287	4,000 Vrms
	8A	0.405	10.287	—
	10	0.475	12.065	4,000 Vrms
	14	0.545	13.843	5,500 Vrms
	16	0.630	16.002	—
	17	0.870	22.098	11,000 Vrms
	18	0.945	24.003	11,000 Vrms
	19	1.120	28.448	14,000 Vrms
	20	1.195	30.353	14,000 Vrms
	74	0.615	15.621	5,500 Vrms
52 ohms———	212	0.332	8.433	—
	213	0.405	10.287	—
	217	0.545	13.843	—
	218	0.870	22.098	—
	219	0.945	24.003	—
	220	1.120	28.448	—
52.5 ohms———	5	0.332	8.433	3,000 Vrms
53 ohms———	21	0.332	8.433	2,700 Vrms
53.5 ohms———	55	0.206	5.232	1,900 Vrms
	55B	0.206	5.232	—
	58	0.195	4.953	1,900 Vrms
58 ohms———	54A	0.245	6.223	3,000 Vrms
67.5 ohms———	41	0.425	10.795	3,000 Vrms
69.0 ohms———	36	1.180	29.972	—
71 ohms———	34	0.625	15.875	5,200 Vrms
	35	0.945	24.003	10,000 Vrms
72 ohms———	144	0.395	10.033	—
73 ohms———	59	0.242	6.147	2,300 Vrms
	140	0.242	6.147	—

Coaxial Cable Data (*Cont.*)

Impedance	RG/U#	Diameters Inch	Millimeter	Maximum Operating Voltage
74 ohms ———	13	0.420	10.668	4,000 Vrms
	216	0.425	10.795	—
75 ohms ———	6A	0.332	8.433	2,700 Vrms
	11	0.405	10.287	4,000 Vrms
	11A	0.412	10.465	5,000 Vrms
	12A	0.475	12.065	5,000 Vrms
	34B	0.630	16.002	6,500 Vrms
	35B	0.945	25.003	10,000 Vrms
	59B	0.242	6.147	2,300 Vrms
	84A	1.000	25.400	10,000 Vrms
	85A	1.565	39.751	10,000 Vrms
	101	0.588	14.935	—
	164	0.870	22.098	10,000 Vrms
	179A	0.100	2.540	—
	187	0.110	2.794	1,200 Vrms
	216	0.425	10.795	5,000 Vrms
	302	0.206	5.232	2,300 Vrms
	307	0.270	6.858	400 Vrms
	144	0.410	10.414	5,000 Vrms
76 ohms———	6	0.332	8.433	2,700 Vrms
	6A	0.332	8.433	—
	15	0.545	13.843	5,000 Vrms
	108	0.245	6.223	—
78 ohms———	42	0.342	8.687	2,700 Vrms
93 ohms———	62A	0.242	6.147	750 Vrms
	62B	0.242	6.147	750 Vrms
95 ohms———	71	0.250	6.350	750 Vrms
	71B	0.250	6.350	750 Vrms
	22	0.405	10.287	1,000 Vrms
	22B	0.420	10.668	1,000 Vrms
	57	0.625	15.875	3,000 Vrms
	57A	0.625	15.875	3,000 Vrms
	65	0.405	10.287	1,000 Vrms
	111A	0.490	12.446	1,000 Vrms
	130	0.625	15.875	8,000 Vrms
	131	0.710	18.034	8,000 Vrms
	180B	0.145	3.683	1,500 Vrms
	195A	0.155	3.937	1,500 Vrms
125 ohms———	23	0.945	24.003	3,000 Vrms
	63B	0.405	10.287	1,000 Vrms
	79B	0.475	12.065	1,000 Vrms
	181	0.640	16.256	3,500 Vrms
	89	0.632	16.053	—
140 ohms———	102	1.088	27.635	—
185 ohms———	114	0.405	10.287	—

Source: Raymond H. Ludwig, *Electronic Tables, Symbols, Measurements, and Values* (Englewood Cliffs, N.J.: Prentice Hall, 1984), pp. 387–90.

Triac *See* Transistors.

Trigonometrical Functions *See* Mathematical Data.

Truth Tables *See* Logic Circuits.

Tuning Capacitor *See* Capacitors.

Tunnel Diode *See* Diodes.

U

Ultraviolet Radiation That part of the electromagnetic spectrum with wavelengths from 370 to 10 nanometers. It is subdivided into near (370–300 nm), far (300–200 nm), and extreme (200–10 nm).

Unijunction Transistor *See* Transistors.

V

VACUUM TUBES

Transistors have so completely replaced vacuum tubes for all but specialized purposes that their mode of operation has almost been forgotten by most people. Not counting diodes, there are three basic types:

Triode

Tetrode

Pentode

Triode

A triode consists of a glass envelope containing three electrodes in a vacuum. These are:

Cathode

Anode

Grid

The cathode may be a simple tungsten filament which emits electrons when heated to incandescence. This is generally the case in high-power tubes. In others, it is more often a nickel sleeve, coated with an oxide that emits electrons freely when heated. This is done by a heating element inside the cathode, but insulated from it. Hence the name "indirectly-heated cathode."

The anode is a metal plate—it is often called the plate—in the form of a cylinder or box surrounding the cathode.

The grid is a spiral of fine wire between the anode and the cathode, but nearer to the cathode.

In operation, the cathode is connected to the negative side of the power supply and is only a few volts above ground potential. The anode is connected to the positive side of the power supply, which is much higher. This high positive voltage attracts the electrons emitted by the cathode, which flow across the intervening space to become the anode current.

The grid is the control electrode. The voltage on it accelerates or impedes the electrons. If it is sufficiently negative, it will stop the flow entirely. A signal to be amplified is applied between the grid and the cathode and modulates the anode current to produce an amplified and inverted replica of the signal.

Tetrode

A tetrode has four electrodes. In addition to the three in a triode, there is a second grid positioned between the control grid and the anode. This grid is given a positive voltage (not as high as the anode) to accelerate the electron flow. It also acts as a screen between the anode and the grid to reduce interelectrode capacitance that causes feedback, for which reason it is often called the screen grid.

Pentode

A pentode has five electrodes. The extra electrode is a third grid placed between the screen grid and the anode. In the tetrode, the accelerated electrons strike the anode hard enough to knock other electrons out of it. These secondary electrons interfere with the primary electron flow. They are removed by the third grid, which is connected to the cathode either externally, or internally inside the envelope, for which reason it is called the suppressor grid.

Modern Vacuum Tubes

There are still applications where vacuum tubes must be used. These include:

> High-power transmitting and industrial tubes
> Klystrons, magnetrons, and traveling-wave tubes
> Cathode-ray tubes
> Television picture tubes and camera tubes
> X-ray tubes
> Photomultiplier tubes
> Image intensifier tubes

High-Power Transmitting and Industrial Tubes

These tubes are for applications where much heat is generated, for which reason they are made of metal. Air cooling is usually satisfactory for anode dissipation up to 50 kilowatts, using fins and blowers. For power higher than this, water or vapor cooling is used.

TABLE V-1 Water and Vapor (Steam) Cooling Compared

Cooling method	Temperature °C					Ratio
	Ambient	Inlet	Outlet	Mean	Differential	
Vapor	45	60	100	80	35	1
Water	45	50	70	60	15	2.3

Klystrons

Klystrons begin to be useful at 400 MHz, and are available for frequencies up to 20 GHz. The majority of applications are below 2 GHz, where continuous power outputs of 25 kW are available. At the lowest frequencies, output power may be as high as 1 MW.

Electrons are emitted from a cathode, accelerated, and formed into a beam by electrodes that constitute an *electron gun*. Traveling at a constant velocity, the beam enters a drift tube. Coils surrounding the tube create a magnetic field that prevents the electrons in the beam from spreading out. The tube leads to a resonant cavity, which is adjusted to resonate at the same frequency as that of an r.f. signal coupled into it by means of a small loop antenna. In each successive half-cycle of the r.f. electric field, the electrons are either accelerated or decelerated so that, as they leave the resonant cavity and continue along the drift tube, the fast ones catch up with the slow ones to form bunches. These then enter a second cavity, which is tuned to be resonant at the same frequency so that an r.f. electric field is created by the *density-modulated* electron beam. Another small loop antenna picks up this r.f. signal, which is then transmitted to the antenna or another load. The spent beam that emerges from the second cavity travels into a collector, where the electrons are absorbed by a positive charge. (*See* Figure V-1.)

Figure V-1 Elements Inside Envelope of Two-Cavity Klystron—[6]

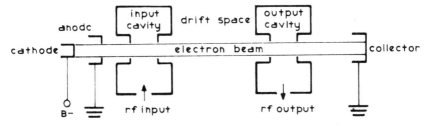

Variations of this arrangement are the reflex klystron and the multicavity klystron. In the reflex klystron, there is only one cavity. After the electron beam passes through it a first time, it is reflected back through it a second time. This type of klystron is used as an oscillator more often then it is used as an amplifier.

The two-cavity klystron has a rather narrow bandwidth. To obtain a wider bandwidth, additional resonant cavities are used. These are stagger-tuned to be resonant at frequencies above and below a center frequency. Up to seven cavities are not uncommon, but four is the most popular number.

Magnetrons

The magnetron is a microwave oscillator with a cross-section as shown in Figure V-2. A cylindrical anode surrounds the cathode. Electrons are emitted by the cathode, but a strong magnetic field produced by external coils causes them to circulate around the cathode instead of going to the anode.

The anode is not only the positive electrode but also contains cavities that are resonant near the desired r.f. output frequency. These cavities produce an r.f. electric field that also rotates in the space between the anode and the cathode.

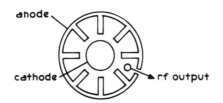

Figure V-2 A Magnetron is a Hollow Metal Cylinder.

In the cross-section, the anode has the appearance of a wheel, with the cathode as the hub. The "spokes" are partitions that form resonant cavities. (*See* text.) The coil structure that produces the magnetic field is not shown. — [6]

The interaction between this field and the circulating electrons forms them into bunches, as in the klystron. The resulting r.f. signal is coupled out through a vacuum window into an external waveguide or coaxial line.

The range of frequencies available from magnetrons is 1 to 100 GHz, with peak output power up to 10 MW, and mean output power up to 100 kW.

Traveling-Wave Tubes

A traveling-wave tube (Figure V-3) is a microwave amplifier that has an electron gun. Like a klystron, it beams a stream of electrons through two resonant cavities. Between the cavities is a slow-wave structure, often in the form of a helix. Its purpose is to make the r.f. energy travel along the helix from the first cavity to the second at the same velocity as the electron beam, forming the electrons into bunches. These induce voltages on the slow-wave structure which reinforce those already present. As a result, when the r.f. signal reaches the second cavity, it has been amplified. The electrons in the beam are then trapped by a collector.

The gain depends on the length of the slow-wave structure. The original helix structure of tungsten is still used, but because it is difficult to cool, it is limited to an output power of 2 kW. Higher powers (up to 1 MW) are made possible by using slow-wave structures with bars and rings, or wedges of copper, by which heat is dissipated more efficiently.

Figure V-3 Traveling-Wave Tube—[6]

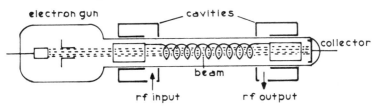

Cathode-Ray Tube

A cathode-ray tube also has an electron gun that produces a beam of electrons. The object here is to focus this beam to come to a fine point on a luminescent screen at the opposite end of the tube. The tube is funnel-shaped, with a narrow neck containing the electron gun, from which it flares out to give a wide screen.

In electrostatic deflection, the electron beam is aimed by the voltages on two pairs of plates inside the tube, between which it passes. One pair deflects it vertically; the other, horizontally, as shown in Figure V-4.

Figure V-4 Cathode-Ray Tube
Many tubes have a focusing anode between the first and second anodes shown here. The focusing anode is then the second anode, and the second anode shown here is the third anode. The anodes and control grid are often called "lenses" because they shape and aim the electron beam in a manner analogous to optical lenses.—[6]

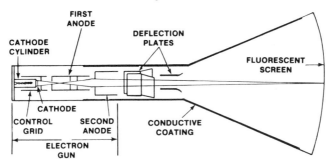

The function of the screen, of course, is to provide a visible indication of the position of the deflected electron beam at any instant. It is made by depositing a thin layer of phosphor on the inside of the faceplate of the tube. This material glows where it is struck by the electron beam. The light emitted is called fluorescence. After the electron beam has moved to a new position, the light decays, but while it persists, it is called phosphorescence. Table V-2 shows the principal types of phosphor.

TABLE V-2   Principal Types of CRT Phosphor

Designation JEDEC	WTDS	Fluorescent color	Phosphorescent color	Persistence (ms)
P1	GJ	Yellowish-green	Yellowish-green	1 to 100
P4	WW	White		0.01 to 1
P7	GM	Blue	Yellowish-green	100 to 1000
P11	BE	Blue	Blue	0.01 to 1
P31	GH	Green	Green	0.01 to 1
P33	LD	Orange	Orange	>1000
P39	GR	Green	Green	100 to 1000
P43	GT	Yellowish-green	Yellowish-green	1 to 100
P45	WB	White		1 to 100

The brightness of the display depends upon the number of electrons striking it and their velocity. The number of electrons is controlled by the grid, as in other vacuum tubes, which repels more or less of them back to the cathode according to the negative voltage on it. A highly negative voltage on the grid cuts the beam off entirely. This is called blanking.

The initial velocity of the electrons depends upon the three anodes in the electron gun. The first anode is a disk or short cylinder held at a constant positive voltage with respect to the cathode of about 1 to 2 kilovolts. The electric field thus produced brings the electrons to focus at a point between this anode and the grid. From this point, the electrons begin to diverge again, but are brought to a second focus on the screen by the voltages on the second and third anodes.

The second anode is called the focusing anode, and its voltage is about 250 volts with respect to the anode. This can be varied to obtain a sharp focus. The third anode has about the same voltage as the first anode. It accelerates the electrons toward the screen.

On the inside of the flared portion of the envelope is a conductive coating with the same positive charge as the third anode. It collects any electrons released from the screen by secondary emission.

In early CRTs, secondary electrons would build up on the screen and cause the primary electrons to slow down as they approached it. This would reduce the light output from the screen. Modern screens have a thin layer of aluminum deposited on the inner side of the phosphor screen. This layer is connected to the conductive coating, to which any electrons sticking to the screen are conducted. Another advantage of the aluminum layer is that it reflects light from the phosphor forward. Previously, this light shone back down the tube and was lost.

The velocity of the primary electrons could be increased further by increasing the voltage on the third anode. However, increasing the voltage makes the beam "stiffer" so that higher potentials are required to deflect it. This difficulty has been met by making the conductive layer on the inside of the flared portion of the envelope in the form of a spiral. The end of the spiral nearest to the third anode is at the same voltage, but the voltage along the spiral increases as it nears the screen, reaching a maximum of 10 to 20 kilovolts. In this way, the electrons receive their maximum acceleration *after* they have passed the deflection plates. Consequently, this arrangement is called *post-deflection acceleration.*

Cathode-ray tubes are also made with a screen that retains the display after its source has been disconnected. These are called memory tubes. In addition to the internal structure described above, they have *flood guns* that flood the screen with low-energy electrons. These do not make the phosphor glow, but give it a negative charge. When the *writing gun* (the gun that produces the electron beam) operates, its high-energy electrons cause the phosphor to glow and release large numbers of secondary electrons from the written area. The latter now has a positive charge, so that even after the writing gun stops, the image it made on the screen continues to glow, because the flood-gun electrons landing on it are accelerated by its positive charge.

Television Picture Tube

The picture tube in a television receiver has many features in common with the cathode-ray tube described above. However, it has a much larger screen, and therefore much more energy is required to deflect the electron beam, which is also more intense. The beam is therefore deflected magnetically by deflection coils positioned on the outside of the tube at the point where the flare begins.

Although the monochrome picture tube resembles the CRT closely in other respects, the color picture tube has three electron guns, and therefore three electron beams. Three different phosphors that produce red, green, and blue when excited by the corresponding electron beam are combined in the screen, and a perforated metal mask close to the inner surface of the screen ensures that each beam excites the correct phosphor. (*See* Figure V-5.) The color elements in the screen are very small, so that they blend together, and the viewer is not aware of them.

Figure V-5 Two Shadow-Mask Systems for Color Picture Tubes
  (a) With round holes and guns arranged in a "delta" configuration.
  (b) With slit openings and guns in line.—[6]

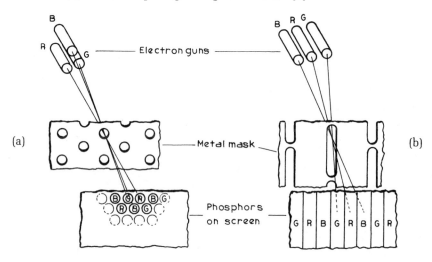

(a)

(b)

Electron guns

Metal mask

Phosphors on screen

Television Camera Tubes

Figure V-6 shows an image orthicon tube in schematic form. This is the camera tube most widely used in broadcasting. A standard camera lens projects an optical image on the photocathode, which is an optically flat glass plate coated on the inside with a light-sensitive material. Electrons are liberated from the photocathode in proportion to the amount of light falling on each part of it.

Figure V-6 Image Orthicon Camera Tube—[6]

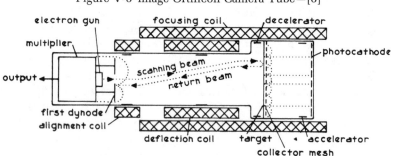

The liberated electrons are accelerated toward the surface of a thin semiconducting target and focused on it magnetically. They strike this target with sufficient energy to release a large number of secondary electrons. The latter are collected by a mesh screen that lies parallel and close to the target.

Where a large number of primary electrons strikes the target, the loss of secondary electrons is correspondingly larger, making that area more positive. Conversely, where a smaller number of electrons strikes the target, that area is less positive. Because the target is extremely thin, these potentials appear on both sides of it.

At the other end of the tube is an electron gun. The electron beam from this gun is made to scan the rear surface of the target by magnetic deflection coils surrounding the tube. These electrons have a low velocity. They are further decelerated as they approach the target so that they will not produce any secondary emission electrons.

If the area of the target being scanned is a bright area it has a higher positive charge than a dark area. A bright area therefore absorbs more electrons, and fewer return from it. A dark area absorbs less, so more are returned.

The return beam of electrons enters a photomultiplier (explained below), and is amplified to become a video output signal.

In color television the camera has three or four image orthicon tubes, and the optical image is split by color-selective filters to form red, green, and blue images. Where four tubes are used, the fourth tube views the scene directly, and produces a black and white image that becomes the Y signal. Otherwise the Y signal is formed from the color signals in a matrix.

X-Ray Tubes

Figure V-7 shows a schematic diagram of a typical diagnostic X-ray tube. Electrons are emitted from the indirectly heated cathode and are attracted by the high voltage on the anode assembly. This is a block of copper, with a piece of tungsten embedded. The electrons strike it with considerable energy, and X-rays radiate in all directions. The angle of the tungsten target causes a large number to radiate in a direction toward the side of the tube, where a small aperture in the lead shield allows them to emerge.

In addition to diagnostic tubes there are also therapeutic tubes. The latter require an efficient cooling apparatus since they are operated over longer periods of time.

Figure V-7 A Diagnostic X-Ray Tube
A lead shield would normally surround the tube. Inside the evacuated glass envelope, a very high voltage on the anode causes electrons emitted by the indirectly heated cathode to strike the tungsten target with great force. Some of these electrons penetrate deeply into the tungsten atoms. Such a penetrating electron ejects an electron from one of the inner shells. The vacancy is immediately filled by another electron from the next higher shell. However, as this electron

Figure V-7 *Continued*

has to lose energy in dscending to the lower shell, it emits a quantum of x-radiation. The energy difference between the shells determines the frequency of the radiation:

$$f = (E_2 - E_1)/h$$

where: h = Planck's constant.

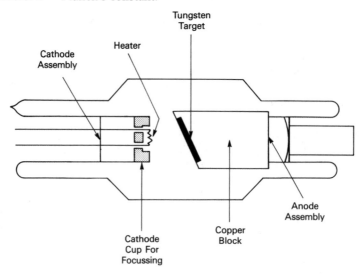

Photomultiplier

A photomultiplier tube has a photocathode that emits electrons when light falls on it. These are attracted by the positive voltage of an adjacent electrode called a dynode, and they strike it with enough force to release secondary electrons. The number of secondary electrons is greater than the number of primary electrons. In turn, the secondary electrons are attracted to a second dynode with a higher voltage. Again the number of secondary electrons liberated is greater than the number of incident electrons. This dynode is followed by more dynodes, each amplifying the electron-beam current until it reaches a collecting anode, where the beam current becomes the output current.

The parameters of a photomultiplier that are of interest to the user are:

Material and spectral response of photocathode

Details of voltage divider network required for dynodes

Anode dark current

Supply voltage required for particular gain. (The current gain of a photomultiplier is typically 10^6 or 10^7.)

Image Intensifier

In an image intensifier, an image of the scene to be viewed is focused on the photocathode of the tube, which emits electrons in response to the incident photons. The electrons are accelerated to strike a luminescent screen. Because each incident photon on the photocathode releases many electrons, a gain in intensity is obtained. In this way, an intensified image of a dimly lit scene is obtained.

Similar tubes, used for surveillance, in which the photocathode material is sensitive to nonvisible photons (for example, infrared light) but produces a visible image on the luminescent screen, are called *image converters.*

Variable Resistor *See* Resistors.

Voltage Divider *See* Power Sources.

Voltmeter *See* Meters.

W

Wattage *See* Power.

WAVEGUIDES AND CAVITIES

Waveguides

R.f. energy is propagated through a waveguide as an electromagnetic field. Waveguides are metal tubes, with cross-sections that are either rectangular, tubular, or elliptical. The first named is the most widely used.

Figure W-1 shows the dimensions of a rectangular waveguide. These dimensions determine the lowest frequency for which it can be used, given by:

$$\lambda_{co} = 2a$$

where:

λ_{co} = the wavelength corresponding to the cutoff frequency, in meters.

a = the inside width of the waveguide, in meters.

λ = c/f.

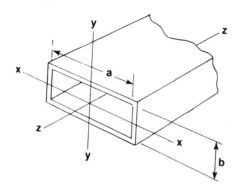

Figure W-1 Dimensions of Rectangular Waveguide—[6]

Higher frequencies can be transmitted. The dimension b is not critical with regard to frequency, but does determine the voltage level at which the waveguide arcs over. As a general rule, a is about 0.7 times the wavelength in space, and b is from 0.2 to 0.5 times the wavelength in space.

The electromagnetic field in a waveguide consists of an electric field and a magnetic field at right angles to each other (as when radiating in space). If the electric field lines are parallel with the Y axis, as shown in Figure W-2, the waveguide is said to be operating in the TE (transverse electric) mode. If the magnetic lines of force are parallel with the Y axis, the waveguide is operating in the TM (transverse magnetic) mode.

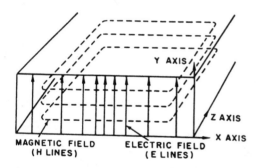

Figure W-2 $TE_{1,0}$ Mode

In the $TE_{1,0}$ mode, there is one intensification of the electric field (E lines) in the wide dimension of the waveguide, none in the narrow dimension. One intensification corresponds to one peak of a sine wave, or a half-wave variation.—[6]

The expression TE has subscript numbers to indicate the number of half-waves in the wide and narrow dimensions of the waveguide. The most often used mode is $TE_{1,0}$, which means the electric field has one half-wave in the wide dimension and none in the narrow dimension, as shown in Figure W-2. This mode is called the dominant mode and is the one having the cutoff frequency for that waveguide.

Energy is coupled in or out of a waveguide by means of a small antenna placed parallel with the electric field lines, or by means of a small loop of wire that cuts the magnetic lines of force (a transformer). Fields inside the waveguide may also be linked through slots or holes in the wall.

The characteristic impedance of a rectangular waveguide in either the *TE* or *TM* mode is given by:

$$Z_o = 120\pi(\lambda_g/\lambda)$$

where:

λ_g = the wavelength in the waveguide, in meters.

λ = the wavelength in space, in meters.

The wavelength in the waveguide is given by:

$$\lambda_g = \lambda/\sqrt{1 - (\lambda/2a)^2}$$

Resonant Cavities

A length of waveguide short-circuited (closed) at both ends will be resonant when:

$$2h = l(\lambda_g/2)$$

where:

h = length of the waveguide, in meters.

$l = 1, 2, \ldots$, but not 0, in the *TE* mode.

A cylindrical cavity will be resonant when:

$$\lambda = 1/[(1/4h)^2 + (1/\lambda_{co})^2]^{1/2}$$

$(\lambda_{co}$ = waveguide cutoff wavelength)

Some cylindrical cavities have pistons that can be adjusted to tune to a desired frequency.

Wavelength *See* Frequency.

Wye Circuit *See* Tee or Wye Network.

Z

Zener Diode *See* Diodes.

SOURCES OF SOME
FIGURES AND TABLES

[1]   DOUGLAS-YOUNG, J., *Complete Guide to Reading Schematic Diagrams,* 2nd Edition, Parker Publishing Company, Inc. (1979)

[2]   DOUGLAS-YOUNG, J., *Complete Guide to Reading Schematic Diagrams,* 3rd Edition, Prentice-Hall, Inc. (1988)

[3]   DOUGLAS-YOUNG, J., *Discovering Electronics, with Useful Projects and Applications,* Prentice-Hall, Inc. (1986)

[4]   MIDDLETON, R.G., *Designing Electronic Circuits,* Prentice-Hall, Inc. (1986)

[5]   THOMAS, H.E., *Handbook for Electronic Engineers and Technicians,* 2nd Edition, Prentice-Hall, Inc. (1965)

[6]   DOUGLAS-YOUNG, J., *Illustrated Encyclopedic Dictionary of Electronics,* 2nd Edition, Prentice-Hall, Inc. (1987)

[7]   LUDWIG, R.H., *Illustrated Handbook of Electronic Tables, Symbols, Measurements and Values,* 2nd Edition, Prentice-Hall, Inc. (1984)

[8]   DOUGLAS-YOUNG, J., *Microelectronics: A Standard Manual and Guide,* Prentice-Hall, Inc. (1984)

[9]   DOUGLAS-YOUNG, J., *Technician's Guide to Microelectronics,* Parker Publishing Company, Inc. (1978)